D1232059

NUMERICAL PROBLEMS IN
ADVANCED PHYSICAL CHEMISTRY

Numerical Problems
in Advanced
Physical Chemistry

J. H. WOLFENDEN
New Hampshire Professor of Chemistry
at Dartmouth College

R. E. RICHARDS F.R.S.
Reader in Physical Chemistry
University of Oxford, Fellow and Tutor
Lincoln College

E. E. RICHARDS
Lecturer, Somerville College, Oxford

SECOND EDITION

CLARENDON PRESS · OXFORD
1964

Oxford University Press, Amen House, London E.C.4

GLASGOW   NEW YORK   TORONTO   MELBOURNE   WELLINGTON
BOMBAY   CALCUTTA   MADRAS   KARACHI   LAHORE   DACCA
CAPE TOWN   SALISBURY   NAIROBI   IBADAN   ACCRA
KUALA LUMPUR   HONG KONG

Printed in Great Britain by
Butler & Tanner Ltd., Frome and London

Preface to the Second Edition

The purposes of the second edition are the same as those of its predecessor but we have tried to bring it closer to the advancing frontiers of physical chemistry. To this end almost a quarter of the problems in the first edition have been discarded, several have been rewritten in terms of present perspectives and fifty new problems have been added in areas which have originated or have developed notably since the appearance of the first edition. We have sought to use original papers containing relatively 'raw' experimental observations; although this has sometimes compelled us to use papers chronologically rather early in the development of the topic concerned, such papers are more likely to include the main features of theoretical interpretation within their own compass rather than to cover them by allusion to a long series of earlier papers. We have not thought it necessary to reduce terminology and usage to perfect uniformity; as a rule these will be found to reflect the practices of the paper on which the problem is based.

A selection of numerical problems from examination papers in the Final Honour School of Chemistry at Oxford have been added (without notes but with answers) in the form of an appendix. These problems are straightforward exercises requiring between twenty and forty-five minutes' work. They may be used as an elementary introduction to some of the longer problems in the book.

Our indebtedness to authors of various papers in providing supplementary information about experimental detail is noted in the text. We are also grateful to Messrs. P. D. Bartlett, R. P. Bell, E. J. Bowen, W. T. Doyle, D. H. Everett, E. W. R. Steacie and W. H. Stockmayer for valuable suggestions and comment; our obligation to those who gave useful advice in the preparation of the first edition continues.

v

We are especially indebted to Professor Dorothy Hodgkin for reviewing and supplementing the problems on crystal structure which she contributed to the first edition, to Dr. R. F. Barrow, who provided the material for Problems 17 and 121, and to Professor R. K. Laidler who formulated Problems 108 and 109 at our request.

Hanover, N.H.,   J. H. W.
  Oxford   R. E. R.
January 1964   E. E. R.

Contents

* See p. xv.

HETEROGENEOUS EQUILIBRIA

EQUILIBRIA IN SOLUTION

* See p. xv.

ix

THERMODYNAMIC PROPERTIES

* See p. xv.

ELECTRICAL CONDUCTIVITY AND MISCELLANEOUS ELECTROCHEMISTRY

* See p. xv.

KINETICS AND PHOTOCHEMISTRY

SPECTROSCOPY AND MOLECULAR STRUCTURE

CRYSTAL STRUCTURE (by Professor D. Hodgkin)

* See p. xv.

* See p. xv.

Notes on the Use of the Book

1. A table of the more important physico-chemical constants and conversion factors will be found at the end of the book. These are the values that were used in calculating the 'Answers'. Such values are liable to continual revision, usually as a result of fresh experimental information, but occasionally as a consequence of some agreed change in the units to be employed, such as the recent adoption of the 'unified' or 'carbon-12' scale of atomic masses. E. R. Cohen, K. M. Crowe, and J. W. M. DuMond, *The Fundamental Constants of Physics* (Interscience, London, 1957), or J. H. Sanders, *The Fundamental Atomic Constants* (Oxford University Press, 1961), provide useful surveys of the field; A. Labbauf, *J. Chem. Ed.*, **39**, 282, 1962, describes the history and consequences of the carbon-12 scale. Very few problems in the book require the refinement of precision exemplified by these discussions.

2. The (relatively few) problems which require logarithms of more than four figures are so designated in the notes relating to them. Desk calculators are much more accessible to students nowadays and their use is to be encouraged. Chapter 12 of E. Bright Wilson, *An Introduction to Scientific Research* (McGraw-Hill, New York, 1952), provides useful advice on numerical computations.

3. Problems of substantially more than average length are marked with an asterisk.

4. The reference at the head of each problem is to the paper or papers from which the principal data of the problem are taken. It is always worth the student's while to consult this reference.

5. It is better to work out solutions in a note-book rather than on loose paper and it is often convenient to keep one side of the page for logarithms and jottings, while the opposite side is

used for the principal steps in the calculation and for any incidental tables.

6. When, as must frequently happen, the same sequence of mathematical operations is to be performed on a series of data, it makes for accuracy as well as lucidity to arrange the results of the successive stages of the calculation in the form of a table.

7. It is very helpful to have a comprehensive series of mathematical tables (reciprocals, square roots, exponentials, &c.) such as may be found, for example, in the *Handbook of Chemistry and Physics* (Chemical Rubber Publishing Co., Cleveland), which also contains a wide range of chemical and physical constants. Barlow's Tables, edited by L. J. Comrie (Spon, London, 1960), providing squares, cubes, square roots, cube roots, and reciprocals of all integers up to 12500, can also be a valuable labour-saving device.

8. For reasons noted at the beginning of the 'Answers' section on p. 225 the student's answers, correctly worked, will not always be identical to the last digit with those quoted in the book or with those contained in the original paper on which the problem is based.

9. In the graphical representation of data it is far from easy to avoid the occasional misplotting of points. The operation of checking plotted points is most reliably performed by *putting away* the numerical data used in plotting the graph, reading off and writing down the coordinates of all points from the graph and then comparing the result with the original numerical data.

10. The sign of electrode potentials used in the problems follows the convention recommended by the International Union of Pure and Applied Chemistry (see, for example, *J. Am. Chem. Soc.*, **82**, 5518, 1960). This convention, sometimes referred to as the 'European' convention, leads to values that are often called 'reduction potentials'; under it the alkali metals have large *negative* electrode potentials and the electrode potentials of the various forms of calomel electrode all have a *positive* sign.

Fundamental Constants, Atomic and Molecular Weights

Problems 1 to 4 are concerned with some of the classical studies of the fundamental constants. More recent work leading to the now accepted values is well reviewed and discussed by E. R. Cohen, K. M. Crowe, and J. W. M. Dumond, *The Fundamental Constants of Physics* (Interscience, London, 1957).

1 AVOGADRO'S NUMBER DETERMINED FROM THE SEDIMENTATION OF COLLOID PARTICLES

J. Perrin, *Ann. de Chimie et de Physique*, **18**, 1, 1909 (cf. Perrin, *Atoms*, transl. Hammick (London, 1923), ch. iii).

Perrin determined Avogadro's number by measuring the distribution of an aqueous emulsion of rubber latex, whose particles were of known radius and density, under the influence of gravity.

An emulsion of latex, of density 1·206, in water was centrifuged to obtain particles of uniform size. Their radius, measured microscopically and also by the application of Stokes's law to their rate of fall under gravity, was 0·212 μ. The number of particles (averaged over a period of time) in the field of view of a microscope at various vertical heights was as follows:

Height	Average number of particles
5 μ	4·00
35 ,,	1·88
65 ,,	0·90
95 ,,	0·48

1

Taking the temperature of the experiment as 15° C, calculate Avogadro's number from the first and third and from the second and fourth observations respectively.

NOTE: This is an application of the so-called 'barometric' equation which represents the sedimentation equilibrium brought about by the opposed effects of thermal agitation and gravity. It owes its name to the fact that it may be used to calculate the change in density of the atmosphere with increasing height above the earth's surface. The same equation is used in the ultra-centrifuge experiments of Svedberg (cf. Problem 10) where the value of Avogadro's number is assumed and the equation is used to calculate the size of large molecules.

2 AVOGADRO'S NUMBER FROM THE RATE OF DIFFUSION OF COLLOID PARTICLES

J. Perrin, *Ann. de Chimie et de Physique*, **18**, 1, 1909 (cf. Perrin, *Atoms*, transl. Hammick (London, 1923), ch. iv).

Perrin measured the Brownian motion of a number of latex particles suspended in water. From the records of the paths of a series of fifty particles the mean squares of the displacement along a given arbitrary axis of direction were calculated for intervals of 30 seconds. The radius of the granules was 0.212μ and the viscosity of water at the temperature of the experiment (14° C) was 0.012 poise.

The following table gives the mean square of the displacement after various intervals of time:

Time (sec)	Mean square of the displacement $cm^2 \times 10^{-8}$
30	45
60	86.5
90	140
120	195

Calculate the Avogadro number for each value of the mean square displacement and also a mean value for the Avogadro number.

NOTE: This method for the evaluation of N depends like the sedimentation method upon the fact that colloid particles behave like very large molecules. There is no distinction of kind between the visible displacement of a colloid particle and the diffusion of a molecule. The equation employed in the solution of this problem treats the displacement of the colloid particle as a process of diffusion in which the large size of the colloid particle in comparison with the molecules of the suspending medium permits the calculation of the frictional force resisting motion by Stokes's law. [The poise is the absolute unit of viscosity; it corresponds to a resistance to shear of 1 dyne per cm², where the velocity gradient perpendicular to the shearing plane (and direction of motion) is 1 cm/sec per cm.]

Among later adaptations of this method may be mentioned that of Fletcher (*Physikal. Zeit.*, **12**, 202, 1911; oil-drops in air) and Kappler (*Ann. Physik.*, **11**, 233, 1931; displacements of a very light mirror by random molecular bombardment).

3 * THE ELECTRONIC CHARGE FROM OIL-DROP EXPERIMENTS

R. A. Millikan, *Phil. Mag.*, **34**, 1, 1917.

Millikan measured the rate of movement of charged oil-drops under the influence of gravity alone and under the combined influence of gravity and an electric field.

The measurements were carried out at 23° C, at which temperature the densities of the oil and air (at 760 mm) were 0·9199 and 0·0011923 respectively, the viscosity of air being 0·00018226 poise. The drops were timed over a distance of 1·0220 cm. The parallel plates between which the potential difference was applied were 1·49174 cm apart.

The observations overleaf relate to three different oil-drops.

(i) Neglecting the deviations from Stokes's law, calculate the apparent radius and apparent electronic charge for each drop.

(ii) Plot the two-thirds power of the apparent electronic charge against the reciprocal of the product of the air pressure and the apparent radius of the drop, and extrapolate to find the true value of the electronic charge.

Drop No.		5	12	14
Potential difference (volts)		4661	4661	4651
Air pressure (cm)		75·00	36·61	36·80

No. 5		No. 12		No. 14	
t_G	t_F	t_G	t_F	t_G	t_F
39·95	28·77	29·19	90·53	47·78	66·79
39·99	28·70	29·35	89·61	47·40	354·00
40·14	65·78	29·32	34·14	47·57	65·91
39·93	39·59	29·14	34·12	47·70	36·70
40·09	39·65	29·11	49·07	..	..

Time of fall under gravity $= t_G$.
Time of ascent under gravity and electrical field $= t_F$.

R. A. Millikan, *Electrons, Protons*, &c. (Chicago and Cambridge, 1935), ch. v.

R. A. Millikan, *The Electron*, ed. by *J. W. M. Dumond* (Chicago, 1963), ch. 5.

NOTE: It is convenient to begin by converting the times of fall under gravity into a mean velocity of fall and performing a similar operation upon the times of ascent in the electric field; these velocities should be tabulated for each drop together with the sum of the velocities with and without the field. The greatest common divisor of these sums, which is employed in the calculation of apparent electronic charge, is readily found by inspection. In calculating the latter, as in calculating the apparent radius of each drop, it is worth noting that the greater part of the mathematical expression used is common to all three drops; it is therefore convenient to work out these common factors at the outset.

Note that the potential gradient must be expressed in electrostatic units; for the meaning of 'poise' see the notes on Problem 2. From the slope of the graph of (apparent electronic charge)$^{\frac{2}{3}}$ against $1/(\text{pressure} \times \text{apparent radius})$ the rate of linear deviation from Stokes's law may be obtained and a second approximation to the radii of the drops may be made. These new radii may then be used to draw a fresh graph of $e^{\frac{2}{3}}$ against $1/pa$, whose extrapolation leads to a more accurate value of the electronic charge; in practice, however, the further approximation leads to a relatively insignificant change in the value of the electronic charge and the result of the first approximation may be adopted. It will be understood that the use of a selection of the data for three drops, out of the twenty-five measured by Millikan, introduces a much greater uncertainty than attaches to Millikan's final result.

Criticisms of this work are well summarized in *The Particles of Modern Physics* by J. D. Stranathan (Blakiston, Philadelphia, 1942), pp. 56–63.

4 PLANCK'S CONSTANT FROM THE PHOTO-ELECTRIC EFFECT

R. A. Millikan, *Phys. Rev.*, **7**, 355, 1916.

Millikan exposed a freshly cut sodium surface *in vacuo* to monochromatic radiation of various frequencies from a quartz–mercury arc and collected the photo-electrons emitted in a Faraday cylinder connected with an electrometer. He measured the electrometer deflexion caused by 30 seconds' illumination when various potentials were applied to the sodium surface relative to the Faraday cylinder. In addition to the externally applied potential there was a contact potential between the sodium surface and the oxidized copper Faraday cylinder; this contact potential, which may be assumed to be constant during the experiment, made the sodium positive to the Faraday cylinder.

Below are tabulated Millikan's results for the three frequencies selected by him as being among the most reliable:

Wave-length 5461 $\mathring{A}$		3650 $\mathring{A}$		3126 $\mathring{A}$	
Applied voltage	Electrometer deflexion	Applied voltage	Electrometer deflexion	Applied voltage	Electrometer deflexion
−2·257	28	−1·157	67·5	−0·5812	52
−2·205	14	−1·105	36	−0·5288	29
−2·152	7	−1·0525	19	−0·4765	12
−2·100	3	−1·0002	11	−0·4242	5
..	..	−0·9478	4	−0·3718	2·5

(i) For each frequency, plot the deflexion against the applied voltage and hence estimate the minimum applied voltage which, together with the unknown contact potential, prevents the fastest photo-electrons from reaching the Faraday cylinder.

(ii) Plot these minimum voltages against the frequency of

the incident radiation; from the slope of the line and Millikan's value for the electronic charge ($4 \cdot 774 \times 10^{-10}$ e.s.u.) calculate Planck's constant.

R. A. Millikan, *Electrons, Protons*, &c. (Chicago and Cambridge, 1935), ch. x.

R. A. Millikan, *The Electron*, ed. by *J. W. M. Dumond* (Chicago, 1963), ch. 10.

NOTE: The extrapolation to ascertain the minimum stopping voltage is a good deal more arbitrary than was originally suspected, although the error introduced is probably not very serious. The matter is discussed by Du Bridge (*Phys. Rev.*, **43**, 727, 1933) and Roehr (*Phys. Rev.*, **44**, 866, 1933).

5 THE ATOMIC WEIGHT OF LANTHANUM BY MASS-SPECTROMETER

M. G. Inghram, R. J. Hayden, and D. C. Hess, *Phys. Rev.*, **72**, 967, 1947.

Examination in a mass-spectrometer of the ions emitted by a tungsten filament coated with lanthanum sesquioxide discloses peaks at masses 154, 155, 156, and 157. The last three peaks are attributable to $La^{139}O^{16}$, $La^{139}O^{17}$, and $La^{139}O^{18}$ respectively. A range of arguments makes it almost certain that the first peak is due to the ion $La^{138}O^{16}$ disclosing the presence of a hitherto unsuspected isotope of lanthanum.

An analysis of the heights of the peaks showed that the isotopic constitution of lanthanum is 99·911 per cent of atoms of mass number 139 and 0·089 per cent of atoms of mass number 138. The packing fraction for lanthanum is $-3 \cdot 2 \times 10^{-4}$; the conversion factor from physical to chemical atomic weights on the pre-1961 physical atomic weight scale ($O^{16} = 16 \cdot 0000$) was $1 \cdot 000275$; the atomic weight of oxygen on the now internationally accepted unified (physical–chemical) scale ($C^{12} = 12 \cdot 0000$) is 15·9994.

> Calculate the atomic weight of lanthanum (i) on the pre-1961 chemical scale, (ii) on the unified scale.

NOTE: This paper contains a discussion of the possible sources of error in the measurements as well as providing an illuminating example of the lines of argument used in establishing the identity of ions responsible for various peaks. An interesting feature of the 'new' isotope of mass 138 is that its nucleus might be expected to be unstable; no observable radioactivity had however been observed in lanthanum; it was discovered eventually in 1950.

The unified atomic weight scale is discussed by E. A. Guggenheim (*J. Chem. Ed.*, **38**, 86, 1961 with erratum pointed out on p. 131) and by A. Labbauf (ibid., **39**, 282, 1962).

6 ATOMIC WEIGHTS AND ISOTOPIC COMPOSITION

R. T. Birge, *Rev. Mod. Phys.*, **1**, 1, 1929; W. F. Giauque and H. L. Johnston, *J. Am. Chem. Soc.*, **51**, 1436, 1929; H. C. Urey and G. K. Teal, *Rev. Mod. Phys.*, **7**, 34, 1935; F. W. Aston, *Nature*, **135**, 541, 1935.

In 1927 Aston compared the masses of hydrogen and oxygen in the mass-spectrograph and obtained the ratio: $1 \cdot 00778 \pm 0 \cdot 00015$ to 16. At that time the accepted value for the atomic weight of hydrogen, derived from a large number of chemical determinations of atomic weight, was $1 \cdot 00777 \pm 0 \cdot 00002$.

(i) What inference was it reasonable to draw from these data as to the isotopic simplicity or complexity of the two elements?

In 1929 Giauque and Johnston showed from an examination of absorption spectra that atmospheric oxygen contains atoms of mass numbers 16, 17, and 18 in relative abundance now believed to be 99·758, 0·0373, and 0·2039 per cent respectively.

(ii) What modification does this lead to in the inferences drawn in (i)? Express your conclusion in quantitative terms.

In 1935 Aston redetermined the H : O ratio in the mass spectrograph and obtained the new value of $1 \cdot 0081 \pm 0 \cdot 0001$ to 16.

(iii) Can this revised value be reconciled with the existence of the heavy isotope of hydrogen of mass number 2, discovered by Urey in 1931, present in water to the extent of about $0 \cdot 0145 \pm 0 \cdot 0005$ per cent?

NOTE: This sequence of data tells the story of the discovery of deuterium; the fortunate consequences of the error in Aston's earlier determination of the H : O ratio are obvious. E. Wichers (*J. Am. Chem. Soc.*, **78**, 3235, 1956) provides an interesting modern discussion of the relation between the 'physical' and 'chemical' scales of atomic weight. The adoption in 1961 of a 'unified' atomic weight scale, based on $C^{12} = 12 \cdot 0000$, by both chemists and physicists promises to make the distinction between the two scales of purely historical interest. A. Labbauf (*J. Chem. Ed.*, **39**, 282, 1962) discusses the genesis of the unified scale.

Because of the large number of significant figures in some of the quantities involved, one or two steps in the problem are best done directly and without the use of logarithms. It is of interest to compare the results obtained in this problem with the most recent values for the masses and abundances of the nuclides involved (see, for example, Appendix G of G. Friedlander and J. W. Kennedy, *Nuclear and Radiochemistry* (Wiley, New York, 1955).

7 ISOTOPIC MASSES FROM THE ENERGY LIBERATED IN NUCLEAR REACTIONS

E. D. Klema and G. C. Phillips, *Phys. Rev.*, **86**, 951, 1952.

The Einstein mass–energy equivalence equation can be applied to the energy liberated in a nuclear reaction to provide rather exact information about the difference between the masses of the 'reactant' and 'resultant' nuclides. Bombarding particles of definite energy can be obtained by passing the beam of particles from an accelerator through a magnetic analyser and the energy of the particles ejected after nuclear reaction can be measured by the strength of the magnetic field required to curve them into a pre-determined trajectory. It is easy to show that, if measurements are restricted to particles ejected at a known angle (e.g. 90°) to the bombarding beam, the energy liberated in the nuclear reaction can be calculated without knowing the energy and trajectory of the residual nucleus. Physicists use the symbol 'Q' for the energy released in nuclear reactions.

Klema and Phillips used a beam of deuterons from a Van de Graaff accelerator to bombard carbon. A magnetic analyser showed that for the nuclear reaction $C^{12}(d,p)C^{13}$ the Q value was $2 \cdot 732 \pm 0 \cdot 006 \times 10^6$ electron-volts. If the isotope masses of hydrogen, deuterium, and carbon-12 are $1 \cdot 008142$, $2 \cdot 014735$, and $12 \cdot 003804$ respectively on the physical scale, calculate the isotopic mass of carbon-13.

NOTE: It is interesting to compare the result of this calculation with the very exact determination of the *ratio* of the masses of the same two carbon isotopes from microwave spectra in Problem 9. A discussion by H. E. Duckworth of the small discrepancies in the mass of C^{13} as determined from Q values and from microwave spectroscopy will be found in *Rev. Mod. Phys.*, **29**, 767, 1957.

The present status of various methods of comparing nuclear masses is usefully discussed by K. T. Bainbridge in ch. 1 of the volume edited by H. Hintenberger, *Nuclear Masses and their Determination* (Pergamon, New York, 1957), and also in part 9, ch. 2 of E. U. Condon and H. Odishaw, *Handbook of Physics* (McGraw-Hill, New York, 1958). The adoption of the unified (carbon-12) scale of atomic masses will make the numerical values quoted above obsolete.

8 GASEOUS DENSITIES

B. Lambert and C. S. G. Phillips, *Phil. Trans.* A., **242**, 415, 1950.

Lambert and Phillips measured the relative densities of nitrogen, methane, and oxygen by means of a gas microbalance. In three sets of measurements the following mean pressures of gas were required for zero balance:

N_2	.	.	230·730 mm	139·642 mm	85·584 mm
CH_4	.	.	402·476	243·691	149·527
O_2	.	.	202·007	122·248	74·924

(i) Calculate the pressure ratios CH_4/N_2 and N_2/O_2 for each set and plot the ratios against nitrogen pressure. From the extrapolated ratios, find the atomic weights of nitrogen and carbon, taking O = 16·0000 and H = 1·0080.

(ii) If the compressibility, a, defined by the equation

$$PV = P_0 V_0 (1 - aP) \qquad (P \text{ in atmospheres})$$

is 0·00068 for oxygen, calculate the compressibility of nitrogen.

NOTE: (i) Carry your pressure ratio calculation to six significant figures.

(ii) Express the pressure ratio (P_{N_2}/P_{O_2}) in terms of the extrapolated pressure ratios and of the compressibilities, and deduce an expression for the slope of your pressure ratio plot.

The paper by Lambert and Phillips gives interesting details about the method of pressure measurement and about the purification of the gases.

9 THE DETERMINATION OF ATOMIC MASSES BY MICROWAVE SPECTROSCOPY

R. C. Mockler and G. R. Bird, *Phys. Rev.*, **98**, 1837, 1955.

The frequencies at which gases absorb microwave radiation can be measured with great accuracy so that microwave spectroscopy can provide remarkably exact information about the rotational energy states of molecules. Mockler and Bird studied the microwave absorption of the unstable radical CS produced by an electrical discharge in carbon disulphide vapour. In the vibrational ground state the frequency of the absorption line for the lowest rotational transition (from $J = 0$ to $J = 1$) was found to be 48991·000±0·006 megacycles per second for $C^{12}S^{32}$ and 46247·472±0·020 megacycles per second for $C^{13}S^{32}$. For the lighter of these radicals the correction for rotation–vibration interaction (α) is 177·544±0·026 megacycles per second and this correction factor may be assumed to be inversely proportional to the three-halves power of the reduced mass for a series of isotopic combinations.

(i) Calculate the ratio of the moments of inertia of the two

10

radicals in the hypothetical state when the nuclei are stationary at their equilibrium separation.

(ii) Calculate the ratio of the atomic masses of C^{12} and C^{13}.

NOTE: The very high resolution and accuracy of microwave spectroscopy, applied to the isotopic shift in the pure rotation spectrum of a molecule, makes it possible to compare isotopic masses with an accuracy comparable with that attainable by mass-spectrographic and nuclear reaction measurements. The theory and experimental technique of the method are discussed by S. Geschwind, G. R. Gunther-Mohr, and C. H. Townes (*Rev. Mod. Phys.*, **26**, 444, 1954). The error that would be introduced by ignoring vibrational–rotational interaction is of the order of two parts in ten thousand; Mockler and Bird themselves took into account not only this correction but one for the centrifugal distortion of the molecule. The mass ratio obtained for C^{12}/C^{13} is not very sensitive to the value assumed for the ratio of the masses of S^{32} and C^{12}. In Problem 7 the masses of the same pair of isotopes are calculated from the energy liberated in a nuclear reaction; the note appended to that problem gives references to reviews of the methods available for measuring nuclear masses.

10 THE MOLECULAR WEIGHT OF 'BENCE-JONES' PROTEIN BY THE ULTRA-CENTRIFUGE

T. Svedberg and B. Sjogren, *J. Am. Chem. Soc.*, **51**, 3594, 1929.

The weight of large molecules such as proteins may be determined by measurements of the concentration gradient set up when the solution is subjected to an intense field of force (in this case *c.* five thousand times *g*) in the Svedberg ultra-centrifuge. The concentration of different strata of the solution is measured by their light absorption at suitable wave-length.

Below are tabulated typical results for the determination of the molecular weight of 'Bence-Jones' protein:

The solution centrifuged was a 0·05 per cent solution of the protein in a phosphate buffer (pH = 5·5). The partial specific volume of the (centrifugable) solute was 0·749; the density of the solvent was 1·006. The speed of the rotor carrying the cell was 10300 revolutions per minute and the temperature of the experiment was 293·3° K.

The concentrations of solution c_1 and c_2 at distances x_1 and x_2 from the axis of rotation, which are set out below, were obtained by comparing photographically the absorption of light from a mercury vapour lamp (filtered through chlorine and bromine) by the given stratum of solution with that absorbed by a M/500 solution of potassium dichromate contained in a second cell on the same rotor:

x_1	x_2	c_1	c_2
(cm)		(per cent)	
5·73	5·68	0·054	0·048
5·58	5·53	0·0382	0·0342

Calculate the mean molecular weight of the protein.

NOTE: The principle of this method is the same as that underlying Perrin's evaluation of Avogadro's number by sedimentation equilibrium of a colloid suspension. Here Avogadro's number is assumed and the mass of the solute determined. The lower mass of the protein (relative to Perrin's suspended colloid) necessitates the use of a greatly enhanced field of force, which, unlike the gravitational field, is not uniform but varies with the distance from the axis of rotation.

Since the potential energy of the molecules, as derived from the centrifugal acceleration, is calculated in mechanical units, the gas constant must be expressed in ergs/°K/mole.

Since the pioneer work of Svedberg the importance of molecular weight determinations for substances of biological interest has provoked intensive exploration of all the ways in which sedimentation studies can be used for this purpose. Sedimentation equilibrium, sedimentation velocity, and the approach to sedimentation equilibrium (J. W. Archibald, *J. Phys. Chem.*, **51**, 1204, 1947) have all been used. The sedimentation equilibrium method, using very small depths of solution (1–3 mm) to accelerate the attainment of equilibrium, is still important; K. E. Van Holde and R. L. Baldwin (*J. Phys. Chem.*, **62**, 734, 1958), D. A. Yphantis (*Annals, New York Academy of Science*, **88**, 586, 1960), or C. Tanford (*The Physical Chemistry of Macromolecules*, Wiley, New York, 1961, ch. 4 and 6) may be consulted.

11* THE MOLECULAR WEIGHT OF POLYISOBUTYLENE FROM MEASUREMENTS OF OSMOTIC PRESSURE AND VISCOSITY

P. J. Flory, *J. Am. Chem. Soc.*, **65**, 372, 1943.

Osmotic pressure measurements were carried out on samples of polyisobutylene which had been separated by precipitation from benzene solution with acetone into fractions of widely differing molecular size. Membranes of swollen cellophane and of denitrated collodion were used in the osmometer and equilibrium was established after several hours at 25° C.

The following table gives the concentration (in grammes of polymer per 100 cm³ of solution) and the osmotic pressure (in grammes weight per cm²) for solutions of a single fraction of polyisobutylene in cyclohexane and in benzene:

In cyclohexane		In benzene	
Concentration	Osmotic pressure	Concentration	Osmotic pressure
2·00	10·58	2·00	0·82
1·50	5·73	1·00	$0·37_5$
1·00	2·42	1·00	$0·40_5$
0·76	1·32	0·50	$0·15_5$
0·61	0·65	0·50	$0·17_5$
0·34	0·30		

(i) Plot the ratio of osmotic pressure to concentration against the concentration for each solvent and from the limiting value of the ratio at zero concentration, calculate the average molecular weight of the fraction.

For a series of more narrowly fractionated samples of polyisobutylene the following table gives the relative viscosity in diisobutylene solution at 20° and the osmotic pressure (in the same units as above) in cyclohexane solution at 25°. All measurements relate to a concentration of 0·5 g/100 cm³ of solution.

13

Sample	Relative viscosity η_r	Osmotic pressure
1	1·281	2·05
2	1·203	2·94
3	1·164	3·66
4	1·071	11·97

(ii) Calculate for each sample the value of $\dfrac{\ln \eta_r}{c}$, where 'c' represents the concentration of the solution in g/100 cm³. The limiting value of this ratio at zero concentration is the 'intrinsic viscosity' of the solution. Flory showed that for the above dilute solutions the value of the ratio itself differed by less than 2 per cent from the true intrinsic viscosity.

(iii) Calculate the average molecular weight of each of the four samples from the osmotic pressure. In estimating the value of osmotic pressure/concentration at zero concentration you may assume, as is justified by other data in Flory's paper, that curves of this ratio plotted against concentration for each of the fractions are identical in shape and differ only in vertical displacement.

(iv) Examine the form of the relationship between average molecular weight and the approximation to the intrinsic viscosity calculated in (ii) by plotting the logarithm of the former against the logarithm of the latter.

NOTE: C. E. H. Bawn, *Chemistry of High Polymers* (Interscience, New York, 1948), ch. 5; P. J. Flory, *Principles of Polymer Chemistry* (Cornell U.P., Ithaca, 1953), ch. 7; C. Tanford, *The Physical Chemistry of Macro-molecules* (Wiley, New York, 1961), ch. 4 and 6.

Two of the commonest methods of estimating the molecular weight of polymers are illustrated by this problem. Osmotic pressure measurements are experimentally exacting but, if extrapolated to zero concentration from suitably low concentrations, are regarded as a reliable source of information for molecular weights. Viscosity measurements are, on the other hand, carried out very readily but the relation of the results to molecular weights have been the subject of spirited discussion ever since Staudinger made his original, now admittedly over-simplified but undeniably fruitful, suggestion. See, for example, discussions by

M. Huggins (*Ind. and Eng. Chem.*, **35**, 980, 1943), M. A. Lauffer (*Chem. Rev.*, **31**, 561, 1942) or ch. 6 of P. W. Allen, *Techniques of Polymer Characterisation* (Butterworth, London, 1959). The viscosity method is not an *absolute* method and always requires calibration based on molecular weight information derived from another method with a more solid theoretical foundation, such as osmotic pressure measurements. The empirical relationship between viscosity data and molecular weights illustrated in part (iv) depends on close structural similarity among the different polymers concerned and is vitiated by structural differences such as branching.

The assumption of 'identity of shape' used in part (ii) is something of an over-simplification; W. R. Krigbaum and P. J. Flory (*J. Am. Chem. Soc.*, **75**, 1775, 1953) or ch. 4 of Tanford's book (*v.s.*) may be consulted.

A significant complication when, as is normally the case, a mixture of polymers is involved, is that different methods give different kinds of averaging of the molecular weight.

The type of osmometer used by Flory is illustrated in *Helv. Chim. Acta*, **23**, 430, 1940; for a new type of osmometer particularly suitable for very low osmotic pressures see B. Enoksson (*J. Polymer Science*, **6**, 575, 1951).

Gaseous Equilibria

12 THE DISSOCIATION OF IODINE VAPOUR

G. Starck and M. Bodenstein, *Z. Elektrochem.*, **16**, 961, 1910.

A known weight of iodine was sealed up in a quartz bulb and the pressure developed by the vapour at various temperatures was measured with a quartz-fibre manometer. The following data were obtained in one of the experiments:

Amount of iodine = 1·958 millimoles
Volume of bulb = 249·8 cm³
(virtually independent of temperature).

Temperature (°C)	Pressure (mm)
800	558·0
1000	748·0
1200	1019·2

Assuming that both molecular and atomic iodine behave as ideal gases, calculate (i) K_p in mm and (ii) K_c in moles per litre at each temperature, and hence (iii) an approximate value for the heat of dissociation at constant volume at 1000° C.

NOTE: This is a straightforward calculation of the two kinds of equilibrium constant together with an application of the van't Hoff isochore. The units in which the equilibrium constants are expressed should be clearly stated; unnecessary confusion is liable to arise in equilibrium constant calculations unless some convention is consistently applied in selecting reactants or resultants for the numerator of the constant; in this book the *resultants* of the reaction will be put in the numerator. A table of reciprocals is useful in this as in all problems involving the isochore or algebraically similar calculations (cf. Problem 17).

13 THE HEAT OF DISSOCIATION OF FLUORINE MEASURED BY ITS RATE OF EFFUSION AT DIFFERENT TEMPERATURES

H. Wise, *J. Phys. Chem.*, **58**, 389, 1954.

The rate of effusion of a gas at low pressures through a small opening with thin edges is given by the expression

$$w = Pat\sqrt{(M/2\pi RT)}$$

where w is the weight (in grammes) of gas diffusing in time t (in seconds), P is the pressure of the gas (in dynes/cm²), a is the area of the orifice (in cm²), M is the molecular weight of the gas, T is the absolute temperature, and R is the gas constant (in ergs mole^{-1} °K^{-1}). If the rate of effusion of a diatomic gas is measured at T_1 at which the orifice has an area a_1 and the gas is undissociated and again at temperature T_2 at which the orifice has an area a_2 (due to thermal expansion) and the degree of dissociation of the gas is α, the two rates of effusion may be calculated by means of the above equation, assuming that the atomic and molecular species diffuse independently at the higher temperature.

(i) Deduce an expression for the ratio of the masses of gas effusing per second under these conditions in terms of the temperatures (T_1, T_2), orifice areas (a_1, a_2), pressures (P_1, P_2), and the degree of dissociation of the gas at the higher temperature.

(ii) Rearrange the result of (i) so as to obtain the degree of dissociation at temperature T_2 as an explicit function of $T_1, T_2, a_1, a_2, P_1, P_2$ and the rates of fall of pressure due to effusion ($d \ln P_1/dt$ and $d \ln P_2/dt$).

Wise used such an expression to measure the temperature

variation of the dissociation of fluorine and hence its heat of dissociation. The low pressures required for the validity of the basic equation are particularly suitable for the realization of substantial dissociation at relatively low temperatures. Fluorine contained in a Pyrex vessel of about one litre capacity at room temperature diffused through a sharp-edged circular nickel orifice (0·0185 cm in diameter). The temperature of both the orifice and a long wide nickel cylinder connecting it to the Pyrex vessel were controlled by an electric furnace which surrounded them. The pressure of fluorine in the storage vessel and its rate of fall owing to effusion were measured by a Pirani gauge. Measurements were carried out in the neighbourhood of 10^{-4} mm pressure.

The following data are taken from Wise's paper:

Temperature $(^{\circ}K)$	P $(atmos \times 10^7)$	$\dfrac{d \log_{10} P}{dt}$ $(sec^{-1} \times 10^4)$	Effective aperture (see note)
298	5·27	11·00	2·146
572	7·28	9·76	2·689
658	7·80	8·71	2·857

(iii) Calculate the degree of dissociation and the equilibrium constant (in atmosphere units) of the dissociation of fluorine at 572° K and 658° K.

(iv) Estimate the approximate heat of dissociation of fluorine.

NOTE: The energy of the F–F bond was the subject of lively discussion in the decade preceding the appearance of Wise's paper which was one of those contributing to the acceptance of a much lower value than had formerly been regarded as reasonable. A paper by M. G. Evans, E. Warhurst, and E. Whittle, *J. Chem. Soc.*, 1524, 1950, written as the evidence against the erroneous higher value was beginning to accumulate, provides an interesting account of the conflict of views; cf. Problem 54.

The pressure recorded in the second column is that of the gas at the heated orifice (and therefore the pressure controlling the dissociation as measured); it differs from that measured in the storage vessel (maintained at 298°) because of the difference in temperature of storage vessel

18

and orifice. The pressure listed has been corrected for this effect known as 'thermal transpiration'.

The variation of the orifice area with temperature was studied by measurements of the diffusion of argon in the apparatus over the same temperature range. The fourth column gives a value proportional to the orifice area which also takes into account effects due to the difference in temperature between the gas whose pressure is being measured and that diffusing through the orifice.

(i) In a mixture of fluorine molecules and atoms the partial pressure of each species is readily related to the degree of dissociation and the total pressure.

(ii) The mathematical rearrangement to be carried out here is required because the rate of effusion was measured not in terms of rate of mass-transfer but in terms of the rate of fall of pressure in the storage vessel, which was at room temperature throughout.

14* THE EQUILIBRIUM AND KINETICS OF THE DISSOCIATION OF GASEOUS HYDROGEN IODIDE

A. H. Taylor, jr., and R. H. Crist, *J. Am. Chem. Soc.*, **63**, 1377, 1941.

The dissociation of hydrogen iodide is one of the most carefully investigated of all gas reactions. Its original study by Bodenstein (1893–1899) is one of the classical investigations of physical chemistry and since then it has been repeatedly used as a proving ground for hypotheses concerning both chemical equilibrium and reaction velocity.

In a modern study of the reaction Crist and Taylor measured the equilibrium constant over a range of temperature, approaching the equilibrium from both sides, and measured the reaction rates for forward and backward reactions. The reaction was carried out in fused quartz bulbs; their contents could be analysed after a given period of reaction or at equilibrium with standard sodium thiosulphate and alkali.

The equilibrium constant

The following data relate to two of their individual experiments at two different temperatures; in the first of these hydrogen and iodine (not in stoichiometric proportions) were heated together and in the second hydrogen iodide was decomposed. In all cases concentrations are given in (moles/cm³) × 10⁵.

Temperature (°K)	Time of heating (min)	[H₂] At start	[I₂]	[H₂]	[HI]
			At equilibrium		
698·6	515	1·1337	0·07378	0·45647	1·3544
666·8	2202	. .	0·13953	0·13953	1·0791

(i) Calculate the equilibrium constant at each temperature for the reaction: $2HI = H_2 + I_2$.

These constants are subject to error owing to the diffusion of hydrogen through quartz at these temperatures. Independent measurements of the rate of this diffusion with reaction cells such as those used showed that the equilibrium constants calculated above must be reduced by 1·3 per cent and 1·7 per cent respectively to correct for the diffusion of hydrogen.

(ii) Using equilibrium constants corrected in this way calculate the mean heat content change over the temperature range for the dissociation of one mole of hydrogen iodide into the gaseous elements.

The rate of decomposition of hydrogen iodide

Similar analyses carried out on reaction mixtures before equilibrium was attained (where the shorter reaction time eliminated the need for a correction for hydrogen diffusion) were used to measure the rate of decomposition of hydrogen iodide. The results of two such experiments follow, with the same concentration units as those used above:

Temperature (°K)	Time of reaction (sec)	[HI] at start	[I₂] after reaction
698·6	10800	1·2178	0·07787
666·8	18000	1·5187	0·04800

20

(iii) Bearing in mind that this is a reversible reaction whose equilibrium constant was calculated in (ii), calculate the second-order rate constant (in cm^3 $mole^{-1}$ sec^{-1}) at each temperature.

(iv) From the results of (iii) calculate the activation energy of the reaction corrected for the variation of molecular velocity with temperature.

(v) As a test of the simple form of the collision theory of reaction rates, which assumes that every collision between reactant molecules in which the relative kinetic energy along the line of centres exceeds the activation energy will lead to reaction, calculate the molecular diameter that must be postulated for the hydrogen iodide molecule in order to account for the rate constant at $666 \cdot 8°$ K calculated in (iii), using the activation energy calculated in (iv).

NOTE: (iii) The calculation of the forward rate constant of a reversible reaction from the equilibrium constant and concentration against the time data is sometimes quite complicated but in this particular case the calculation is comparatively simple. The rate law:

$$dx/dt = k(a-x)^2 - k'\left(\frac{x}{2}\right)^2,$$

where $(a-x)$ is the concentration of hydrogen iodide at time t, leads on integration to the expression

$$\ln\left[\frac{x(a-2x_e) + ax_e}{a(x_e - x)}\right] = k\frac{2a(a - x_e)}{x_e}t$$

where $(a - x_e)$ is the concentration of hydrogen iodide at equilibrium (see A. A. Frost and R. G. Pearson, *Kinetics and Mechanism*, Wiley, New York, 1961, pp. 187–8). This expression is readily shown to be equivalent to the one used by Taylor and Crist:

$$k = \frac{K^{\frac{1}{2}}}{0 \cdot 4343ta}\log_{10}\left(\frac{\alpha + Z}{\alpha - Z}\right)$$

where K is the equilibrium constant for the decomposition, Z is the fraction of hydrogen iodide decomposed after time t and α is defined by the expression $\alpha = 2K^{\frac{1}{2}}(1 - Z)$. Taylor and Crist's form is somewhat more convenient for computation.

(iv) For the correction of the energy of activation for the variation of collision number with temperature, see Hinshelwood, *Kinetics of Chemical Change* (Oxford, 1940), p. 55, or A. A. Frost and R. G. Pearson,

21

Kinetics and Mechanisms (Wiley, New York, 1961), p. 24. This correction usually is little larger than the experimental uncertainty.

(v) The number of collisions per cm^3 per sec in a gas containing n molecules per cm^3 is $2n^2\sigma^2\sqrt{\left(\dfrac{\pi RT}{M}\right)}$, where σ is the collision diameter of the molecules and M is the molecular weight of the gas. The proportion of collisions with a relative kinetic energy along the line of centres greater than E is

$$e^{\frac{-E}{RT}}.$$

In applying these relations it is well to remember (a) that two molecules of hydrogen iodide are decomposed in every fruitful collision, (b) that the rate constants obtained in (iii) are based on the concentration unit of one mole per cm^3, (c) that the gas constant used in the collision number expression must be expressed in erg mole^{-1} °K^{-1} units.

15 * THE DEACON EQUILIBRIUM AND THE ELECTROMOTIVE FORCE OF THE HYDROGEN–OXYGEN CELL

G. N. Lewis, *J. Am. Chem. Soc.*, **28**, 1380, 1906; F. Dolezalek, *Z. physik. Chem.*, **26**, 321, 1898.

The equilibrium constant of the Deacon process was investigated by passing a mixture of hydrogen chloride and oxygen in known proportions into a heated reaction vessel containing pumice coated with cupric chloride; equilibrium was attained after several hours and a specimen of the equilibrium mixture was transferred to an evacuated vessel, and the ratio chlorine/hydrogen chloride was measured by titration with potassium iodide and alkali. A selection of the experimental results is tabulated below:

T (°C)	Pressure in reaction vessel (atmospheres)	moles O$_2$ / moles HCl (initial)	moles O$_2$ / moles HCl (final)
352	1·00	0·927	5·440
352	0·93	0·297	0·495
386	0·98	3·270	19·700
386	0·96	0·488	1·460

(i) Calculate the mean value of $K_p \left(= \dfrac{p_{H_2O}^{\frac{1}{2}} p_{Cl_2}^{\frac{1}{2}}}{p_{HCl} p_{O_2}^{\frac{1}{4}}} \right)$ at both temperatures and hence the heat-content change for the reaction in this temperature range.

(ii) Compare the latter value with that derived from the following thermochemical data:

$$\tfrac{1}{2}H_2 + \tfrac{1}{4}O_2 = \tfrac{1}{2}H_2O_{gas} \qquad \Delta H = -28900 \text{ cal}$$
$$\tfrac{1}{2}H_2 + \tfrac{1}{2}Cl_2 = HCl_{gas} \qquad \Delta H = -22000 \text{ cal}$$

The e.m.f. of the cell

$$H_2(Pt) \mid HCl \text{ aq.} \mid Cl_2(Pt)$$
$$\quad \text{1 atm} \quad \text{6·50 N} \quad \text{1 atm}$$

at 30° C was found by Dolezalek to be 1·145 volts; the vapour pressure of water is 31·5 mm and that of hydrogen chloride above its 6·50 N solution is 0·71 mm at 30°.

By combining the data of Lewis and Dolezalek calculate:

(iii) the free energy change of the reaction

$$\tfrac{1}{2}H_2 \quad + \quad \tfrac{1}{4}O_2 = \tfrac{1}{2}H_2O_{liquid} \text{ at } 30° \text{ C};$$
$$\text{1 atm} \qquad \text{1 atm}$$

(iv) $K_p \left(= \dfrac{p_{H_2}^{\frac{1}{2}} p_{O_2}^{\frac{1}{4}}}{p_{H_2O}^{\frac{1}{2}}} \right)$ for the dissociation of water at 30° C;

(v) the e.m.f. at 30° C of the reversible cell ('Knall-gaskette')

$$H_2 \quad \mid \quad H_2O \quad \mid \quad O_2$$
$$\text{1 atm} \quad \text{liquid} \quad \text{1 atm}$$

NOTE: (i) It is convenient to begin by calculating the algebraic relation between x, the proportion of HCl decomposed, and the initial and final oxygen/hydrogen chloride ratios; x may then be tabulated for the four experiments. The equilibrium constant

$$\frac{p_{H_2O}^{\frac{1}{2}} p_{Cl_2}^{\frac{1}{2}}}{p_{HCl} p_{O_2}^{\frac{1}{4}}}$$

may be expressed algebraically in terms of x, the total pressure and the initial oxygen/hydrogen chloride ratio and calculated numerically for each case.

(ii) In comparing the thermochemical value for ΔH with that derived from the van't Hoff isochore, it should be realized that the two results relate to different temperatures; to reduce them to the same temperature would involve a knowledge of the specific heats of the reactants and resultants and the application of Kirchhoff's law (cf. Problem 16).

23

(iii) From Dolezalek's e.m.f. measurement we can calculate the net work involved in the reversible formation of hydrogen chloride at its partial pressure over a 6·5 N aqueous solution from hydrogen and chlorine at one atmosphere. In calculating the free energy change of this reaction, it must not be forgotten to reduce the result to the standard pressure unit (the atmosphere). This result may then be combined additively with the free energy change for the Deacon process, calculated from its equilibrium constant at 30° C, to give the free energy of formation of water-vapour at one atmosphere. Since the free energy of formation of liquid water is asked for, the vapour pressure of water at 30° is provided.

(iv) K_p for the dissociation of water at 30° C is directly calculable from the free energy of formation at the same temperature by means of the van't Hoff isotherm.

(v) The e.m.f. of the hydrogen–oxygen cell, which is calculable directly from the free energy of formation of liquid water, is not accessible by direct experiment as the oxygen electrode does not behave reversibly (cf. T. P. Hoar, *Proc. Roy. Soc.* A, **142**, 628, 1933).

For a discussion on the hydrogen–oxygen fuel cell, see G. J. Young, *Fuel Cells* (Reinhold, New York, 1960); see Problem 16.

16 * THE DISSOCIATION EQUILIBRIA OF STEAM AND THE OXIDES OF CARBON

F. T. E. Rhead and R. V. Wheeler, *J. Chem. Soc.*, **100**, 1140, 1911; I. Langmuir, *J. Am. Chem. Soc.*, **28**, 1357, 1906.

Rhead and Wheeler studied the equilibrium

$$CO_2 + C \rightleftharpoons 2CO$$

by analysing samples of the gas taken from a heated silica bulb containing the reaction mixture. The data shown in the table at the top of the facing page are taken from their results.

(i) Calculate a mean value of K_p for each temperature.

(ii) Calculate the heat-content change of the reaction at 1173° K, and compare the result with that derived from the following heats of combustion at 290° K:

$$C + O_2 = CO_2; \qquad \Delta H = -94250 \text{ cal}$$
$$CO + \tfrac{1}{2}O_2 = CO_2; \qquad \Delta H = -67960 \text{ cal}$$

Temperature (°K)	Total pressure (atmospheres)	Percentage CO_2 in equilibrium mixture
1073	2·57	26·45
	1·23	16·12
1173	2·30	6·92
	0·65	2·17
1323	2·09	0·92
	1·59	0·71

(iii) From your graph of $\log_{10} K_p$ against $1/T$, estimate K_p at 1400° K.

Langmuir measured the dissociation of carbon dioxide at atmospheric pressure into carbon monoxide and oxygen at a hot platinum wire with the following results:

Temperature (°K)	Percentage dissociation
1395	0·0140
1443	0·0250
1498	0·0471

(iv) Calculate K_p at each temperature.

(v) Calculate the heat-content change of the reaction and compare the results with the thermochemical data given in (ii).

(vi) From the graph of $\log_{10} K_p$ against $1/T$ calculate K_p at 1400° K.

(vii) From the results of (iii) and (vi) calculate the e.m.f. at 1400° K of the hypothetical fuel cell in which the reaction

$$C + O_2 = CO_2$$

takes place reversibly.

The molar heats at constant pressure of carbon, oxygen, and carbon dioxide are given by the equations:

$$C: \quad C_p = 1·64 + 0·0017T;$$
$$O_2: \quad C_p = 6·50 + 0·0010T;$$
$$CO_2: \quad C_p = 7·0 + 0·0071T - 0·00000186T^2.$$

(viii) Calculate the e.m.f. of the fuel cell at 298° C.

Using the hot-wire method Langmuir obtained the following results for the dissociation of steam at atmospheric pressure:

Temperature ($°K$)	Percentage dissociation
1457	0·0144
1537	0·0270

(ix) Calculate K_p for the water–gas equilibrium

$$CO_2 + H_2 \rightleftharpoons CO + H_2O$$

at 1400° K from Langmuir's two sets of results.

NOTE: In calculating equilibrium constants from analytical data it often saves confusion to begin by formulating the equilibrium constant algebraically in terms of the quantities measured experimentally. In (ii), (iii), and (vi) the variation of heat-content change with temperature is ignored. (vii) involves the calculation of the experimentally unmeasurable equilibrium $C + O_2 = CO_2$ from two related equilibria accessible to direct measurement; it further illustrates how information from gaseous equilibria enables us to calculate the e.m.f. of a cell of great potential technical importance; for a discussion of 'fuel cells' see R. G. H. Watson, *Research*, **7**, 34, 1954, and G. J. Young, *Fuel Cells* (Reinhold, New York, 1960). In (viii) the variation of free energy change with temperature must be calculated in the more rigorous manner which takes into account the variation of heat-content change with temperature.

17* DISSOCIATION OF IODINE FROM SPECTROSCOPIC DATA

G. Herzberg, *Molecular Spectra: vol. i. Diatomic Molecules* (Van Nostrand, New York, 1950).

The following properties have deen determined spectroscopically:

For iodine molecules:
ground state $= {}^1\Sigma_g^+$; vibration frequency $= 213·5$ cm^{-1}
internuclear distance $= 2·667$ Å; dissociation energy, D_0,
$$= 12442 \text{ cm}^{-1}$$

The ground state of the iodine atom is a multiplet, the lowest level being ${}^2P_{\frac{3}{2}}$ with ${}^2P_{\frac{1}{2}}$ lying 7598 cm^{-1} above it.

Weight of one atom of iodine $= 210\cdot72 \times 10^{-24}$ g.

$$\frac{hc}{k} = 1\cdot4385 \text{ cm deg.}$$

(i) Calculate the equilibrium constant of the reaction
$$I_2 \rightleftharpoons 2I$$
at $0°$ C, $800°$ C, and $1200°$ C.

(ii) Compare the results with direct experimental measurements of Starck and Bodenstein, Z. *Elektrochem.*, **16**, 965, 1910 (cf. Problem 12).

NOTE: This is a straightforward exercise in the calculation of partition functions and their use for the calculation of thermodynamic properties. The problem divides itself into (a) the evaluation of $E\Delta_0^\circ/T$ and (b) the evaluation of the free energy function $(G° - E_0^\circ)/T$. (a) usually involves the calculation of the heat content function and comparison with calorimetric measurements of ΔH, but in this simple case it has been determined accurately by spectroscopic methods. (b) is carried out by calculation of the partition functions of the atoms and molecules from their energy levels.

Heterogeneous Equilibria

18 THE THERMAL ANALYSIS OF ANTIMONY–GOLD ALLOYS

R. Vogel, *Z. anorg. Chem.*, **50**, 145, 1906.

The results of the thermal analysis of mixtures of gold and antimony are tabulated below. The first column gives the atomic percentage of antimony in the alloy; the second column gives the temperature at which solid begins to separate; the third column gives the temperature of the invariant equilibrium (i.e. of the horizontal part of the cooling curve); and the fourth column gives the duration in seconds of this latter period of temperature arrest.

Atomic percentage Sb	First separation of solid (°C)	Invariant equilibrium (°C)	Temperature arrest (sec)
0	1064	1064	110
15·12	728	360	160
22·06	581	361	220
28·61	472	360	310
34·83	357	357	310
40·73	396	360	230
51·66	443	360	80
56·74	455	360	40
61·58	458	359	10
66·21	460	460	380
70·64	494	460	280
86·51	580	460	60
100	631	631	300

(i) Construct the phase-rule diagram for the system, showing the temperature-arrest–time curve on the same graph.

(ii) What intermetallic compounds are formed?

(iii) Label the areas into which the diagram may be divided.

NOTE: The data in this problem relate to an unusually simple alloy system; for information regarding the thermal analysis of more complicated systems see W. Hume-Rothery, J. W. Christian, and W. B. Pearson, *Metallurgical Equilibrium Diagrams* (Institute of Physics, London, 1952), or F. N. Rhines, *Phase Diagrams in Metallurgy* (McGraw-Hill, New York, 1956).

19 THE SYSTEM BERYLLIUM SULPHATE–POTASSIUM SULPHATE–WATER

H. T. S. Britton and A. J. L. Allmand, *J. Chem. Soc.*, **119**, 1463, 1921.

The equilibrium of the above system (including any double salts formed) at $25°$ C was investigated by dissolving in water

Saturated liquid phase			Wet residue		
Composition of 100 g of solute		Grammes of water associated with 100 g of solute	Composition of 10 g of an-hydrous salts		Grammes of water per 100 g of an-hydrous salt
K_2SO_4	$BeSO_4$		K_2SO_4	$BeSO_4$	
100	0	830	..	..	..
80	20	550	97·9	2·1	67
72	28	438	94·6	5·4	84
62·8	37·2	241	69·7	30·3	38
62·3	37·7	251	62·4	37·6	17
56·7	43·3	385	61·8	38·2	42
30·8	69·2	402	60·9	39·1	40
16·2	83·8	249	56·4	43·6	43
15·2	84·8	218	38·3	61·7	83
9·8	90·2	220	1·8	98·2	93
6·5	93·5	230	0	100	68·5
0	100	234	0	100	68·5

above 25° C weighed quantities of the two sulphates in varying relative amounts; the solution was allowed to cool down to 25° C and stirred at that temperature for several days. After allowing the solid phase to settle, portions of the clear supernatant liquid and of the wet solid were separately analysed with the results shown in the table on page 29.

Plot the number of grammes of water associated with 100 g of the mixed anhydrous sulphates in the liquid phase and in the wet residue respectively against the percentage composition of the mixed anhydrous salts. Deduce the nature of the solid phase in equilibrium with the solution when varying relative amounts of the two sulphates are present.

NOTE: This illustrates the 'residue' method in which the composition of the solid phase may be derived graphically from the composition of the saturated solution and that of a corresponding 'residue' consisting of the saturated solution mixed with the solid phase; two or more such pairs of compositions are needed for each solid phase. The method of plotting is often known as the 'Jänecke' rectangular diagram. G. L. Cunningham and T. S. Oey (*J. Am. Chem. Soc.*, **77**, 799, 1955) provide a later example of a 'Jänecke' diagram constructed by the residues method.

20 THE SYSTEM FERRIC CHLORIDE–AMMONIUM CHLORIDE–WATER

H. W. B. Roozeboom, *Z. physik. Chem.*, **10**, 145, 1892.

The equilibrium was investigated at 15° C by shaking up various mixtures of the two salts with water and analysing the saturated solution and solid phase respectively for iron and for total chloride. The table at top of facing page gives the composition of the solution, expressed as moles of salt per 100 moles of water, and of the solid phase:

From these data plot the composition of the saturated solution using as abscissae the moles of NH_4Cl per 100

Solution			Solid phase
NH$_4$Cl (moles)	FeCl$_3$ (moles)		
0	9·30 ⎫		FeCl$_3$,6H$_2$O
1·09	9·57 ⎭		
1·36	9·93 ⎫		
2·79	8·71 ⎪		(NH$_4$Cl)$_2$,FeCl$_3$,H$_2$O
5·22	7·65 ⎬		
10·78	6·21 ⎭		
7·82	6·75	7·29 ⎫	
7·70	5·03	4·40 ⎪	Mixed crystals
7·76	3·83	3·06 ⎬	per cent, FeCl$_3$
9·60	1·70	0·94 ⎭	
11·88	0		NH$_4$Cl

moles of H$_2$O and as ordinates the moles of FeCl$_3$ per 100 moles of H$_2$O, and hence deduce:

(i) The best conditions for getting the double salt;

(ii) the consequence of evaporating isothermally at 15° C the following solutions:

FeCl$_3$ (moles)	NH$_4$Cl (moles)	H$_2$O (moles)
8·0	0·8	100
6·0	6·0	100
2·0	6·0	100

NOTE: A convenient feature of this method of plotting a double salt equilibrium is that the consequence of evaporating isothermally any unsaturated solution is immediately ascertained by producing the line joining the intersection of the two axes to the point corresponding to the solution in question, until it intersects one of the solubility lines.

21 THE SYSTEM LITHIUM OXIDE–CHROMIUM TRIOXIDE–WATER

F. A. H. Schreinemakers, *Z. physik. Chem.*, **55**, 71, 1906.

The equilibrium of the lithium chromates with water was investigated at 30° by shaking various proportions of the two oxides with water and analysing the saturated solution and the wet solid phase. The following results are expressed in percentages by weight:

Saturated solution		Residue	
Percentage CrO_3	Percentage Li_2O	Percentage CrO_3	Percentage Li_2O
0	7·09	..	..
6·98	7·74	4·32	18·54
16·56	8·88	10·08	19·55
33·61	12·88	24·36	19·39
37·41	14·30	44·55	17·41
37·49	13·31	51·07	16·38
40·28	10·85	50·3*	14·4*
43·40	11·80	53·79	14·07
45·13	9·51	56·08	10·19
47·94	7·95	58·02	9·23
57·03	6·43	65·56	8·73
63·29	6·00	68·24	8·92
67·81	5·68	80·45	3·78
63·98	3·50	87·83	1·11
63·25	2·14	85·91	0·75
62·28	..	..	..

(i) Plot the data in the form of a triangular diagram, identify the solid phases, and label the areas.

(ii) Estimate from the diagram the solubility in pure water of the chromates of lithium.

NOTE: This system is typical of a large number where the formation of acid or basic salts makes it expedient to select the basic and acidic oxides as components. The composition of the residue marked with an asterisk was not measured by Schreinemakers; it has been calculated so as to define one of the solid phases. The original paper explains fully the indirect determination of a solid phase by the method of 'residues'; it also contains an investigation (and diagram) of the more complicated equilibria obtaining in the analogous system K_2O—CrO_3—H_2O.

For examples of more recent studies of ternary system the series of papers by A. E. Hill in the *J. Am. Chem. Soc.* may be consulted; of these papers that of Hill and J. E. Ricci (*J. Am. Chem. Soc.*, **53**, 4305, 1931) is characteristic and contains a discussion of methods of indirect analysis of the solid phase. A. C. Nixon and R. E. Smith (*J. Phys. Chem.*, **60**, 1422, 1956) also provide a later example of a triangular diagram constructed by the 'residues' method.

22* THE VAPOUR PRESSURE AND LATENT HEAT OF VAPORIZATION OF ZIRCONIUM DIOXIDE FROM EFFUSION MEASUREMENTS

M. Hoch, M. Nakata, and H. L. Johnston, *J. Am. Chem. Soc.*, **76**, 2651, 1954.

The vapour pressure of zirconium dioxide was measured by its rate of effusion from a tantalum 'Knudsen' cell containing a small orifice of known area with the following results:

Temperature (°K)	Time of effusion (sec)	Area of orifice (cm²)	Loss of weight of cell due to effusion (g)
2282	16304	0·0211	0·0381
2175	32658	0·0210	0·0181
2089	43823	0·02043	0·0074
2046	70123	0·02042	0·0056

(i) Assuming that the vapour has the formula ZrO_2, calculate the vapour pressure at each temperature.

(ii) Plot the logarithm of the vapour pressure against the reciprocal of the absolute temperature and by the method of least squares evaluate the coefficients in the equation:

$$\log_{10} p = A - B/T.$$

If the molar heat capacities at constant pressure of the solid and gaseous oxide are given by the equations:

$$C_p \text{ (solid)} = 17 \cdot 80 - 4 \cdot 00 \times 10^5 \times T^{-2}$$
$$C_p \text{ (gas)} = 10,$$

(iii) calculate the apparent heat-content change of vaporization at absolute zero from the least squares equation obtained in (ii) and these heat capacity data, using a 'sigma' plot.

33

(iv) Write an equation for the heat-content change of vaporization as a function of the absolute temperature.

NOTE: (i) The use of five significant figures in the effusion times given in the table is, of course, superfluous. The weight losses given are all corrected for the fact that the effusion orifice had finite thickness (c. 0·01 inch). The equation for the rate of effusion gives the vapour pressure in dynes/cm² if the gas constant expressed in ergs mole^{-1} °K^{-1} is used.

(ii) The method of least squares (see E. Bright Wilson, *An Introduction to Scientific Research* (McGraw-Hill, New York, 1952), pp. 217–219), is a useful way of eliminating the subjective factor in finding the 'best' straight line here.

(iii) The 'sigma' plot is a method of dealing with the temperature variation of equilibrium when heat capacity data are available to correct for the variation of enthalpy change with temperature. It is described in R. R. Wenner, *Thermochemical Calculations* (McGraw-Hill, New York, 1941), pp. 92–93 and 109–12, and in G. N. Lewis and M. Randall, *Thermodynamics*, revised by K. Pitzer and A. K. Brewer (McGraw-Hill, New York, 1961), p. 175. In computing 'sigma' it is convenient to evaluate $\log_{10} p$ at rounded values of $1/T$ by the least squares equation obtained in (ii). The omission of the T^{-2} term in the equation for the heat capacity of the solid oxide will be found to make a difference in the value of the apparent heat content change of vaporization at absolute zero that is small enough to be within the experimental error. The heat-content change at absolute zero obtained in (iii) is probably quite different from the true heat-content change on vaporization at absolute zero; the two values would only be identical if the heat capacity equations used were valid down to absolute zero.

23* THE EQUILIBRIUM CONSTANT FOR THE REDUCTION OF ZINC OXIDE BY CARBON MONOXIDE

E. C. Truesdale and R. K. Waring, *J. Am. Chem. Soc.*, **63**, 1610, 1941.

The reduction of zinc oxide by carbon monoxide at temperatures above the boiling-point of zinc (907° C) is a crucial reaction in the metallurgy of zinc and it is therefore important to know the equilibrium constant of the reaction:

$$ZnO(s) + CO(g) = Zn(g) + CO_2(g)$$

Truesdale and Waring passed mixtures of carbon monoxide, carbon dioxide, and nitrogen of known composition at a carefully measured rate of flow into an electric furnace containing a briquet of zinc oxide hanging from one arm of a balance. From measurements of the rate of loss of weight of the briquet the composition of the effluent gas can be calculated; provided that equilibrium had been established at the surface of the briquet the equilibrium constant can then be calculated. The purpose of adding carbon dioxide to the influent mixture was to assure the attainment of equilibrium during the short contact time between gases and briquet.

The table below, containing data from two of the experiments of Truesdale and Waring, tabulates successively the temperature of the briquet, the rate of gas input corrected to n.t.p., the composition of the input gas, the value of atmospheric pressure at the time of the experiment, and the rate of loss of weight of the briquet in grammes per minute, derived from weight measurements carried out over a substantial period.

Tem-perature ($°C$)	Gas input cm^3/min at n.t.p.	Composition of influent gas			Atmo-spheric pressure (mm)	Rate of loss of weight g/min
		Molar percentage				
		CO	CO_2	N_2		
1002	183·6	47·45	51·45	1·10	750·1	0·0206
1105	182·2	46·35	50·50	3·25	750·1	0·0594

(i) Calculate at each temperature the composition of the effluent vapour and hence the equilibrium constant of the reaction in atmosphere units.

(ii) Neglecting the dependence of heat of reaction on temperature estimate the heat-content change of the reaction at 1053° C.

The heat capacities of the participants in the reaction are expressed by the following equations:

$$ZnO(s) \ C_p = 11·40 + 1·45 \times 10^{-3}T - 1·824 \times 10^5/T^2$$
$$CO \qquad = 6·60 + 1·20 \times 10^{-3}T$$

$$\text{Zn(g)} \quad = 4 \cdot 97$$
$$\text{CO}_2 \quad = 10 \cdot 34 + 2 \cdot 74 \times 10^{-3} T - 1 \cdot 955 \times 10^5 / T$$

over the range $273°$ K–$1400°$ K, where T represents the Kelvin temperature. From a range of calorimetric data Truesdale and Waring calculated that the heat content change for the reaction at $298 \cdot 1°$ K (with zinc as a vapour) is 46803 ± 50 calories.

(iii) Calculate the equation expressing the heat-content change of the reaction as function of temperature.

(iv) Using this equation and the value of the equilibrium constant at $1105°$ C obtained in part (i) calculate the equation expressing the free energy change of the reaction with temperature.

NOTE: (i) It is convenient to begin by calculating the input of each gas in millimoles per minute. The rate of loss of weight of the briquet leads to the rate of formation of zinc in similar units and thence to the composition of the effluent.

(iii) and (iv). The development of equations expressing the variation of enthalpy change and of free energy change with temperature is discussed in ch. 15 of G. N. Lewis and M. Randall, *Thermodynamics*, revised by K. Pitzer and A. K. Brewer (McGraw-Hill, New York, 1961).

24 THE THERMODYNAMICS OF THE REDUCTION OF DOLOMITE BY FERROSILICON

L. M. Pidgeon and J. A. King, *Discussions, Faraday Soc.*, **4**, 197, 1948; O. Kubaschewski and E. L. Evans, *Metallurgical Thermochemistry* (Pergamon, London, 1956), p. 371.

The production of magnesium by the reduction of calcined dolomite with ferrosilicon was carried out on an industrial scale in Canada and the U.S. during the Second World War. The iron plays no part in the reduction process and to a first approximation the process can be represented by the equation

$$2\text{MgO} + 2\text{CaO} + \text{Si} = \text{Ca}_2\text{SiO}_4 + 2\text{Mg}.$$

At the temperature of the reaction magnesium is in the vapour state and all other substances are solid.

Pidgeon and King measured the equilibrium pressure of magnesium by passing a known volume of hydrogen (serving as an inert gas) through a column of the hot reaction mixture which had been briquetted, crushed, and screened to appropriate size beforehand. The entrained magnesium vapour was condensed on steel wool and weighed. Control experiments showed that at the flow-rates used saturation of the carrier gas with magnesium was established and that its subsequent condensation was complete. A total pressure of 765 mm was maintained in all experiments.

The results of some of their experiments over a range of temperatures are tabulated below:

| Temperature (°C) | Hydrogen | | Weight of magnesium condensed (g) |
| | Flow rate (cu ft/min) | Total volume passed (cu ft) | |
	(corrected to n.t.p.)		
1100	0·0099	2·900	1·192
1150	0·0096	2·900	2·232
1190	0·0048	1·353	1·715

(i) Calculate the equilibrium pressure of magnesium vapour at each temperature.

(ii) Plot the logarithm of the equilibrium pressure against the reciprocal of the absolute temperature and evaluate suitable values for the numerical coefficients, A and B, in the equation:

$$\log p = -\frac{A}{T} + B.$$

Kubaschewski and Evans in their book provide extensive tables of thermodynamic data for a large number of elements and compounds of possible metallurgical importance. Their tables include the following standard free energy equations germane to the reduction process under consideration:

$2CaO(s) + SiO_2(s) = Ca_2SiO_4(s),$ $\Delta G = -30200 - 1·2T$ (298°–1700° K)

$Si(s) + O_2(g) \quad\;\; = SiO_2(s),$ $\Delta G = -210600 - 3·0T \; \log T + 52·22T$
                                                      (298°–1700° K)

37

$$2\text{Mg(g)} + \text{O}_2\text{(g)} \quad = 2\text{MgO(s)}, \quad \Delta G = -363200 - 14 \cdot 74T \log T$$
$$+ 151 \cdot 4T$$
$$(1380\text{--}2500^\circ \text{ K})$$

(iii) From these equations deduce an equation for the variation with temperature of the standard free energy change of the reaction whose equation is given in the first paragraph.

(iv) From the equation obtained in (iii) calculate the logarithms of the equilibrium pressures of magnesium at 1100° C and 1190° C and plot these values on the graph obtained in (ii).

NOTE: In calculating the equilibrium pressure of magnesium from the mass condensed, it should be remembered that a constant *total* pressure is maintained in the reaction vessel so that the hydrogen expands during its saturation with magnesium. This effect is readily corrected by first calculating the approximate pressure of magnesium, ignoring this factor. (See the Notes to Problem 34.)

In parts (iii) and (iv) do not forget that standard free energies for gases relate to one *atmosphere* pressure and that ΔG in (iii) relates to the formation of *two* gramme-atoms of magnesium.

(1 cubic foot = 28·316 litres.)

25 THE FEASIBILITY OF THE REDUCTION OF METALLIC OXIDES INFERRED FROM FREE ENERGY EQUATIONS

F. D. Richardson and J. H. E. Jeffes, *J. Iron Steel Inst.*, **60**, 261, 1948.

Although the thermodynamically rigorous equation for the variation of the free energy change of a chemical reaction with temperature, based on the Gibbs–Helmholtz relation, often contains five or six terms, such an equation is cumbersome and sometimes gives an impression of accuracy unjustified by the data used. Richardson and Jeffes have shown that for many high temperature equilibria of potential metallurgical interest a simple linear equation of the form

$$\Delta G^\circ = A + BT$$

is adequate for many purposes over a wide temperature range and often does full justice to the experimental information available.

Below are tabulated coefficients in the above equation adopted by Richardson and Jeffes for the standard free energy of formation of a number of oxides with an indication of the temperature range over which the individual equations are applicable. The metals (except for aluminium and chromium in the upper of the two temperature ranges) and their oxides are all solid over the temperature ranges quoted.

Reaction	A	B	Temperature range
$2C + O_2 = 2CO$	-53400	$-41\cdot90$	298°–2500° K
$2CO + O_2 = 2CO_2$	-135100	$41\cdot50$	298°–2500° K
$\frac{4}{3}Al + O_2 = \frac{2}{3}Al_2O_3$	-256600	$43\cdot3$	298°–930° K
,, ,,	-257500	$44\cdot3$	930°–2318° K
$2Co + O_2 = 2CoO$	-111800	$34\cdot35$	298°–1763° K
$\frac{4}{3}Cr + O_2 = \frac{2}{3}Cr_2O_3$	-178500	$41\cdot40$	298°–1868° K
,, ,, ,,	-183740	$44\cdot21$	1868°–2500° K

The standard free energy of formation of each oxide is given in calories and relates to the amount of oxide formed in the relevant equation.

(i) Construct a graph showing the temperature variation of the standard free energy change of the five reactions tabulated.

(ii) From examination of the graph comment on the thermodynamic feasibility of

    (a) reducing alumina with carbon at 1300° K,

    (b) reducing chromic oxide with carbon or with carbon monoxide at 2000° K.

(iii) Calculate the dissociation pressure of chromic oxide at 1400° K.

(iv) Calculate the ratio of the pressures of carbon monoxide and dioxide that would be in equilibrium with a mixture of cobalt and cobaltous oxide at 1000° K.

NOTE: Except for the oxides of carbon the free energy data may well be in error by 5 kilocalories; meticulous plotting is therefore unnecessary in (i). Since the standard state of gaseous components is one atmosphere pressure, it is arithmetically simplest to express pressures in atmospheres. The usefulness of simplified and approximate forms of the free energy equation is discussed in the original paper and also by O. Kubaschewski and E. L. Evans, *Metallurgical Thermochemistry* (Pergamon, London, 1956), pp. 219–21.

26 THE STUDY OF A HETEROGENEOUS EQUILIBRIUM BY THE EFFUSION CELL METHOD

M. Farber and A. J. Darnell, *J. Phys. Chem.*, **59**, 156, 1955.

At temperatures between 500° K and 750° K titanium trichloride disproportionates according to the equation

$$2TiCl_3(s) = TiCl_4(g) + TiCl_2(s).$$

In this temperature range $TiCl_3$ is a solid of small but measurable vapour pressure, $TiCl_4$ is a gas, and $TiCl_2$ is a solid of negligible vapour pressure. The measurement of the pressure of $TiCl_4$ in equilibrium with the two solid chlorides leads to the free energy change of the disproportionation reaction and the measurement of the equilibrium pressure of $TiCl_3$ vapour over a range of temperatures leads to its latent heat of sublimation.

Farber and Darnell investigated this problem using an effusion cell to measure the pressures concerned. An effusion cell is a small vessel, usually of metallic construction, with a minute orifice not greater than the mean free path of the gas whose effusion is being measured. Under these circumstances the pressure of any gas inside the effusion cell may be deduced from its rate of effusion, provided that the molecular weight and temperature of the gas, and the size of the hole are known. Corrections are necessary for the fact that the orifice is not in an infinitely thin plate but has a finite depth so that molecules collide with its wall and with each other while passing through the orifice. The method is particularly suitable for low pressures and high temperatures.

The results in the table below relate to measurements at two temperatures:

Temperature (°K)	Length of run (hours)	Weight of effused material (g)		Corrected area of hole (cm)	Correction for deviation from free molecular flow
		$TiCl_4$	$TiCl_3$		
636	5·5	0·0320	0·00097	0·01325	1·224
732	2·6	0·223	0·0120	0·00393	1·304

(i) Calculate the equilibrium pressures of the two volatile chlorides at each temperature.

(ii) Calculate the free energy change of the disproportionation reaction at each temperature and hence the heat-content change of the reaction.

(iii) Calculate the latent heat of sublimation of titanium trichloride.

NOTE: The paper on which this problem is based was presented at a symposium on 'High Temperature Chemical Reactions'; other papers in the symposium published simultaneously in the same journal illustrate other applications of the effusion cell method. E. Miescher (*Helv. Phys. Acta*, **14**, 507, 1941), F. Metzger (ibid., **16**, 323, 1943), L. Brewer, P. W. Gilles, and F. A. Jenkins (*J. Chem. Phys.*, **16**, 797, 1948), and R. S. Bradley and T. G. Cleasby (*J. Chem. Soc.*, 1681, 1953) provide other examples of the diversity of problems susceptible of attack by the effusion cell technique. The masses of effusate quoted in the table are based on the steady effusion rate established after a short period of abnormally fast effusion; for the masses corrected in this way and deviating slightly from those quoted in Table II of the original paper we are indebted to the courtesy of Dr. Farber. The correction factor in the final column is applied to the mass of effusate to arrive at the

41

(higher) mass that would have effused through an orifice in an infinitely thin plate.

27 THE ADSORPTION OF CARBON MONOXIDE ON MICA

C. E. H. Bawn, *J. Am. Chem. Soc.*, **54**, 72, 1932.

The following measurements were made of the adsorption of carbon monoxide on a mica surface of total area 6239 cm² enclosed in a glass vessel at 90° K and 193° K respectively.

Glass vessel only (blank experiments)		Glass vessel and mica	
Pressure of gas (cm)	Volume adsorbed (cm³ corrected to s.t.p.)	Pressure of gas (cm)	Volume adsorbed (cm³ corrected to s.t.p.)
90° K			
0·00132	0·00498	0·00056	0·1082
0·00344	0·00797	0·00105	0·1339
0·00852	0·01114	0·00453	0·1717
		0·00545	0·1769
		0·00791	0·1889
		0·01059	0·1960
193° K			
0·00252	0·00080	0·00121	0·00075
0·00534	0·00283	0·00597	0·00624
0·00829	0·00434	0·0138	0·0150
0·0120	0·00553	0·0225	0·0229

(i) Plot the adsorption isothermals for carbon monoxide on mica at both temperatures.

(ii) Fit the results at 90° K, if possible, to a Langmuir adsorption equation and evaluate the constants.

(iii) Find the percentage of the surface covered at saturation at the lower temperature, taking the diameter of the carbon monoxide molecule (derived from viscosity data) as 3·5 Å.

NOTE: A simple algebraic transformation of the Langmuir adsorption equation leads to the following relation between the amount adsorbed (x) and the pressure (p):

$$\frac{p}{x} = \frac{1}{ab} + \frac{p}{b},$$

where a and b are constants whose significance may be ascertained by converting the above relation back to the Langmuir equation. A graph of p/x against p will test the conformity of the data with the Langmuir equation and enable its constants to be evaluated.

In estimating the percentage of surface covered, the area occupied by each molecule may be taken as equal to the square of its diameter. Bawn used the diameter taken from the liquid state instead of that derived from viscosity data.

28 THE ADSORPTION OF NITROUS OXIDE ON CHARCOAL, USING THE 'SORPTION BALANCE'

J. W. McBain and G. T. Britton, *J. Am. Chem. Soc.*, **52,** 2198, 1930.

The adsorption of various gases on charcoal was measured by means of a 'sorption balance'; this consists of a platinum bucket, containing the adsorbent, which is suspended in the gas to be adsorbed by means of a silica helix whose increase in length records the mass of gas adsorbed. The table below relates to nitrous oxide at 20° C:

Mass of charcoal = 0·1023 g
Sensitivity of helix = 15·25 cm extension/g
Volume of charcoal and bucket = 0·06087 cm³

Pressure of nitrous oxide (atmospheres)	Density of gas at this pressure (g/cm³)	Extension of helix (cm)
0·6	0·000923	0·237
4·0	0·00758	0·288
9·7	0·0199	0·289
19·8	0·0464	0·279
38·0	0·107	0·225

(i) Making the appropriate buoyancy correction, calculate the mass of gas (x) adsorbed at each pressure.

(ii) Compare the results graphically with the Freundlich isotherm ($x = kp^{1/n}$) and the Langmuir equation $\left(x = \dfrac{abp}{1+ap} \right)$.

NOTE: The pressure of nitrous oxide in this research was varied by changing the temperature of an excess of liquid nitrous oxide, kept in the lower part of the adsorption vessel.

Conformity with the Langmuir equation is conveniently tested (cf. Problem 27) by plotting p/x against p.

29* THE MEASUREMENT OF SURFACE AREA BY ADSORPTION ISOTHERMS

L. A. Wooten and C. Brown, *J. Am. Chem. Soc.*, **65**, 113, 1943.

In connexion with a study of the correlation of surface area with the thermionic emission of oxide-coated cathodes, Wooten and Brown sought to determine the area by measuring the adsorption of ethylene on the cathode at very low temperatures. The very low pressures involved, which were measured with a McLeod gauge, made it possible to measure relatively small surface areas.

The following measurements were carried out on a cathode coated with 17·6 milligrammes of mixed barium and strontium carbonates at $-183°$ C, at which temperature the vapour pressure of ethylene is $30·60 \times 10^{-3}$ mm. The first column shows the pressure of ethylene gas in equilibrium with the cathode and the second column shows the amount of gas adsorbed on the cathode, expressed in cm^3 of gas corrected to 1 mm pressure and $25°$ C.

Pressure (mm) $\times 10^3$	Gas adsorbed (cm^3—mm)
22·30	10·34
12·70	7·85
7·30	6·42
4·48	5·52
2·74	4·98
1·85	4·60
1·32	4·33

(i) By an appropriate graphical method examine the conformity of the data with the Langmuir adsorption isotherm.
(ii) By means of the Brunauer–Emmett–Teller equation calculate the effective surface area of the cathode, assuming the cross-section of the adsorbed ethylene molecule to be $17·55 \times 10^{-16}$ cm^2.
(iii) Make a similar calculation of effective surface using the Harkins–Jura (*J. Am. Chem. Soc.*, **66,** 1366, 1944) equation and assuming with R. L. Burwell, P. A. Smudski, and T. P. May (*J. Am. Chem. Soc.*, **69,** 1525, 1947) that the value of '*k*' in this equation is 5·16 cm^{-1} for ethylene.

NOTE: Several methods have been developed for measuring the surface area of porous and finely divided solids by a study of adsorption isotherms of selected gases in the neighbourhood of or below their boiling-points. Under these conditions physical absorption of multi-layers of gas is believed to occur and various devices may be used to estimate the point corresponding to the completion of the first mono-layer. The problem above illustrates two of the best known techniques using this approach to the problem of surface area. The data of Wooten and Brown are somewhat unusual in the extremely low pressure range in which they worked, a circumstance that enabled them to measure very small surface areas. The subject is reviewed by P. H. Emmett (*Ind. and Eng. Chem.*, **37,** 639, 1945), and more extensively in ch. xi of A. W. Adamson, *The Physical Chemistry of Surfaces* (Interscience, New York, 1960).

30 ADSORPTION AT AN AIR–SOLUTION INTERFACE MEASURED BY THE MICROTOME METHOD; AN EXPERIMENTAL TEST OF THE GIBBS ADSORPTION ISOTHERM

J. W. McBain and R. C. Swain, *Proc. Roy. Soc.* A, **154**, 608, 1936.

The adsorption at the interface between air and aqueous solutions of hydrocinnamic acid was measured by shaving off a surface layer about 0·1 mm thick by a small microtome blade moving at a speed of about 35 ft per second and comparing by interferometer the concentration of the solution thus collected with that of the bulk of the solution.

The area of the trough from which the surface film was abstracted was 310 cm². One interferometer division corresponded to a concentration of $2·25 \times 10^{-6}$ g of hydrocinnamic acid per gramme of water. The following results are selected from the paper of McBain and Swain:

Concentration of bulk of solution g/1000 g water	Weight of surface layer collected (g)	Concentration difference (interferometer divisions)
3·987	1·9	5·3*
	2·6	4·2*
1·498	1·6	4·2
	1·5	5·4

* Corrected by blank experiments for a small evaporation error.

(i) Calculate the surface adsorption in grammes per square centimetre for each experiment.

(ii) Calculate the surface adsorption corresponding to a

monomolecular layer of vertical molecules with a cross-section of 24 Å^2.

The following surface-tension data (communicated privately by the courtesy of Professor McBain) relate to hydrocinnamic acid solutions at approximately the same temperature, which may be taken as 22° C:

Concentration g/1000 g water	Surface-tension (dynes/cm)
0·5026	68·88
0·9617	66·39
1·5007	63·63
1·7506	61·10
2·3515	59·20
3·0024	56·06
4·1146	52·50
6·1291	47·24

(iii) Plot the graph of surface tension against concentration, and hence calculate by the approximate form of the Gibbs adsorption equation, using concentrations instead of activities, the theoretical adsorption at the two concentrations for which experimental adsorption data are given.

NOTE: The adsorption data obtained by this method of measurement at a *static* air–solution interface are in much closer harmony with the Gibbs adsorption equation than those obtained in most earlier measurements by the stream-of-bubbles method; in the latter the surface excess carried away by a stream of bubbles of air (or a liquid hydrocarbon) passing through the solution was measured. The experimental verification of the equation is discussed by N. K. Adam, *The Physics and Chemistry of Surfaces* (Oxford, 1958), by A. E. Alexander and P. Johnson, *Colloid Science* (Oxford, 1949), and by A. W. Adamson, *The Physical Chemistry of Surfaces* (Interscience, New York, 1960).

Equilibria in Solution

---

31 THE IONIZATION CONSTANT OF HYDROXYLAMINE FROM SPECTROPHOTOMETRIC MEASUREMENTS

R. A. Robinson and V. E. Bower, *J. Phys. Chem.*, **65**, 1279, 1961.

The ionization constant of an acid or base can be determined by spectrophotometric measurements of its partially neutralized solutions of known composition containing an acid–base indicator whose ionization constant is known. This method was used by Robinson and Bower to measure the thermodynamic ionization constant of the hydroxylammonium ion. The indicator used was 3,4-dinitrophenol, which is yellow in basic solutions and almost colourless in acidic solutions; the optical density at 400 millimicrons is a measure of the extent to which the indicator is in its basic form; it may be assumed that in 0·01 M HCl solution the indicator is entirely in the acid form and that in 0·01 M NaOH solution the indicator is entirely in the basic form.

Robinson and Bower measured the optical density of solutions of hydroxylamine hydrochloride partially neutralized by sodium hydroxide in the presence of a known concentration of indicator (Table I); the optical densities of the same concentration of indicator in 0·01 M HCl and 0·01 M NaOH were also measured (Table II). The observations below at 25° C are taken from their work.

TABLE I

Molarity of hydroxylamine hydrochloride	Molarity of free hydroxylamine (and also of sodium chloride)	Molarity of indicator	Optical Density (D)
0·05668	0·02904	0·000068	0·688
0·06478	0·01464	0·000056	0·438

TABLE II

Molarity of indicator	Optical density	
	in 0·01 M HCl (D_1)	in 0·01 M NaOH (D_2)
0·000068	0·024	0·925
0·000056	0·023	0·768

It was already known from spectrophotometric measurements of the indicator in buffer solutions of known pH that the thermodynamic ionization constant of 3,4-dinitrophenol is $10^{-5\cdot42}$.

Assuming that the activity coefficient (γ) of univalent ions is related to the ionic strength (I) by the semi-empirical equation:

$$-\log \gamma = \frac{0\cdot50\sqrt{I}}{(1+\sqrt{I})} - 0\cdot2I$$

calculate the thermodynamic ionization constant of the hydroxylammonium ion for each of the two salt–base mixtures.

NOTE: At a fixed total concentration of indicator the concentration present in the basic form may be assumed to be proportional to the excess of the observed optical density over that observed in 0·01 M HCl; this relation leads to a simple connexion between the ratio $(D-D_1)/(D_2-D)$ and the relative amounts of indicator in acid and basic form. When this relationship is combined with the expressions for the thermodynamic ionization constants of the indicator and of the hydroxyl ammonium ion, the activity of the hydronium ion may be eliminated and an expression readily deduced for the quantity desired in terms of optical density data, the ionization constant of the indicator, the salt–base ratio in the hydroxylamine solution and its ionic strength. The semi-empirical equation relating activity coefficient to ionic strength is due to C. W. Davies (*J. Chem. Soc.*, 2093, 1938); the activity coefficient of neutral molecules may be taken as unity.

32 THE ACID AND BASIC DISSOCIATION CONSTANTS OF AN AMPHOLYTE ('SULPHADIAZINE') DETERMINED FROM ITS SOLUBILITY IN BUFFERS OF VARYING pH

H. A. Krebs and J. C. Speakman, *J. Chem. Soc.*, 593, 1945.

The influence of hydrion concentration on the degree of dissociation of a weak acid leads to progressively lower solubility (S) of a sparingly soluble acid in solutions of increasing acidity. In solutions of sufficiently low pH the acid will be completely undissociated and the solubility under these conditions (S_0) can be equated to the concentration of undissociated acid, whose value must be constant in the saturated solutions at any value of the pH. These considerations may be used to determine the dissociation constant of a sparingly soluble acid by measuring its solubility in buffers of varying pH; the method is also obviously applicable to bases.

Krebs and Speakman employed these principles to measure *both* dissociation constants of the ampholyte 'sulphadiazine' (2-sulphanilamidopyrimidine) by solubility measurements covering both the range of pH in which basic dissociation predominated and that in which acid dissociation determined the solubility. The solubility was measured by a colorimetric method in a series of buffers at a constant ionic strength of 0.1 with the following results:

pH (at saturation) .	1·00	1·55	2·31	3·06	4·89	6·01	6·35	7·56
S (mg/100 ml) . .	68	25·2	9·3	6·9	6·33	8·5	11·1	86

(i) Over the pH range 4·5–6·5, where acid dissociation predominates, plot the solubility against the reciprocal of the hydrion concentration and extrapolate to find S_0.

(ii) Plot $\log_{10}(S/S_0-1)$ against pH over the complete range and from the graph determine the acid and basic dissociation constants of sulphadiazine.

NOTE: (i) In the case of an ampholyte S_0 cannot be determined from the solubility in very acid solutions since under these conditions the basic dissociation will predominate. It is therefore necessary, as suggested above, to carry out the extrapolation from solubility data in the (higher) pH range where only acid dissociation plays a significant role.

(ii) In the case of a weak acid the expression for the thermodynamic dissociation constant when combined with the fact that $S_0 = [HA]$ leads to the equation, using fairly obvious symbols:

$$S = S_0 + S_0 K_a f_{HA}/a_{H^+} f_{A^-}$$

Put into logarithmic form this equation is the basis for the procedure suggested in the second step of the problem. A closely similar relation can be deduced for the basic dissociation. The two dissociation constants obtained are the 'acidity constant' $K'_a = \dfrac{a_{H^+}[A^-]}{[HA]}$ and the 'basicity constant' $K'_b = \dfrac{[H_2A^+]}{[HA]a_{H^+}}$ of J. N. Bronsted (*Chem. Rev.*, **5**, 293, 1928) rather than the thermodynamic dissociation constants of the ampholyte. By assuming a plausible value for the activity coefficient of a singly charged ion at the ionic strength of the experiments the former are readily converted to the latter.

33 ACTIVITY COEFFICIENTS AND TRANSPORT NUMBERS OF HYDROGEN CHLORIDE IN METHANOL FROM ELECTROMOTIVE FORCE MEASUREMENTS

G. Nonhebel and H. B. Hartley, *Phil. Mag.*, **50**, 729, 1925.

The e.m.f. at 25° C of the cell

$$H_2 \mid HCl \text{ in MeOH} \mid AgCl.Ag$$

at various concentrations of hydrogen chloride (expressed in moles/litre) is tabulated below:

c	e.m.f. (volts)
0·00211	0·3041
0·004265	0·2712
0·007749	0·2445
0·01353	0·2207

(i) Find by graphical extrapolation the e.m.f. of the cell at unit activity of hydrogen chloride ('E_0').

(ii) Find with the aid of the graph the activity coefficient of 0·01 N hydrogen chloride.

The e.m.f. at 25° C of the cell

$$\text{Ag.AgCl} \mid \text{HCl in MeOH} \mid \text{HCl in MeOH} \mid \text{AgCl.Ag}$$
$$c = 0·01235 \qquad c = 0·001002$$

with a flowing liquid junction is 0·0844 volt.

(iii) Find the transport number of the hydrion in this concentration region.

NOTE: 'E_0' is conveniently found by plotting the function

$$E_0' = \left(E + \frac{2RT}{F} \ln c \right)$$

against $\sqrt{c}$ and extrapolating to zero concentration. The interpolation necessary in (iii) to find the e.m.f. of the cells *without* liquid junction at $c = 0·01235$ and $0·001002$ is best carried out on the graph used to evaluate E_0.

The calculation of transport numbers from the ratio of the electromotive force of concentration cells with and without liquid junctions is only approximate where there is a finite concentration difference. A more rigorous treatment, involving the differential of e.m.f. with respect to concentration, will be found in the work of A. S. Brown and D. A. MacInnes (*J. Am. Chem. Soc.*, **57**, 1356, 1935) embodied in Problem **39**, where the e.m.f.s of concentration cells with liquid junction are combined with directly measured transport numbers to calculate activity coefficients, thus reversing (and refining) the procedure of the present problem.

34 ACTIVITY COEFFICIENTS OF CONCENTRATED AQUEOUS HYDROCHLORIC ACID SOLUTIONS FROM VAPOUR-PRESSURE MEASUREMENTS

S. J. Bates and H. D. Kirschmann, *J. Am. Chem. Soc.*, **41**, 1991, 1919; G. A. Linhart, ibid., **39**, 2601, 1917.

The partial pressure of hydrogen chloride over its aqueous solutions at 25° C was measured by Bates and Kirschmann by passing a large volume (between 50 and 200 litres) of air at 760 mm pressure successively:

(a) over the hydrochloric acid solution,
(b) through dilute caustic soda (to absorb the acid),
(c) over pure water,
(d) through a series of U-tubes containing calcium chloride and sulphuric acid respectively (to absorb the water).

The following table gives the results obtained:

Concentration of hydrochloric acid (moles/litre)	Equivalents of halide absorbed in caustic soda $\times 10^3$	Weight of water absorbed in U-tubes (g)	Partial pressure of water above the solution (mm)
3·021	0·0521	2·870	19·8
4·570	0·3118	2·416	16·8
5·559	0·7552	1·895	14·7
7·546	4·920	1·175	11·0
8·256	9·116	0·961	9·6

The fourth column is interpolated from measurements by Linhart. The vapour pressure of water at 25° C is 23·76 mm.

(i) Calculate the partial pressure of hydrogen chloride over the solutions and plot the results against the concentration.
(ii) From e.m.f. data the mean activity of the *ions* in 5 N hydrochloric acid is 12·55. Calculate the mean activity of

53

the ions in hydrochloric acid in the least and most concentrated of the solutions whose vapour pressure was measured.

NOTE: In calculating the partial pressure of hydrogen chloride allowance must be made for the expansion of the air on passing from the acid saturator to the water saturator owing to the fact that the vapour pressure of pure water is greater than the sum of the partial pressures of HCl and H_2O over the acid solution, while the total pressure in the apparatus always remains atmospheric. This correction, which is discussed by Bates and Kirschmanm, is conveniently made by first calculating the partial pressure of HCl, neglecting p_{HCl} in the expansion term; this first approximation may then be used in a corrected expression to obtain a second approximation to the partial pressure. The second approximation differs from the first appreciably at the two highest concentrations only.

The form of the vapour-pressure–concentration curve is interesting in the extremely low concentration of hydrogen chloride molecules which it suggests at stoicheiometric concentrations below 5 N (cf. Problem 64).

In the second part of the problem it is necessary to interpolate the partial pressure of HCl at 5 N; for this purpose a c–log p graph is convenient. The mean activity of the ions obtained in the most concentrated solution illustrates the impracticability of explaining the free energy data of hydrochloric acid solutions in terms of the Arrhenius theory.

35* ACTIVITY COEFFICIENTS OF AQUEOUS HYDROCHLORIC ACID SOLUTIONS FROM ELECTROMOTIVE FORCE MEASUREMENTS

H. S. Harned and R. W. Ehlers, *J. Am. Chem. Soc.*, **54**, 1350, 1932; Harned and Ehlers, ibid., **55**, 2179, 1933.

Harned and Ehlers made a series of measurements of the e.m.f. of the cell

$$H_2 \mid HCl \text{ aq.} \mid AgCl.Ag$$

over a wide range of temperatures and concentrations. The table following is selected from their results at 20° C.

	Molality (m)	Electromotive force (E)
Series I	0·003661	0·51200
	0·005314	0·49395
	0·008715	0·46987
	0·013407	0·44899
	0·021028	0·42726
Series II	0·10266	0·35211
	0·48968	0·27535
	1·2045	0·22432
	2·3802	0·17552
	2·9566	0·15645
	4·0875	0·12307

(i) From the data of Series I plot the function

$$\left(E + \frac{2RT}{F} 2{\cdot}303 \log_{10} m - \frac{RT}{F} 2{\cdot}303 m^{\frac{1}{2}}\right)$$

against the molality, and by extrapolation to zero molality find the value of the e.m.f. of the cell at unit activity (E_0).

(ii) Deduce from the graph the activity coefficient in 0·01 m solution.

(iii) From the slope of the graph deduce the value of the constant b in the equation

$$\log_{10} \gamma = -0{\cdot}50 m^{\frac{1}{2}} + bm.$$

(iv) From E_0 and the data of Series II calculate the activity coefficient of the solutions measured, and hence sketch a rough graph of the variation of the activity coefficient with the square root of the molality.

NOTE: The data of this problem are probably more accurate and relate to a wider concentration range than those of Problem 48; the concentrations are expressed in terms of 1000 g of solvent instead of 1 litre of solution. The method of extrapolation suggested in (i) is based on the equation for the variation of activity coefficient with concentration in dilute solution:

$$\log_{10} \gamma = -0{\cdot}50 m^{\frac{1}{2}} + bm,$$

where 0·50 is the constant of the limiting Debye–Hückel equation and b is an empirical constant. When this equation is combined with the thermodynamic equation

$$E_0 - E = \frac{2RT}{F} 2{\cdot}303 \log_{10} \gamma m,$$

the reason for the form of the extrapolation function will be realized. This method of extrapolation places less reliance on the results obtained in very dilute solution than the method used in Problem 33. The graph obtained in (iv) illustrates the characteristic variation of the activity coefficient of a strong electrolyte over a wide concentration range. In the second of the two papers quoted will be found the derivation of a variety of thermodynamic properties of hydrochloric acid solutions from e.m.f. data.

Chapter 10 of H. S. Harned and B. B. Owen, *The Physical Chemistry of Electrolytic Solutions* (Reinhold, New York, 1958), discusses the theory of this type of measurement in great detail. Chapter 11 of the same volume is devoted to the physical chemistry of hydrochloric acid solutions.

Do not overlook the detail that the measurements were carried out at 20° C; at this temperature $\dfrac{2RT \ln 10}{F} = 0\cdot 11633$ volt.

36 ESTIMATES OF THE CONCENTRATION OF UNDISSOCIATED MOLECULES IN AQUEOUS HYDROCHLORIC ACID

S. J. Bates and H. D. Kirschmann, *J. Am. Chem. Soc.*, **41,** 1991, 1919; J. H. Ellis, ibid., **38,** 737, 1916; G. A. Linhart, ibid., **39,** 2601, 1917; K. Fajans, *Trans. Faraday Soc.*, **23,** 357, 1927; L. Ebert, *Naturwissenschaft*, **13,** 393, 1925.

The concentration of hydrogen chloride molecules in dilute solutions may be roughly estimated provided (*a*) that the partial pressure of hydrogen chloride above the solution (which is experimentally unmeasurable except in concentrated solution) can be calculated, and (*b*) that the partition coefficient of the molecules between water and the gas phase can be estimated by plausible analogy with that of structurally similar compounds.

(*a*) *The vapour pressure of hydrogen chloride over its dilute aqueous solutions.*

The vapour pressure of concentrated solutions of hydrochloric acid at 25° C has been measured by Bates and Kirschmann with the following results:

Molality (moles per 1000 g water)	Vapour pressure (mm)
3·240	0·00780
3·952	0·01724
5·041	0·0557
5·364	0·0791

The e.m.f. of the cell $H_2 \mid HCl\, aq. \mid Hg_2Cl_2 . Hg$ has been measured at the same temperature by Ellis and by Linhart; the following results are taken from their work:

Molality	e.m.f.
4·484	0·15506
0·0100	0·5110

(i) Calculate from the above data the experimentally inaccessible vapour pressure of hydrogen chloride above its m/100 solution.

(b) *The partition coefficient of hydrogen chloride molecules between the aqueous solution and the gas phase.*

Method 1 (Fajans). We may assume that the partition coefficient for hydrogen chloride molecules is the same as the 'over-all' partition coefficient of hydrogen cyanide. The partial pressure of hydrogen cyanide over a 2·92 m solution is 167 mm at 18° C.

(ii) On this basis calculate the concentration of hydrogen chloride molecules in 0·01 m HCl from the result of (a).

Method 2 (Ebert). Ebert pointed out that for aqueous solutions of the alkyl halides the quotient

$$\frac{\text{v.p. of halide above solution}}{(\text{concentration in solution}) \times (\text{molecular volume of halide})}$$

is very roughly constant at a given temperature and independent of the alkyl radical.

Assuming that it is justifiable to extend the principle to the hydrogen halides, (iii) calculate the order of magnitude of the concentration of hydrogen chloride molecules in 0·01 m HCl from the result of (a) and the following data. The vapour pressure of propyl chloride above its 0·0346 m aqueous solution is 280 mm at 20° C. The molecular volumes of propyl and hydrogen chlorides may be taken as 88 and 30 respectively.

NOTE: The calculation of the vapour pressure over the 0·01 m solution depends on the identity of the net work derived from the transfer of hydrogen chloride from one solution to another whether it is performed electrically in a concentration cell or by distillation through the gas phase. The necessary interpolation of the vapour pressure of hydrogen chloride over a 4·484 m solution is readily made from a graph of the logarithm of the v.p. against the molality; rough interpolation only is necessary since the result is to be used to calculate an order of magnitude.

37 ACTIVITY COEFFICIENTS OF COBALTAMMINE SALTS FROM SOLUBILITY MEASUREMENTS

J. N. Brönsted and V. K. LaMer, *J. Am. Chem. Soc.*, **46**, 555, 1924.

The Debye–Hückel theory of strong electrolytes was tested by measuring the solubility at 15° C of complex cobaltammine salts of various valency types in solutions of other salts ('solvent salts') of various valency types. The solubility was measured by a Kjeldahl estimation of the solution of the solvent salt after it had percolated slowly through a long column of the solid complex salt. Below are tabulated typical results for two cobaltammine salts.

Solute salt: $[Co(NH_3)_4(NO_2)(CNS)][Co(NH_3)_2(NO_2)_2C_2O_4]$ (1–1 valent)

Solvent salt	Concentration of solvent salt (*equivs/litre*)	Solubility of complex salt (*equivs/litre* $\times 10^4$)
KNO$_3$	0	3·355
	0·0010	3·418
	0·0050	3·572
	0·0100	3·669
K$_3$[Co(CN)$_6$]	0·0010	3·464
	0·0020	3·556
	0·0050	3·687

Solute salt: [Co(NH$_3$)$_6$][Co(NH$_3$)$_2$(NO$_2$)$_2$C$_2$O$_4$]$_3$ (3–1 valent)

Solvent salt	Concentration of solvent salt (equivs/litre)	Solubility of complex salt (equivs/litre × 10^4)
KNO$_3$	0	1·5123
	0·0010	1·6167
	0·0020	1·6983
BaCl$_2$	0·0010	1·6452

(i) Evaluate the activity coefficients of the two solute salts graphically by plotting $\log \left(\dfrac{\text{solubility in solvent salt}}{\text{solubility in pure water}} \right)$ against the square root of the ionic strength and extrapolating to zero ionic strength.

(ii) Plot the logarithm of the activity coefficient of each of the solute salts against the square root of the ionic strength of the solution, and compare the result with the straight lines predicted by the limiting equation of the Debye–Hückel theory:

$$-\log_{10} f = 0{\cdot}50 z_1 z_2 \sqrt{\mu},$$

where z_1, z_2 are the valencies of the ions of the solute salt and μ is the ionic strength of the solution.

NOTE: Since the activity coefficient is inversely proportional to the solubility, the quantity plotted in part (i), $\log s/s_0$, is equal to $\log f_0/f$. It is readily seen that the graph required in part (ii) is a line parallel to the one drawn in part (i), and may be drawn on the same sheet.

Deviations from the limiting equation of Debye and Hückel are often found, notably in the case of unsymmetrical high valency salts. Examples of these deviations, which are in harmony with Brönsted's 'principle of the specific interaction of ions', are described by V. K. LaMer and R. G. Cook (*J. Am. Chem. Soc.*, **51**, 2622, 1929), and V. K. LaMer and F. H. Goldman (ibid., **51**, 2632, 1929). This method of measuring activity coefficients is discussed by H. S. Harned and B. B. Owen, *The Physical Chemistry of Electrolytic Solutions* (Reinhold, New York, 1958), pp. 586–91, and by C. B. Monk, *Electrolytic Dissociation* (Academic Press, London, 1961), ch. v.

38^* ACTIVITY COEFFICIENTS OF AQUEOUS SOLUTIONS OF BUTANOL FROM FREEZING-POINT MEASUREMENTS

W. D. Harkins and R. W. Wampler, *J. Am. Chem. Soc.*, **53**, 850, 1931.

Harkins and Wampler measured the freezing-point depression of aqueous solutions of butanol. The following table is selected from their results in dilute solution:

Molality (m)	Freezing-point depression ΔT ($°C$)
0·004134	0·007669
0·019330	0·035588
0·02420	0·04452
0·03982	0·07300
0·05206	0·09505
0·08067	0·14679
0·09746	0·17680

(i) Calculate for each concentration the function j defined by the equation $j = 1 - \dfrac{\Delta T}{\lambda m}$, where λ is the molecular depression at infinite dilution and has the value 1·858°, and plot j/m against the molality.

(ii) Read off from the curve interpolated values of j/m at 0·01 m, 0·03 m, 0·05 m, and 0·10 m.

(iii) From these interpolated values of j/m and the corresponding values of m, calculate by graphical integration the activity coefficient of butanol at these molalities.

NOTE: The quantity j/m is very sensitive to experimental error in very dilute solution, but the arbitrary nature of the extrapolation to zero concentration makes very little difference to the final result. The method of graphical integration in which j/m is employed is described by G. N. Lewis and M. Randall, *Thermodynamics*, revised by K. Pitzer and A. K. Brewer (McGraw-Hill, New York, 1961), ch. xxiii in the first edition or ch. xxvi in the second edition, and in other textbooks such as:

J. A. V. Butler, *Chemical Thermodynamics* (Macmillan, London, 1962), ch. xv. The second integral in the expression for the logarithm of the activity coefficient $\left(\text{i.e.} \int_0^m 0.00057\frac{\Delta T}{m}d\Delta T \right)$ may be neglected, since for the solutions under consideration its effect on the activity coefficient is barely appreciable below 0·1 m. The activity coefficients obtained should be compared with those of a uni-univalent electrolyte at the same molalities (*c.* 0·90 at 0·01 m and *c.* 0·78 at 0·1 m).

The technique necessary for precise measurements of freezing-point depression are discussed by G. Scatchard, P. T. Jones, and S. S. Prentiss (*J. Am. Chem. Soc.*, **54**, 2676, 1932) and by P. G. M. Brown and J. Prue (*Proc. Roy. Soc.* A, 232, 320, 1955). The latter authors used such measurements for estimating ionic association in bi-bivalent salts.

39* ACTIVITY COEFFICIENTS OF SODIUM CHLORIDE SOLUTIONS FROM THE ELECTROMOTIVE FORCE OF CONCENTRATION CELLS WITH LIQUID JUNCTION AND TRANSPORT NUMBERS

A. S. Brown and D. A. MacInnes, *J. Am. Chem. Soc.*, **57,** 1356, 1935.

The transport numbers of electrolytes have not infrequently been determined (cf. Problem 48) from a comparison of the e.m.f. of concentration cells 'with' and 'without liquid junction'. Brown and MacInnes reversed this procedure by evaluating activity coefficients from the e.m.f. of 'cells with liquid junction' taken together with transport numbers obtained by the accurate moving-boundary method.

They measured at 25° C the e.m.f. of the cell:

$$\text{Ag.AgCl} \quad \left| \quad \begin{matrix} \text{NaCl aq.} \\ C_1=0.09953 \end{matrix} \quad \right| \quad \begin{matrix} \text{NaCl aq.} \\ C_2 \end{matrix} \quad \right| \quad \text{AgCl.Ag}$$

and the transport number of sodium in sodium chloride for various values of C_2, with the following results:

C_2 (equivs/litre)	E.m.f. (millivolts)	Transport number of sodium at C_2
$0 \cdot 004984_9$	$-56 \cdot 45_0$	$0 \cdot 3930_4$
$0 \cdot 006978_6$	$-49 \cdot 90_7$	$0 \cdot 3924_9$
$0 \cdot 019934_4$	$-29 \cdot 80_4$	$0 \cdot 3902_4$
$0 \cdot 03985_5$	$-16 \cdot 81_8$	$0 \cdot 3882_8$
$0 \cdot 05976_2$	$- 9 \cdot 31_7$	$0 \cdot 3870_0$
$0 \cdot 09953_3$	0	$0 \cdot 3854_5$

(i) If f_1 be the activity coefficient at $C_1 = 0 \cdot 09953$ and f_2 be the value for any other concentration C_2, calculate for the first five solutions the value of $\Delta \log_{10} f$ defined by $\Delta \log_{10} f = \log_{10} f_2 - \log_{10} f_1$.

The 'first approximation' equation for activity coefficients of the Debye–Hückel theory is $-\log_{10} f = \dfrac{\alpha \sqrt{C}}{1 + \beta C}$, where α is $0 \cdot 5056$ for aqueous uni-univalent electrolytes at 25° C and β is equal, under the same conditions, to the distance of closest approach of the ions multiplied by $3 \cdot 27 \times 10^7$.

(ii) Examine graphically whether the activity coefficient data for sodium chloride conform with an equation of this type.

(iii) Evaluate from the graph the distance of closest approach of the ions.

(iv) Determine the activity coefficients of the most dilute and the most concentrated solutions.

NOTE: It is only recently that the moving-boundary method has been sufficiently refined to give transport number data suitable for the method of determining activity coefficients illustrated in this problem. The method is particularly valuable for electrolytes in which one of the constituent ions does not provide a convenient reversible electrode and where, therefore, concentration cells 'without liquid junction' are impracticable.

For the method of calculation, which is somewhat complicated by the variation of transport number with concentration, the original paper or the textbook: D. A. MacInnes, *Principles of Electrochemistry* (Dover, New York, 1951), ch. 8, should be consulted; it is an interesting example of the reduction of somewhat recalcitrant experimental data. The graphical integration of the third term in equation (11) (p. 1361 of the paper) should be done by cutting out and weighing the area under the curve. It will be found that the fourth term is insignificant at the three highest concentrations and may be neglected.

In testing the conformity with the Debye–Hückel equation, $\log_{10} f$ for the most concentrated solution (the term A in the paper) may be taken as -0.11 for a first approximation.

Alternative methods of computation will be found in the papers of W. J. Hornibrook, G. J. Janz, and A. R. Gordon (*J. Am. Chem. Soc.*, **64**, 513, 1942), T. Shedlowsky (ibid., **72**, 3680, 1950), and F. H. Spedding, P. E. Porter, and J. M. Wright (ibid., **74**, 2781, 1952). Discussion and further references may be found in C. B. Monk, *Electrolytic Dissociation*, Academic Press, London, 1961), ch. 4.

40* THE IODINE–TRI-IODIDE EQUILIBRIUM, THE FREE ENERGY OF FORMATION OF SILVER IODIDE, AND THE STANDARD POTENTIAL OF THE IODINE ELECTRODE

G. Jones and B. B. Kaplan, *J. Am. Chem. Soc.*, **50**, 1845 and 2066, 1928.

The iodine–tri-iodide equilibrium

A solution of iodine in aqueous potassium iodide was equilibrated (through the vapour phase) with an unsaturated solution of iodine in pure water containing a trace of sulphuric acid to prevent hydrolysis. The iodine content (free and combined) of the two solutions was estimated by means of arsenious acid. Below are the results of three such experiments:

Experiment . . .	A	B	C
Temperature . . .	25° C	25° C	0° C
Potassium iodide concentration (moles/litre) .	0·0200	0·3333	0·02000
Total iodine in KI solution (moles/litre) . . .	0·0023668	0·003491	0·0016505
Iodine in aqueous solution (moles/litre) . . .	0·0001745	0·00001471	0·00006201

Assuming that the concentration of free iodine is the same in each pair of equilibrated solutions and that no poly-iodides higher than I_3' are formed in solutions so dilute in iodine, calculate:

(i) the equilibrium constant $\dfrac{[I'][I_2]}{[I_3]}$ at 25° and 0° C;

(ii) the heat of formation of the tri-iodide ion.

The free energy of formation of silver iodide

The e.m.f. of the cell

$$\text{Ag.AgI} \mid \underset{0·02\text{ N}}{\text{KI}} \mid \underset{0·02\text{ N}}{\text{KI}} + I_2 \text{ (unsaturated)} \mid \text{Pt}$$

was measured at 25° and 0° C using in the right-hand half of the cell the tri-iodide solutions analysed in experiments *A* and *C* above. The e.m.f.s observed were 0·6611 volt (using solution *A* at 25° C) and 0·6537 volt (using solution *C* at 0° C). The solubility of iodine in pure water (corrected for the slight hydrolysis as determined by conductivity measurements) is 0·00132 mole/litre at 25° C and 0·000635 at 0° C.

Neglecting the variation of activity coefficients with concentration and assuming that the liquid junction potential diminishes the observed e.m.f. at 25° C by 0·0007 volt and at 0° C by 0·0005 volt, calculate:

(iii) the e.m.f. at 25° and 0° C of the cell

$$\text{Ag} \mid \text{AgI}_{\text{solid}} \mid I_{2\text{ solid}};$$

(iv) the free energy of formation of silver iodide at each temperature;

(v) the entropy change in the reaction in cal/degree;

(vi) the heat of formation of silver iodide.

The standard potential of the iodine electrode

The e.m.f. of the cell

$$\text{Pt} \mid \underset{\substack{0·02\text{ N} \\ \text{saturated} \\ \text{with iodine}}}{\text{KI}} \mid \underset{0·10\text{ N}}{\text{KCl}} \mid \text{Hg}_2\text{Cl}_2 . \text{Hg}$$

is $-0·3200$ volt at 25° C.

The e.m.f. of the cell

$$\text{Pt} \mid \underset{\substack{0 \cdot 02 \text{ N} \\ \text{with iodine at} \\ \text{concentration of } A}}{\text{KI}} \mid \underset{\substack{0 \cdot 02 \text{ N} \\ \text{saturated} \\ \text{with iodine}}}{\text{KI}} \mid \text{Pt}$$

is 0·0371 volt at 25° C. The liquid junction

$$\underset{\substack{0 \cdot 02 \text{ N} \\ \text{with iodine at} \\ \text{concentration } A}}{\text{KI}} \mid \underset{\substack{0 \cdot 10 \text{ N}}}{\text{KCl}}$$

has a potential difference of 0·0010 volt, the iodide solution being at the higher potential.

(vii) If the activity coefficient of 0·02 N KI is 0·89, and that of iodine in its solutions may be taken as unity, calculate the standard electrode potential of iodine at 25° C on the deci-normal calomel scale.

NOTE: The method of equilibration through the gas phase is free from the errors (due to emulsification and slight mutual solubility of the two solvents) associated with the investigation of the iodine–tri-iodide equilibrium by distribution experiments with a non-polar solvent.

Since the activity coefficients of iodide and tri-iodide ions, being of the same valency, are likely to be substantially the same, and since the activity coefficient of the iodine molecules will be virtually unity at such low concentrations, the thermodynamic equilibrium constant (expressed in activities) will be almost indistinguishable from the equilibrium constant (expressed in concentrations) calculated here.

(iii) involves a correction for the liquid junction potential, as given, and the correction of the right-hand electrode potential to the value it would have in a solution simultaneously saturated with iodine and 0·02 N in *free* I'; the latter correction is made neglecting the variation of activity coefficients with concentration (i.e. identifying activity ratios with concentration ratios). The e.m.f. of the cell $\text{Ag} \mid \text{AgI}_s \mid \text{I}_{2s}$ is, of course, independent of the concentration of the intervening electrolyte, provided it is saturated with silver iodide and iodine.

The result of (v) may be compared with the data of Problem 65; Jones and Kaplan's discussion of the entropy of formation of silver iodide illustrates the difficulties sometimes associated with the experimental verification of the third law of thermodynamics.

(vii) By the standard electrode potential of iodine is meant the potential of an inert metal electrode immersed in a solution simultaneously saturated with iodine and containing *free* iodide ion at unit activity.

In the calculation the potential of the liquid junction

KI	KI
0·02 N	0·02 N
saturated with I_2	with iodine at concentration of A

may be neglected.

The sign convention must be carefully observed in this problem; the electromotive forces of the three cells as written give the potential of the right-hand electrode relative to the left-hand electrode. Note 10 on p. xvi should also be consulted.

41 THE DISSOCIATION CONSTANT OF MONOCHLORACETIC ACID DETERMINED BY CATALYTIC MEASUREMENTS

C. Grove, *J. Am. Chem. Soc.*, **52**, 1404, 1930 (cf. J. N. Brönsted and C. Grove, ibid., **52**, 1394, 1930).

The hydrolysis of the acetals is well adapted to the catalytic measurement of hydrogen-ion concentrations, partly because there is no appreciable general acid–base catalysis, the hydrogen ion being the only catalytically effective molecular species, and partly because the linear salt effect has been accurately determined by Brönsted and Grove. Grove applied the method to measure the dissociation of monochloracetic acid; the rate of hydrolysis of the acetal was measured dilatometrically in the presence of varying concentrations of pure monochloracetic acid; dimethyl acetal was used for the more dilute solutions, and the less catalytically sensitive ethylene acetal was used at the higher concentrations. Below are tabulated the hydrogen-ion concentrations (corrected for salt effects) at various concentrations of monochloracetic acid.

Concentration of acid (moles per litre)	Concentration of hydrion (gramme-ions per litre)
0·003	0·00151
0·005	0·00212
0·010	0·00327
0·015	0·00416
0·100	0·0120
0·300	0·0217

(i) Calculate the dissociation constant K_c (in concentration units) and plot the result against the square root of the ionic strength of the solution (μ).

(ii) By graphical methods or otherwise, express the variation of K_c with μ in an equation of the form:

$$\log K_c = \log K_a + \sqrt{\mu} - \beta\mu,$$

and hence evaluate the 'true' or thermodynamic dissociation constant in activity units (K_a).

NOTE: The coefficient of $\sqrt{\mu}$ is unity in the equation

$$\log K_c = \log K_a + \sqrt{\mu} - \beta\mu$$

by a numerical coincidence, since the coefficient α in the Debye–Hückel equation $-\log_{10} f = \alpha z^2 \sqrt{\mu} + \beta\mu$ happens to be almost exactly one-half.

The conformity of K_c with an equation of the type suggested (and its limiting value at zero ionic strength) is readily tested by plotting ($\log K_c - \sqrt{\mu}$) against μ.

42 THE DISSOCIATION CONSTANT OF CALCIUM HYDROXIDE FROM KINETIC MEASUREMENTS

R. P. Bell and J. E. Prue, *J. Chem. Soc.*, 362, 1949.

The depolymerization of diacetone alcohol to form acetone is catalysed by hydroxide ions and for solutions of sodium and potassium hydroxides the rate of reaction is directly proportional to the stoicheiometric hydroxide-ion concentration up to about 0·1 N. With the hydroxides of the alkaline earths the rate of reaction increases less rapidly than the stoicheiometric hydroxide-ion concentration; Bell and Prue attributed this to the incomplete dissociation of the hydroxides and obtained the results tabulated below in the course of a quantitative test of this hypothesis.

The reaction which is first order with respect to diacetone alcohol, was followed by dilatometer in approximately 1 per cent aqueous solution in the presence of various concentrations of metallic hydroxides. The first column gives the concentration of the metallic hydroxide in gramme-equivalents per litre and the second gives the first-order rate constant in decadic logarithms and minutes:

Concentration	Rate constant $\times 10^3$
Sodium hydroxide	
0·01046	2·28
0·02616	5·70
0·04186	9·07
0·0751	16·23
0·1001	21·48
Calcium hydroxide	
0·01442	2·939
0·02162	4·369
0·02882	5·686
0·03569	6·931

(i) For sodium hydroxide plot the quotient of the rate constant divided by the stoicheiometric hydroxide-ion concentration against the latter and estimate the limiting value of the quotient at infinite dilution.

(ii) On the assumptions (a) that the true hydroxide-ion concentration in the calcium hydroxide solutions can be calculated by dividing the rate constant by the limiting value determined in (i) and (b) that any difference between the concentration of hydroxide ion thus computed and its stoicheiometric value is due to incomplete dissociation of the ion $CaOH^+$, calculate the concentration dissociation constant for the process:

$$CaOH^+ = Ca^{++} + OH^-$$

(iii) Calculate the approximate thermodynamic dissociation constant of the process, using the following equation for the activity coefficient f of an ion of charge z in a solution of ionic strength μ:

$$-\log_{10} f = 0{\cdot}5z^2 \frac{\sqrt{\mu}}{1 + \sqrt{\mu}}.$$

NOTE: The kinetic data are adequately accounted for by a conventional type of dissociation equilibrium, whose constant, it is interesting

68

to note, is in good agreement with a value obtained later by C. W. Davies and B. E. Hoyle from solubility measurements (*J. Chem. Soc.*, 233, 1951). There may be room for debate as to the exact physical meaning of such dissociation constants but they seem adequate to account for a wide range of properties for some electrolyte solutions; the note on Problem 81 should be consulted. The activity coefficient equation used is a modification by E. A. Guggenheim (*Phil. Mag.*, **19**, 588, 1935) of the limiting equation of Debye and Hückel; it gives reasonably accurate results over a wider range of ionic strength than the limiting equation.

43^* THE THERMODYNAMIC DISSOCIATION CONSTANT OF ACETIC ACID IN AQUEOUS SOLUTION FROM ELECTROMOTIVE FORCE DATA

H. S. Harned and R. W. Ehlers, *J. Am. Chem. Soc.*, **54**, 1350, 1932.

The e.m.f. at 20° C of the cell (without liquid junction)

$$H_2 \mid CH_3COOH, CH_3COONa, NaCl \mid AgCl.Ag$$
$$ m_1 \qquad\quad m_2 \qquad\quad m_3$$

for varying compositions of the electrolyte is:

m_1 (moles/1000 g water)	m_2	m_3	E_{20} (volts)
0·004779	0·004599	0·004896	0·63580
0·012035	0·011582	0·012426	0·61241
0·021006	0·020216	0·021516	0·59840

The e.m.f. of the cell $H_2 \mid$ HCl (unit activity) $\mid$ AgCl.Ag in these concentration units is 0·2255 volt at 20° C (cf. Problem 35).

Calculate by graphical extrapolation the thermodynamic dissociation constant of acetic acid.

NOTE: The two types of cell of which the e.m.f. is given, when combined 'back to back', constitute a concentration cell without liquid junction for hydrochloric acid, and their combined e.m.f. is determined by the ratio of the activity products $(a_{H^+} \times a_{Cl^-})$ in the two electrolytes. When this relation is formulated and the hydrogen-ion concentration is replaced by

$$K_a \times \frac{m_{HAc}\gamma_{HAc}}{\gamma_{H^+}m_{Ac^-}\gamma_{Ac^-}},$$

an equation is obtained which can be rearranged so that the limiting value at zero ionic strength of one side of the equation is $\dfrac{-RT}{F} \ln K_a$.

An extrapolation to zero ionic strength of the expression constituting this side of the equation will therefore lead to the evaluation of K, the thermodynamic dissociation constant.

In formulating the quantity to be plotted, it is necessary to assume an approximate value of m_{H^+}; this value may be obtained by putting K_c for acetic acid at an approximate value of $1 \cdot 8 \times 10^{-5}$ and working out m_{H^+} from m_1 and m_2.

N.B. In solving this problem five-figure logarithms are necessary.

44 THE THERMODYNAMIC DISSOCIATION CONSTANT AND HEAT OF DISSOCIATION OF WATER FROM ELECTROMOTIVE FORCE MEASUREMENTS

H. S. Harned and W. J. Hamer, *J. Am. Chem. Soc.*, **55**, 2194, 1933 (cf. H. S. Harned and R. W. Ehlers, ibid., **54**, 1350, 1932).

Harned and Hamer determined the thermodynamic dissociation constant and heat of ionic dissociation of water by combining measurements of the e.m.f. of the cell

$$H_2 \mid \underset{0 \cdot 01m}{KOH}, \underset{m}{KCl} \mid AgCl \cdot Ag \quad (Cell\ A)$$

at various values of m and at various temperatures with the e.m.f. of the cell

$$H_2 \mid HCl\ (at\ unit\ activity) \mid AgCl \cdot Ag \quad (Cell\ C)$$

as measured by Harned and Ehlers at the same temperature.

A selection of their results is tabulated below:

Cell A		$T = 15° C$ E_A	$T = 25° C$ E_A
m_{KCl}	= 0·02	1·03147	1·03260
	0·05	1·00883	1·00922
	0·10	0·99181	0·99160
Cell C			
E_0	=	0·22847	0·22239

(i) Plot the function

$$E_A - E_0 + \frac{RT}{F} \ln \frac{m_{KCl}}{m_{KOH}}$$

against the ionic strength of the solution in cell A, and extrapolate to find its limiting value at zero ionic strength for both temperatures.

(ii) Hence evaluate the true dissociation constant of water at both temperatures and the mean heat of dissociation. Compare the latter value with the calorimetric value of 13693 cal obtained at $20° C$ by T. W. Richards and A. W. Rowe (*J. Am. Chem. Soc.*, **44**, 684, 1922).

NOTE: The principle of this problem is the same as that of Problem 43. It is indeed somewhat simpler in application, since it is unnecessary to assume an approximate value for m_{H^+}. The method is discussed in ch. 15 of H. S. Harned and B. B. Owen, *The Physical Chemistry of Electrolytic Solutions* (Reinhold, New York, 1958).

N.B. Five-figure logarithms are necessary for this problem.

45 THE THERMODYNAMIC DISSOCIATION CONSTANT OF WATER, DETERMINED FROM AN EQUILIBRIUM INVOLVING MERCURIC OXIDE AND MERCUROUS BROMIDE

R. F. Newton and M. G. Bolinger, *J. Am. Chem. Soc.*, **52**, 921, 1930.

Newton and Bolinger determined the equilibrium constant of the reaction

$$\tfrac{1}{2}HgO(s) + \tfrac{1}{2}Hg(l) + \tfrac{1}{2}H_2O(l) + Br^- = \tfrac{1}{2}Hg_2Br_2(s) + OH^-$$

by shaking up potassium bromide solution with an excess of mercuric oxide, mercurous bromide, and mercury in a thermostat at 25° C until equilibrium was established; the hydroxide and bromide-ion concentrations of the solution were then measured. Selected results are tabulated below:

Initial weight ratio HgO/Hg_2Br_2	Time of shaking (*hours*)	(OH^-) Gramme-ions per litre	(Br^-) Gramme-ions per litre
1 : 1	26	0·01402	0·06975
	298	0·01370	0·0689
6 : 1	123	0·01856	0·09065
	274	0·01817	0·0896

(i) Calculate the concentration ratio (M_{OH^-}/M_{Br^-}) for each set of observations and estimate the mean value at equilibrium.

The e.m.f. of the two following cells:

$$H_2 \mid NaOH \mid HgO.Hg$$
$$\text{aq.}$$

$$H_2 \mid \quad HBr \quad \mid Hg_2Br_2.Hg$$
$$\text{unit activity}$$

have been measured at 25° C by other authors and found to be 0·9264 and 0·1396 volt respectively, the former being independent of the concentration of sodium hydroxide.

(ii) From these data and the result of (i), calculate the ionic activity product of water at 25° C.

NOTE: The advantage of this method of deriving K_w from e.m.f. measurements over most of its predecessors is that it involves no cells containing liquid junction potentials, which always introduce an element of uncertainty. The work of Harned and Hamer upon which Problem 44 is based is also free from this source of error.

The problem is a straightforward example of the additivity of free energy data. No significant error is introduced at the ionic strengths involved by equating the equilibrium ratio of concentrations to that of activities.

46 A SPECTROPHOTOMETRIC STUDY OF THE INTERACTION BETWEEN IODINE AND AROMATIC HYDROCARBONS

H. A. Benesi and J. H. Hildebrand, *J. Am. Chem. Soc.*, **71**, 2703, 1949 (with supplementary experimental information kindly provided by the authors).

The trend of colour of dissolved iodine in a series of solvents from violet to brown has been generally attributed for some time to progressive interaction between iodine and the molecules of the solvent. In a study which provided strong quantitative support for this view Benesi and Hildebrand showed that the colour changes are associated with intense absorption in the ultra-violet which tends to spread into the violet end of the visible region.

The equilibrium between iodine and a series of aromatic hydrocarbons was studied quantitatively by spectrophotometric measurements in the ultra-violet of various mixtures of iodine and the aromatic hydrocarbons dissolved in an inert solvent such as carbon tetrachloride or n-heptane. Transmissions were measured at the absorption peak, which was assumed to be due entirely to the iodine–hydrocarbon complex, and the absorption of free iodine at this wave-length was neglected.

The measurements in the following table relate to solutions of iodine and benzene in carbon tetrachloride:

Length of cell (cm)	Initial molarity of iodine ($\times 10^5$)	Initial mole fraction of benzene (A)	Percentage transmission (at 2970 Å)
5	3·26	1·000	2·61
2	10·42	0·619	2·20
2	17·4	0·213	3·98
2	43·5	0·0862	1·97

Examine the compatibility of these data with the hypothesis that a complex is formed containing one molecule of iodine and one of the hydrocarbon, estimate the equilibrium constant of the reaction and the molar extinction coefficient of the assumed complex.

NOTE: In formulating an expression for the equilibrium constant it may be noted that, since the concentration of benzene is always much greater than that of either iodine or the iodine–benzene complex, (a) the mole fraction of benzene at equilibrium may be equated to the initial mole fraction, (b) the concentrations of iodine and of complex used in the equilibrium constant may be molarities. If expressions are written down for the equilibrium constant and for the molar extinction coefficient of the complex in terms of measured quantities and of the unknown concentration of the complex, we can eliminate the latter and obtain a relation involving only measured quantities, the desired equilibrium constant and the desired molar extinction coefficient. The linear form of the relation enables the molar extinction coefficient to be obtained graphically and a value for the equilibrium constant can then be calculated from the data for each mixture.

For a discussion of improved methods of calculating acid–base equilibrium constants from spectrophotometric data see, for example, N. J. Rose and R. S. Drago (*J. Am. Chem. Soc.*, **81**, 6138, 1959), and C. P. Nash (*J. Phys. Chem.*, **64**, 950, 1960). L. J. Andrews (*Chem. Rev.*, **54**, 713, 1954) provides a general survey of aromatic molecular complexes of the electron donor–acceptor type. F. J. C. and H. Rossotti, *The Determination of Stability Constants* (McGraw-Hill, New York, 1961), discuss the quantitative study of complex formation in solution comprehensively.

47 THE HYDROLYSIS OF AQUEOUS IODINE SOLUTIONS FROM SPECTROPHOTOMETRIC MEASUREMENTS

T. L. Allen and R. M. Keefer, *J. Am. Chem. Soc.*, **77**, 2957, 1955.

The hydrolytic equilibrium:

$$I_2 + H_2O = H^+ + I^- + HIO \qquad (1)$$

is very rapidly established in aqueous iodine solutions as is the associated tri-iodide equilibrium:

$$I_2 + I^- = I_3^- \qquad (2)$$

whose equilibrium constant may be taken to be 770 litres mole^{-1} at 25° C. The extent of hydrolysis may be deduced from the absorbance at 462 and at 288 millimicrons, if the molar absorbance coefficients of the iodide and tri-iodide ions are known at these wave-lengths.

Two further hydrolytic equilibria

$$I_2 + H_2O = H_2OI^+ + I^- \qquad (3)$$

$$3I_2 + 3H_2O = IO_3^- + 5I^- + 6H^+ \qquad (4)$$

however, complicate the situation. The establishment of equilibrium (4) is sharply retarded by hydrion so that by working in acid solution this hydrolysis may be ignored in freshly prepared iodine solutions. If the expressions for the equilibrium constants for the first three reactions are combined with the condition for electrical neutrality an expression may be obtained involving the three equilibrium constants, of which two are unknown, and the concentrations of hydrion, tri-iodide ion, and molecular iodine.

Allen and Keefer measured absorbances at 462 and 288 millimicrons of freshly made iodine solutions in buffers over a range of pH values with the following results:

	Absorbances (10 mm *cuvettes*)	
pH	462 mμ	288 mμ
4·54	0·919	0·260
4·89	0·905	0·315
5·32	0·914	0·445
5·67	0·650	0·403

The ionic strength of all the solutions was 0·01 at which value the activity coefficient of univalent ions may be taken as 0·905. If the molar absorbance coefficients are as follows:

	I_2	I_3
462	742	1030
288	95	40000

and those of the iodide ion may be neglected, calculate the equilibrium constant of reaction (1).

NOTE: The calculation of the concentrations of molecular iodine and tri-iodide ion in each of the four solutions can be carried out by the solution of simultaneous equations or by successive approximation; matrix methods might be used in more complicated cases than this (see, for example, R. P. Bauman, *Absorption Spectroscopy* (Wiley, New York, 1962), ch. 9 and Appendix 1).

The equilibrium constants for reactions (1), (2), and (3) can be combined with the condition for electrical neutrality so as to eliminate the concentrations of cationic iodine (hydrated), hypoidous acid and iodide ion. This relation can be rearranged so that $K_3 + \dfrac{K_1}{(\mathrm{H}^+)}$ becomes equal to an expression containing only the concentrations of molecular iodine and of the tri-iodide ion K_2 and an activity coefficient term. A plot of this expression against the reciprocal of the hydrion concentration can clearly be used in principle to evaluate both K_1 and K_3.

Over the range of pH of the observations reported above K_3 is negligible in comparison with $\dfrac{K_1}{(\mathrm{H}^+)}$ so that (a) K_3 cannot be determined in this pH range but (b) the plot can be assumed to pass through the origin. We are indebted to Dr. Keefer for the original absorbance data; the value of K_3 quoted in the paper is slightly different from that to be derived from the experimental data above because the former is derived from a wider range of observations including absorbance measurements at 352 mμ.

48* THE MEASUREMENT OF AN ORGANIC HALOGENATION EQUILIBRIUM BY AN ELECTROMETRIC METHOD

R. P. Bell and E. Gelles, *Proc. Roy. Soc.* A, **210**, 310, 1952.

Bell and Gelles studied the equilibrium constants for the reversible halogenation of a number of ketones and related substances in aqueous solution, deducing the equilibrium concentration of free halogen from the potential of a reversible halogen–halide electrode in the solution. The equilibrium constant for the reaction

$$RH + X_2 = RX + H^+ + X^-,$$

where X is a halogen and R is an organic radical, may be derived from measurements of a cell of the following type:

Pt | X_2, X^-, buffer | KCl bridge | X_2, X^-, RH, buffer | Pt.

The substance RH in the right half-cell is partly converted to RX at equilibrium with a consequent shift in the concentrations of X_2 and X^- in the right half-cell, which are initially identical with those in the left half-cell. The same buffer solution is used in both half-cells which were made up to constant ionic strength of 0·10 by the addition of potassium chloride. Liquid junction potentials may be neglected. E.m.f. measurements were made after waiting until equilibrium had been established.

The following data relate to measurements of the iodination of ethyl acetoacetate, which were carried out at 25° C in a buffer whose hydrion concentration was $3·02 \times 10^{-5}$. Expressed in milli-molarities the initial concentrations of ester, iodine, and iodide ion were 24·16, 2·46, and 16·9 respectively. When equilibrium had been attained the e.m.f. of the cell was found to be 99·4 millivolts.

(i) Taking the equilibrium $[I_3^-]/[I_2][I^-]$ as 714 litres/mole, calculate the equilibrium concentrations of iodine, iodide, and tri-iodide ions in the left half-cell.

(ii) Combining the value of $[I^-]^2/[I_2]$ for the left half-cell derived from the results of (i) with the e.m.f. of the cell, calculate the value of the same ratio for the right half-cell.

(iii) Calculate the equilibrium concentrations of the molecular species participating in the iodination reaction and hence its thermodynamic equilibrium constant, assuming an activity coefficient of 0·80 for univalent ions at the ionic strength used in the cell.

NOTE : (i) The 'initial concentrations' are those before either the tri-iodide or the iodination equilibrium is established. This involves the solution of a quadratic equation.

(ii) The equal ionic strengths and similar compositions of the solutions in the two halves of the cell makes it possible to cancel activity coefficient terms in what is a simple concentration cell equation.

(iii) The result of (ii) gives one numerical relation between the equilibrium concentrations $[I^-]_e$ and $[I_2]_e$ in the right half-cell. If the corresponding initial concentrations *before* the establishment of *either* the tri-iodide *or* the iodination equilibrium are represented by $[I^-]_0$ and $[I_2]_0$, it is not difficult to show that the tri-iodide equilibrium condition can be rewritten

$$\frac{[I_2]_0 + [I^-]_0 - [I_2]_e - [I^-]_e}{2[I_2]_e[I^-]_e} = 714.$$

This equation and the result of (ii) provide two equations involving $[I_2]_e$ and $[I^-]_e$, which can readily be converted to a cubic equation in $[I^-]_e$, which can be solved graphically; the trial of two or three values of $[I^-]_e$ between 0·0190 and 0·0200 will be sufficient to identify the solution.

The theoretical interest derived from the comparison and interpretation of equilibrium data of this sort for a range of compounds is illustrated in the original paper. The different values for the tri-iodide equilibrium constant chosen by the investigators of Problems 47 and 48 will be more intelligible after consulting M. Davies and E. Gwynne (*J. Am. Chem. Soc.*, **74**, 2748, 1952).

49 THE DISSOCIATION CONSTANTS OF BENZOIC AND TARTARIC ACID FROM ELECTROMETRIC TITRATION MEASUREMENTS

F. Auerbach and E. Smolczyk, *Z. physik. Chem.*, **110**, 65, 1924.

A series of organic acids were titrated with alkali at 20° C using a quinhydrone electrode against a saturated calomel electrode. The quinhydrone electrode is 0·7029 volt more positive than the hydrogen electrode in solutions of the same hydrion activity; the saturated calomel electrode is +0·2461 volt on the hydrogen scale. These electrode potentials are in accordance with the sign convention described in Note 10 on p. xvi.

Below are tabulated the results for benzoic and tartaric acids:

Benzoic acid

50 cm³ of 0·02114 N benzoic acid titrated with 0·1244 N caustic soda.

cm³ alkali	e.m.f.
0·00	0·2879
1·07	0·2603
2·46	0·2372
4·77	0·2078
6·73	0·1795
7·82	0·1516
8·33	0·1083
8·42	0·0832
8·63	−0·0102
8·67	−0·0204
8·71	−0·0247

Tartaric acid

10 cm³ of 0·1005 N tartaric acid titrated with 0·1244 N caustic soda.

cm³ alkali	e.m.f.
0·00	0·3269
2·00	0·2842
3·50	0·2580
4·00	0·2493
4·50	0·2410
5·00	0·2324
6·00	0·2135

cm³ alkali	e.m.f.
7·00	0·1896
7·80	0·1484
8·00	0·1055
8·09	0·0197
8·12	−0·0072
8·19	−0·0313

(i) Plot the titration curve (e.m.f. or pH against the volume of alkali) of each acid.

(ii) Plot the differential quantity

$$\frac{\Delta \text{ e.m.f.}}{\Delta \text{ volume of alkali added}}$$

against the volume of alkali in the neighbourhood of the end-point for each acid.

(iii) Calculate the dissociation constant of benzoic acid.

(iv) Calculate the two dissociation constants of tartaric acid.

NOTE: *Benzoic acid.* This calculation is based on the assumption that on the acid side of the titration of a weak acid by a strong base

$$K = \frac{(\text{hydrogen-ion concentration})(\text{concentration of salt formed})}{(\text{concentration of un-neutralized acid})},$$

an approximation which neglects the dissociation of the un-neutralized acid and the distinction between activities and concentrations. The neutralization point is ascertained graphically, and the dissociation constant may be calculated from the interpolated e.m.f. at half-neutralization or from the directly observed e.m.f. at some point in the same region.

Tartaric acid. For dibasic acids assumptions similar to those above are made but the equations are more complex; the original paper should be consulted. It is necessary to use e.m.f. measurements for the point of complete neutralization and two other points, not too close together; for the latter, points corresponding to 3·5 and 6 cm³ of alkali respectively are suitable. The shape of the titration curve for tartaric acid may surprise the student whose ideas on the titration of polybasic acids are based too exclusively on phosphoric acid. For the explanation and a discussion of titration curves H. F. Walton, *Principles and Methods of Chemical Analysis* (Prentice-Hall, New York, 1952), ch. 13, may be consulted.

50 THE EQUILIBRIUM BETWEEN FERROUS AND FERRIC IONS

S. Popoff and A. H. Kunz, *J. Am. Chem. Soc.*, **51**, 382, 1929;
S. Popoff, V. B. Fleharty, and E. L. Hanson, ibid., **53**, 1643,
1931.

The ferrous–ferric equilibrium determined by e.m.f. measurements

Popoff and Kunz measured the e.m.f. of the cell

$$\begin{array}{c} \text{HCl} \quad m_1 \\ \text{Pt, H}_2 \mid \text{HCl } m_1 \mid \text{FeCl}_2 \, m_2 \mid \text{Pt} \\ \pi_1 \qquad\qquad \pi_2 \, \text{FeCl}_3 \, m_2 \, \pi_3 \end{array}$$

at 25° C for a series of values of m_1 and m_2. Their results were
corrected for small deviations from equality in the molality of
the ferrous and ferric salts; the value of the right-hand electrode
potential plus the liquid junction potential, $(\pi_2 + \pi_3)$, was then
calculated on the standard hydrogen scale from the known
activity coefficients of aqueous solutions of hydrochloric
acid.

Some of their results are tabulated below:

$m_1 = 0.05$		$m_1 = 0.10$		$m_1 = 0.20$	
m_2	$\pi_2 + \pi_3$	m_2	$\pi_2 + \pi_3$	m_2	$\pi_2 + \pi_3$
0·009431	0·7337	0·009397	0·7282	0·008855	0·7207
0·005318	0·7360	0·004799	0·7295	0·004545	0·7214
0·002554	0·7372	0·002598	0·7302	0·002202	0·7218

(i) Extrapolate $\pi_2 + \pi_3$ for each acid molality to zero salt
concentration.

(ii) Extrapolate these limiting values (from which π_2 has
disappeared) to zero acid concentration and thus evaluate
the standard oxidation–reduction potential of ferrous and
ferric ions.

(iii) Taking the standard potential of the silver electrode

as $+0.7995$, calculate from the result of (ii) the equilibrium constant at $25°$ C of the reaction

$$Ag + Fe^{3+} = Ag^+ + Fe^{2+}$$

and compare your result with the experimental value (extrapolated to zero salt concentration) of 0.128, measured directly by Noyes and Brann.

The chemical determination of the ferrous–ferric equilibrium

Popoff, Fleharty, and Hanson approached the equilibrium point of the reaction

$$2Hg + 2Fe(ClO_4)_3 = 2Fe(ClO_4)_2 + Hg_2(ClO_4)_2$$

at $25°$ from both sides, the equilibrium concentrations being determined by electrometric titration. Their result for two experiments made in the presence of 0.002 M $HClO_4$ were as follows:

$m_{Fe^{++}}$	Hg_2^{++}	$m_{Fe^{+++}}$
0·001546	0·0007712	0·0004542
0·0008301	0·0004153	0·0001698

(iv) Assuming that at these ionic strengths the activity coefficients are given by the equation

$$-\log_{10} f = 0.50 z^2 \sqrt{\mu},$$

where z is the valency of the ion and μ is the ionic strength, calculate the true equilibrium constant (in activities) from each mixture.

(v) From the mean of these two values calculate the standard potential of the ferrous–ferric electrode, taking Lewis and Randall's value of the standard potential of mercury (against mercurous ion) as $+0.7986$.

NOTE: The method of calculation is here fairly completely indicated in the formulation of the problem. The sign of the standard electrode potentials given in the problem is according to the 'European' convention in contrast to that of Lewis and Randall, used in the original paper. In (iv) the equilibrium constant should be calculated in the form

$$\frac{a_{Hg_2^{++}} \cdot a_{Fe^{++}}^2}{a_{Fe^{+++}}^2};$$

reference to the original paper reveals unexpected discrepancies in the equilibrium constants derived from data (not quoted here) obtained in the presence of slightly higher concentrations of perchloric acid; the original paper also shows that very variable equilibrium 'constants' are obtained when calculated on the assumption that the mercurous ion is monatomic. For a later determination of an oxidation–reduction potential by the same method as that of Popoff and Kunz see J. R. Partington and H. I. Stonehill, *Trans. Faraday Soc.*, **31**, 1357, 1935.

It must not be concluded that the careful work reported in the papers on which this problem is based represents the 'last word' on the value of the classic example of an oxidation–reduction potential. Perusal of W. C. Bray and A. V. Hershey (*J. Am. Chem. Soc.*, **56**, 1889, 1934) and of W. C. Schumb, M. S. Sherill, and S. B. Sweetser (ibid., **59**, 2360, 1937) shows how elusive the true value of the oxidation–reduction potential is.

51* THE MEASUREMENT OF ACTIVITY COEFFICIENTS BY ION-EXCHANGE RESINS, USING RADIOACTIVE TRACERS

R. H. Betts and A. N. MacKenzie, *Can. J. Chem.*, **30**, 146, 1952.

The displacement equilibrium between an ion-exchange resin and an electrolyte solution, such as:

$$HR + Na^+(+Cl^-) = NaR + H^+(+Cl^-)$$

is governed by a thermodynamic equilibrium constant

$$K_a = \frac{a_{NaR}[H^+]\gamma_{HCl}^2}{a_{HR}[Na^+]\gamma_{NaCl}^2},$$

where the a terms relate to the activities of the species NaR and HR in the resin phase, $[H^+]$ and $[Na^+]$ are the molalities of hydrion and sodium ion in solution and the γ terms are the activity coefficients of the two electrolytes in the solution. There is cumulative evidence that over limited ranges of composition the ratio of the activities of the two components in the resin phase is indistinguishable from the ratio of their mole fractions.

The distribution of alkali metal ions between a resin and a relatively concentrated solution of hydrochloric acid can be measured at extremely low concentrations by means of radioactive tracers. The application of the equation above to the results can then be used to study the activity coefficient of sodium chloride at extremely low concentrations in the presence of a wide range of concentrations of hydrochloric acid.

Betts and Mackenzie made such measurements using Na^{24}, prepared by neutron-irradiation in the Chalk River pile, to tag the sodium chloride. Mixtures of hydrochloric acid of 'macroscopic' concentration and of tagged sodium chloride at a concentration several orders of magnitude lower were shaken with a known mass of a cation-exchange resin in its acid form until equilibrium had been established. The distribution of sodium ions between solution and resin was measured by Geiger count of the equilibrium solution combined with a similar measurement of the solution before contact with the resin. The mass and exchange capacity of the resin was so large in comparison with the amount of sodium chloride present that in all experiments less than 0·1 per cent of hydrion in the resin had been displaced by sodium ion at equilibrium. Not only was the ratio NaR/HR very low but it varied over a range so limited that the ratio of the activity coefficients of the two species in the resin phase can be treated as constant in the experiments described below.

The observations shown on the facing page (provided by the courtesy of Dr. Betts) relate to experiments carried out with samples of the same batch of resin in dilute and concentrated solutions of hydrochloric acid respectively:

(i) In Experiment 8a the electrolyte concentration is low enough to be in the region of the 'Debye–Hückel limiting law' where the activity coefficients of sodium chloride and hydrochloric acid can be assumed to be equal. With this assumption and those previously mentioned calculate the

84

Experiment No.	8a		12	
Molality of HCl	0·00502		0·8544	
Molality of NaCl	0·00000183		0·000333	
Wt. of resin (grammes) (air-dried)	None	0·0363	None	1·4024
Wt. of Na²⁴Cl solution (grammes)	0·4916	0·9896	0·1985	0·3967
Total wt. of solution (grammes)	50·327	50·825	12·360	12·253
Counts/minute/gramme of solution (corrected for decay) at equilibrium	15254	14831	8670	8891

value of K_a, if the capacity of the acid form of the resin is 4·12 milli-equivalents per gramme.

(ii) With the value of K_a thus derived from Experiment 8a calculate from the data of Experiment 12 the activity co-efficient of sodium chloride at the very low concentration involved in the presence of 0·8544 molal hydrochloric acid. The activity coefficient of the latter may be taken as 0·789.

NOTE: The use of ion-exchange resins for the measurement of activity coefficients was suggested by A. P. Vanselow in 1932 (*J. Am. Chem. Soc.*, **54**, 1307, 1932) but it was not until the use of resins for the separation of fission products in the development of the atom bomb provoked a thorough study of ion-exchange equilibria (and incidentally suggested the simultaneous use of radioactive tracers) that the way was paved for general application. W. C. Bauman, R. E. Anderson, and R. M. Wheaton (*Ann. Rev. Phys. Chem.*, **3**, 123, 1952) or R. E. Connick and S. W. Mayer (*J. Am. Chem. Soc.*, **73**, 1176, 1951) may be consulted for references to post-war developments.

The observations quoted for Experiment 12 have been corrected for preferential uptake of water by the resin, which concentrated the HCl and reduced the total amount of solution; the corresponding correction for Experiment 8a is negligible in view of the low resin/solution ratio.

The first and third columns of figures make it possible to calculate the specific activity of the two tagged sodium chloride solutions used in the two experiments. The material balance-sheet covering the ion-exchange process needs rather careful consideration. The following observations may be helpful: (a) the 'capacity' of a resin measures the number of fixed ionic sites capable of entering into ion exchange, expressed in milli-equivalents per gramme, (b) the molalities of the two sodium chloride solutions do not appear in the final calculation, (c) a little arithmetical complication arises from the need to convert grammes of solution into grammes of water so as to be able to calculate molalities in Experiment 12, (d) further arithmetical complication in the original paper, which do *not* enter into the problem as stated above, arose from the fact that solutions were standardized volumetrically (i.e. on a molarity basis), (e) the solutions used in Experiment 8a are sufficiently dilute not only to cancel the activity coefficient terms but also make weights of solution and of solvent virtually identical.

N.B. Five-figure logarithms are necessary in this problem.

52 AN EXPERIMENTAL TEST OF THE DONNAN THEORY OF MEMBRANE EQUILIBRIUM

N. Kameyama, *Phil. Mag.*, **50**, 849, 1925.

Kameyama investigated the distribution of potassium chloride across a membrane of copper ferrocyanide, deposited on vegetable parchment, between a pure aqueous solution and one containing potassium ferrocyanide, the anion of which cannot pass through the membrane.

$$\begin{array}{c|c} \mathrm{KCl}\ (C_1) & \\ & \mathrm{KCl}\ (C_2) \\ \mathrm{K_4Fe(CN)_6}\ (C_3) & \end{array}$$

Membrane
of
$Cu_2Fe(CN)_6$.

The following equilibrium data are selected from his results, concentrations being expressed in *milli-equivalents* per litre:

Solution 1		Solution 2
$K_4Fe(CN)_6$ (C_3)	KCl (C_1)	KCl (C_2)
17·8	22·2	27·8
42·4	10·7	20·9
80·3	11·1	26·0

Assuming that the activity coefficient of potassium chloride, in pure and mixed salt solutions, depends only on the ionic strength of the solution and that the variation with the ionic strength is given by the following data:

Concentration (millimoles per litre)	10	20	50	100	200	500
$\sqrt{}$(Ionic strength)	0·1	0·1415	0·2237	0·3162	0·4472	0·7071
Activity coefficient	0·922	0·892	0·840	0·794	0·749	0·682

examine the conformity of the experiments with the Donnan theory by using the theory and the principle of ionic strength to calculate, from the concentration data for the potassium ferrocyanide side of the membrane, the concentration of potassium chloride to be expected on the other side of the membrane.

NOTE: Two papers by G. Schmid (*Z. Elektrochem.*, **39**, 384 and 453, 1933) give full details of the experimental technique of membrane studies.

The calculation is facilitated by plotting, for interpolation purposes, a graph of activity coefficient against activity for dilute potassium chloride solutions in addition to the graph of activity coefficient against $\sqrt{}$(ionic strength) which is obviously necessary.

53 THE COMBINATION OF SERUM ALBUMIN WITH CHLORIDE IONS FROM MEMBRANE EQUILIBRIUM MEASUREMENTS

G. Scatchard, I. H. Scheinberg, and S. H. Armstrong, *J. Am. Chem. Soc.*, **72**, 535, 1950.

The interaction of proteins with small ions is a matter of both theoretical and practical interest. It may be studied by equilibrating a protein solution inside a cellophane sac with a solution of the diffusible ion outside the sac; the procedure is sometimes referred to as 'equilibrium dialysis'.

Scatchard, Scheinberg, and Armstrong used this method to measure the combination of human serum albumin with chloride ion. A cellophane sac containing a known amount of serum albumin and water was immersed in a test-tube containing known amounts of sodium chloride and water. The system was brought to equilibrium at 5·0° C by rotating the tightly stoppered test-tube for twenty-seven hours; the motions of a glass bead inside the sac and of the sac inside the test-tube served respectively to stir the inside and the outside solutions. After equilibrium the concentration of sodium chloride outside the membrane was determined by conductance measurements and the volume of solution inside the sac was measured.

The following experimental results, kindly provided by Professor Scatchard, are among those on which the paper cited above is based; they relate to the system after equilibration.

Moles of protein inside sac $\times 10^5$	Total moles of NaCl (inside and outside) $\times 10^5$	Total weight of water (g)	Weight of water inside sac (g)	Molality of NaCl outside sac $\times 10^3$
2·133	12·19	60·54	22	1·834
2·133	420·7	66·37	21	62·44
2·133	2540	65·67	22	385·4

The authors cite reasons for believing that sodium ions are *not* bound by the protein molecules. With this assumption and the further one that the activity coefficients of the uncombined sodium and chloride ions are the same inside the sac as outside, apply the principles of the Donnan equilibrium to calculate the average number of chloride ions bound to each albumin molecule at each sodium chloride concentration.

NOTE: Using the simplifying assumption about activity coefficients indicated above, the Donnan equilibrium provides that the product of the concentration of sodium ions and of chloride ions outside the membrane will be equal to the corresponding product inside the membrane. This relationship together with a material balance sheet for the diffusible ions leads to an expression for the number of moles of chloride ion combined with the albumin and hence to the average number of chloride ions bound to one molecule of the protein.

Biochemical textbooks may be consulted on the importance of membrane equilibria in living organisms. The authors of the present paper show that their results for ion-protein combination can be interpreted in terms of the law of mass action with a correction for electrostatic interaction of combined ions.

Thermodynamic Properties

54 ELECTRON AFFINITIES FROM THE BORN-HABER CYCLE

M. G. Evans, E. Warhurst, and E. Whittle, *J. Chem. Soc.*, 1524, 1950.

Calculate the mean electron affinities of the halogens from the thermodynamic data tabulated below. These are selected values given by Evans, Warhurst, and Whittle where references to the original measurements are given.

In the tables

$Q(MX)_c$ is the heat of formation of $(MX)_c$ from $(M)_c$ and gaseous X_2.

$S(M)_c$ is the heat of sublimation of the alkali metal.

$I(M)$ is the ionization potential of the alkali metal.

TABLE 1

	F_2	Cl_2	Br_2	I_2
$D(X_2)$ kcal mole^{-1}	37 ± 8	$57 \cdot 8$	$46 \cdot 2$	$36 \cdot 1$

TABLE 2

	Li	Na	K	Rb	Cs
$S(M)_c$ kcal mole^{-1}	$39 \cdot 0$	$25 \cdot 9$	$19 \cdot 8$	$18 \cdot 9$	$18 \cdot 8$
$I(M)$ kcal mole^{-1}	$123 \cdot 8$	$118 \cdot 0$	$99 \cdot 7$	$95 \cdot 9$	$89 \cdot 4$

$D(X_2)$ is the dissociation energy of the halogen.

U_0 is the lattice energy of the alkali halide.

Comment on the variation of the electron affinities of the halogens. Cf. Problem 13.

TABLE 3

Salt	$Q(MX)_c$ kcal mole^{-1}	$-U_0$ kcal mole^{-1}	Salt	$Q(MX)_c$ kcal mole^{-1}	$-U_0$ kcal mole^{-1}
LiF	145·6	245·1	LiBr	87·6	189·9
NaF	136·0	216·4	NaBr	90·6	175·9
KF	134·5	193·2	KBr	97·9	161·5
RbF	133·2	183·4	RbBr	99·6	156·1
CsF	131·7	175·9	CsBr	101·5	149·6
LiCl	97·6	201·1	LiI	72·5	176·2
NaCl	98·43	184·0	NaI	76·7	164·4
KCl	104·4	168·3	KI	86·3	152·5
RbCl	105·1	162·1	RbI	88·5	147·9
CsCl	106·3	153·2	CsI	91·4	142·4

55 THE HEAT OF FORMATION OF STEAM AT HIGH TEMPERATURES

G. W. C. Kaye and T. H. Laby, *Table of Physical and Chemical Constants* (Longmans, Green, London, 1958).

The molar heat capacity of a gas can be expressed in the form

$$C_p = a + bT + cT^2 \text{ cal mole}^{-1},$$

where T is the absolute temperature, between about 300° K and 1500° K.

The values of the constants for gaseous H_2, O_2, and H_2O are given in the table.

	a	$b \times 10^3$	$c \times 10^6$
H_2	6·947	−0·200	0·4808
O_2	6·148	3·102	−0·923
H_2O	7·256	2·298	0·283

The heat of formation of liquid water from hydrogen and oxygen (each at 1 atmosphere) is -70.60 kcal mole^{-1} at $25°$ C. The latent heat of vaporization of water at $25°$ C is 13.67 kcal mole^{-1}.

Calculate the heat of formation of steam from hydrogen and oxygen at 1 atmosphere and $1600°$ C.

56 THE ENTROPY OF METHANOL AND THE FREE ENERGY OF ITS FORMATION FROM ITS ELEMENTS

K. K. Kelley, *J. Am. Chem. Soc.*, **51**, 180, 1929.

The following table gives the molar heat capacity at constant pressure of methanol between liquid hydrogen temperature and room temperature.

T $(°K)$	C_p $(cal\ mole^{-1})$
18·80	1·109
27·25	2·292
48·07	5·404
77·61	8·735
118·79	11·64
153·98	14·12
157·46	283·4
164·14	11·29
167·65	11·68
181·09	16·77
221·69	17·08
235·84	17·41
267·01	18·13
292·01	19·11

The transition in the neighbourhood of $157°$ K is a gradual one; $157.4°$ K may be taken as the mean temperature of transition; separate experiments showed that the heat of this transition is 154.3 cal mole^{-1} and that the latent heat of fusion at $175.2°$ K is 757 cal mole^{-1}.

(i) Evaluate graphically the entropy of liquid methanol at $298°$ K.

The heat of combustion of liquid methanol at 298° K is **173·61** kcal and those of graphite and hydrogen at the same temperature are 94·27 kcal/gramme-atom and 68·32 kcal mole^{-1} respectively. The entropies of graphite, hydrogen, and oxygen at 298° K are 1·3 entropy units per gramme-atom and 31·25 and 48·9 entropy units per mole respectively.

Calculate: (ii) the heat of formation, (iii) the free energy of formation, of liquid methanol at 298° K from graphite, gaseous hydrogen, and oxygen.

NOTE: The entropy is evaluated graphically by the usual C_p–$\log_{10} T$ plot; the area under the curve is most easily determined by cutting out and weighing.

The free energy of formation of methanol is readily calculated from the heat-content change and the entropy of methanol and its constituent elements with the aid of the third law of thermodynamics.

57 THE METHANOL SYNTHESIS EQUILIBRIUM FROM ENTROPY DATA

Handbook of Chemistry and Physics, 44th ed. (Chemical Rubber Publishing Co., Cleveland, Ohio, 1962/3).

From the following data determine the thermodynamic feasibility of the synthesis of methanol from carbon monoxide and hydrogen at 25° C.

Entropies at 25° C:

Carbon monoxide	47·30 entropy units mole^{-1}
Hydrogen	31·21 ,, ,, ,,
Liquid methanol	30·3 ,, ,, ,,

Heats of combustion at 25° C:

$CO + \frac{1}{2}O_2 = CO_2$; $\Delta H = -67 \cdot 63$ kcal.

$H_2 + \frac{1}{2}O_2 = H_2O$ liquid; $\Delta H = -68 \cdot 32$ kcal.

$CH_3OH_{liquid} + \frac{3}{2}O_2 = CO_2 + 2H_2O_{liquid}$;

$$\Delta H = -173 \cdot 67 \text{ kcal.}$$

NOTE: This illustrates the value of purely calorimetric data for estimating the thermodynamic feasibility of an important industrial gas reaction. The importance of the compilation of extensive tables of entropies and heats of combustion will be realized. The thermodynamics of this equilibrium are discussed by B. F. Dodge, *Chemical Engineering Thermodynamics* (McGraw-Hill, New York, 1944).

58 THE USE OF FREE ENERGY TABLES

Selected Values of Chemical Thermodynamic Properties, National Bureau of Standards, Circular No. 500 (Washington, 1952).

Tables of standard free energies of formation of substances, though laborious to construct on the large scale, provide a very concise form of expression for a great range of equilibrium data. The rate of proliferation of information of this type makes the construction and use of such tables progressively more indispensable.

From the following extracts from N.B.S. Circular 500 evaluate at 298·16° K the quantities listed below the table:

Substance	Standard free energy of formation (*expressed in kilocalories and relating to one mole at 298·16° K and one atmosphere pressure*)
$C_2H_4(g)$	$+16·282$
$C_2H_4O(g)$	$-2·79$
$Hg(g)$	$+7·59$
$Ag_2O(s)$	$-2·586$
Fe^{++} (hypoth $m = 1$)	$-20·30$
Fe^{+++} (hypoth $m = 1$	$-2·52$
Ag^+ (hypoth $m = 1$)	$+18·430$
Cl^- (hypoth $m = 1$)	$-31·350$
$AgCl(s)$	$-26·224$
$I_2(aq.)$ (hypoth $m = 1$)	$+3·926$
$Br_2(g)$	$+0·751$
$BrCl(g)$	$-0·210$
$CO(g)$	$-32·8079$
$CO_2(g)$	$-94·2598$
$HCOOH(g)$	$-80·24$
$(HCOOH)_2(g)$	$-163·8$
$HCl(aq.)$ (hypoth $m = 1$)	$-31·350$

(*a*) The equilibrium constant for the catalytic oxidation of ethylene to ethylene oxide by oxygen.

(b) The vapour pressure of mercury.

(c) The dissociation pressure of silver oxide.

(d) The ratio of the activities of ferrous and ferric ions in equilibrium with hydrogen gas at one atmosphere and hydrion at unit activity.

(e) The solubility product of silver chloride.

(f) The solubility of iodine.

(g) The partial pressure of bromine chloride present at equilibrium with an equimolecular mixture of chlorine and bromine at a total pressure of 0·100 atmosphere.

(h) The ratio of the partial pressures of carbon monoxide and carbon dioxide in equilibrium with solid carbon at a total pressure of one atmosphere.

(i) The partial pressure of dimer present in formic acid vapour at a total pressure of 0·0100 atmosphere.

(j) The standard electrode potential of the silver–silver chloride electrode.

NOTE: The operations to be performed in this problem are essentially the converse of those required in most of the other problems in the book. Here figures obtained from a work of reference are to be converted into quantities more or less directly observable. All quantities relate to 25° C and further information would be necessary to calculate values at other temperatures. The arithmetical operations are quite simple except in part (i) where the solution of a quadratic equation is inescapable.

The standard state chosen for dissolved substances is discussed by G. N. Lewis and M. Randall, *Thermodynamics* (McGraw-Hill, New York, 1961), pp. 246–8. In all the solutions referred to in this problem, the solvent is water.

59 THE SPECIFIC HEAT OF SALT SOLUTIONS FROM THE TEMPERATURE COEFFICIENT OF THE HEAT OF SOLUTION

S. G. Lipsett, F. M. G. Johnson, and O. Maass, *J. Am. Chem. Soc.*, **49**, 1940, 1927.

The heat of solution of sodium chloride in water at 20° C and 25° C was measured in a rotating adiabatic calorimeter. The results, calculated by the provisional use of previously recorded data for the specific heat of sodium chloride solutions, may be used to calculate the specific heat of these solutions with a considerably higher degree of accuracy. Selected results are tabulated below:

Concentration of final solution (g NaCl/100 g solution)	Heat of solution per mole (cal)	
	20° C	25° C
3·00	+1100	+974
12·00	+774·6	+700·8

The specific heats at 22·5° C of water and solid sodium chloride are 0·9993 and 0·208 cal/g respectively.

Calculate the specific heat of 3·0 and 12·0 per cent aqueous solutions of sodium chloride.

NOTE: The heats of solution recorded above involved the provisional use of specific heat data already available; the relative magnitudes are such that an error of, say, 0·3 per cent in these provisional specific heats leads to an error of only 0·01 per cent in the final specific heat as calculated by Kirchhoff's law: it is clear, therefore, that a second approximation, if necessary, would lead to specific heat values of very high precision. It is, of course, possible to calculate the specific heats without the assumption of provisional values (Richards and Rowe, *J. Am. Chem. Soc.*, **42**, 1621, 1920), but the calculation is laborious. The positive sign corresponds to an *absorption* of heat on solution.

60 THE ENTROPY OF NICKEL

Landolt-Börnstein, *Ergänzungsband*, ii (Springer, Berlin, 1931).

From the following specific-heat data for nickel evaluate graphically its entropy per gramme-atom at 25° C:

Temperature (°K)	Specific heat (cal/g)
15·05	0·000792
25·20	0·00244

Temperature ($°K$)	Specific heat (cal/g)
47·10	0·01438
67·13	0·0311
82·11	0·0411
133·4	0·0728
204·05	0·0925
256·5	0·1010
283·0	0·1062

NOTE: A simple exercise in graphical integration (cf. Problems 56 and 61); the area under the C_p–$\log_{10}T$ curve is most simply determined by cutting out and weighing.

61* HEAT CAPACITIES AND ENTROPIES OF AMMONIUM HYDROXIDE AND AMMONIUM OXIDE

D. L. Hildenbrand and W. F. Giauque, *J. Am. Chem. Soc.*, **75**, 2811, 1953.

The heat capacities of $(NH_4)_2O$ and of NH_4OH were measured over a wide range of temperatures. Selected values of the measurements are given in the tables overleaf.

(i) Evaluate the standard entropy for $(NH_4)_2O$ and for NH_4OH.

(ii) Obtain ΔS_{298} for the reactions

(a) $NH_3(g) + NH_4OH(l) = (NH_4)_2O(l)$
(b) $\quad NH_3(g) + H_2O(l) = NH_4OH(l)$.

S_{298} is 16·72 cal deg^{-1} mole^{-1} for water
46·03 ,, ,, ,, for $NH_3(g)$.

(iii) Compare these values with those obtainable from isothermal data compiled by Scatchard et al. (*Refrig. Eng.*, **53**, 413 (1947)). The relevant data are for

$$NH_4OH(l) + NH_3(l_{satd}) = (NH_4)_2O(l)$$
$$\Delta F_{298} = -434 \text{ cal mole}^{-1}$$
$$\Delta H_{298} = -576 \text{ ,, ,,}$$

for $\qquad H_2O(l) + NH_3(l) = NH_4OH(l)$ at 298° K

$$\Delta F = -1527 \text{ cal mole}^{-1}$$
$$\Delta H = -2109 \quad ,, \quad ,,$$

for $\qquad NH_3(g) = NH_3(l_{satd})$ at 298° K.

National Bureau of Standards Circular 500 give

$$\Delta F = \quad 1298 \text{ cal mole}^{-1}$$
$$\Delta H = -5032 \quad ,, \quad ,,$$

(iv) Find out from the original paper how the authors demonstrated the existence of pure ammonium oxide and of pure ammonium hydroxide.

Heat capacities

(a) *Ammonium oxide*

T (°K)	C_p (cal mole^{-1})	
15	1·085	
20	2·151	
30	4·649	
40	7·666	
50	12·032	
50·84	12·97	
51·58	21·93	
51·63	76·75	
51·65	281	
51·66	429	
51·67	301	Transition
51·69	71·33	Region
51·77	13·73	
51·90	12·50	
52·20	12·52	
53·11	14·01	
57·51	11·36	
58·91	11·35	
55	11·776	
60	11·388	
70	12·491	
100	16·592	
150	22·485	
190	26·667	
194·32 melting-point $L_f = 2352$ cal mole^{-1}		
200	47·552	
230	50·695	
260	53·491	
290	55·795	
300	56·477	

(b) *Ammonium hydroxide*

T $(°K)$	C_p
15	0·419
20	0·924
30	2·185
40	3·536
50	4·845
60	6·114
70	7·333
80	8·486
100	10·643
130	13·603
160	16·344
190	19·030
190·15 melting-point $L_f = 1568$ cal mole^{-1}	
200	28·566
230	31·285
260	33·957
290	36·400
300	37·134

NOTE: Plot the specific heat against $\ln T$ and obtain the standard entropy by graphical integration. The specific heat curve may be extrapolated from 15° K to 0° K by the method of Debye.

$(NH_4)_2O$ shows specific heat anomalies near 52° K. Measure the area under the plot graphically excluding the amount represented by the peaks above $C_p = 12·032$ cal deg^{-1} mole^{-1} in the region of the transition. The heat absorbed during the transition was found to be 74·5 cal mole^{-1}. Make a more detailed plot of the transition region between 50° K and 58·91° K and estimate the centre of gravity of the transition on the temperature scale. Hence obtain the entropy change during the transition.

62 THE HEAT CAPACITY OF LEAD

Landolt-Börnstein, *Tabellen, 5 and 6 Auflagen* (Springer, Berlin, 1936 and 1961).

The heat capacity of lead at constant pressure has the following values at various temperatures:

Temperature $(°K)$	C_p (Joule mole^{-1} deg^{-1})
20	11·01
40	19·57
60	22·43
80	23·69

Temperature ($^\circ K$)	C_p (Joule $mole^{-1}\ deg^{-1}$)
100	24·43
150	25·27
200	25·87
250	26·36
298·15	26·82

The compressibility of lead is $2 \cdot 2 \times 10^{-12}$ dynes^{-1} cm^2, and the coefficient of cubical expansion is $81 \cdot 24 \times 10^{-6}$ deg^{-1}. The atomic weight of lead is 207·2 and its density is 11·34 g/cm^3.

(i) Calculate C_v for lead at the temperatures between 20° K and 298·15° K. The difference between C_p and C_v below 20° K is negligible.

(ii) Compare those data with the predictions of the Einstein specific heat equation, taking the characteristic temperature of lead as 67° K.

(iii) On the basis of the same equation, calculate the proportion of lead atoms having 0, 1, 2, and 5 quanta of vibrational energy at 67° K, 335° K, and 536° K, respectively.

63 THE LATENT HEAT OF VAPORIZATION OF LEAD FROM VAPOUR-PRESSURE DATA

A. C. G. Egerton, *Proc. Roy. Soc.* A, **103**, 469, 1923.

The following values of the vapour pressure of molten lead were derived from measurements of the rate of effusion of the vapour into a vacuum through a hole of known dimensions:

Temperature ($^\circ K$)	Pressure (mm)
895·4	$5 \cdot 87 \times 10^{-4}$
922·1	$1 \cdot 54 \times 10^{-3}$
964·5	$4 \cdot 04 \times 10^{-3}$
1009·7	$1 \cdot 05 \times 10^{-2}$
1045·5	$2 \cdot 55 \times 10^{-2}$

(i) Plot the logarithm of the vapour pressure against the reciprocal of the absolute temperature and either by inspection of your graph or by the method of least squares set up an empirical equation to represent the vapour pressure of lead over the temperature range measured; (ii) calculate the mean latent heat of vaporization over the temperature range; and (iii) estimate the boiling-point of lead at atmospheric pressure.

NOTE: The method of least squares, which is described on p. 413 of F. Daniels, J. W. Williams, P. Bender, R. A. Alberty, and C. D. Cornwell, *Experimental Physical Chemistry* (McGraw-Hill, New York, 1962), provides an objective method of determining the 'best' straight line but it is doubtful whether the experimental data here warrant such a time-consuming procedure. The estimate of the boiling-point involves an extrapolation over a wide temperature range where the latent heat of vaporization might vary substantially; the closeness of the calculated value to the range of observed values is something of a coincidence. R. W. Ditchburn and J. C. Gilmour (*Rev. Mod. Phys.*, **13**, 310, 1941) provide a useful survey of methods of measurement of vapour pressure and their respective ranges of applicability.

64* THE HEAT OF SUBLIMATION OF ZINC

R. F. Barrow, P. G. Dodsworth, A. R. Downie, F. A. N. S. Jeffries, A. C. P. Pugh, F. J. Smith, and J. M. Swinstead, *Trans. Faraday Soc.*, **51**, 1354, 1956.

The heat of sublimation of zinc at 298·2° K can be evaluated by two methods:—

(*a*) using the third law and specific heat data and,

(*b*) from the second law and vapour pressure data.

(*a*) The heat-content change $\Delta H = H_{g_T} - H_{l_T}$ between zinc vapour and liquid zinc at a temperature T, can be obtained from the following steps:

Solid (298) $\longrightarrow$ vapour (298) $\longrightarrow$ vapour (T)

and   Solid (298) $\longrightarrow$ solid (693) $\longrightarrow$ liquid (693) $\longrightarrow$ liquid (T).

(i) Obtain the value of ΔH at some temperature just above the melting-point, using the specific heat data and the heat of fusion, in terms of the heat of sublimation of zinc.

(ii) Obtain ΔH from the entropy data and hence find the heat of sublimation of zinc.

$$C_p(\text{gas}) = 4 \cdot 968 \text{ cal g atom}^{-1} \text{ deg}^{-1}$$
$$C_p(\text{liquid}) = 7 \cdot 50 \text{ cal g atom}^{-1} \text{ deg}^{-1}$$
$$C_p(\text{crystal}) = 5 \cdot 35 + 2 \cdot 40 T \times 10^{-3}$$
$$\text{cal g atom}^{-1} \text{ deg}^{-1}$$

$\Delta H(\text{fusion})$ at 693 Å = 1765 cal g atom^{-1}.

$S_{298}(\text{crystal}) = 9 \cdot 95$ e.u.

At. wt. of zinc = 65·38. m. pt. of zinc = 692·7° K

$S_T(\text{gas})$ can be obtained from the Sackur–Tetrode equation. The ground state of Zn is $^1S_0$ and the first excited state makes no contribution.

(b) Measurements of the vapour pressure of solid zinc were made by an effusion method and the results can be expressed as $\log_{10} p = 9 \cdot 8253 - 0 \cdot 1923 \log_{10} T - 0 \cdot 2623 \times 10^{-3} T - 6862 \cdot 5 T^{-1}$. If ΔC_p is the difference between the heat capacities of gaseous and solid zinc, we can express it in the form

$$\Delta C_p = \Delta a + \Delta b T.$$

The heat of sublimation is

$$\Delta H_0 + \int_0^T \Delta C_p \, dT$$

or $$\Delta H_T = \Delta H_0 + \Delta a T + \tfrac{1}{2} \Delta b T^2$$

(iii) Find ΔH_{298}.

NOTE: The entropy calculated from the Sackur–Tetrode equation must refer to the vapour pressure of the zinc at the appropriate temperature.

The paper by Barrow et al. gives some details of the method of measuring the vapour pressures.

65 THE HEAT OF FORMATION OF SILVER IODIDE AND THE ENTROPY OF IODINE

T. J. Webb, *J. Phys. Chem.*, **29**, 816, 1925.

Precipitated silver iodide was dissolved in aqueous solutions of potassium and sodium iodide; the heat evolution per mole of silver iodide was 2281 and 1784 cal respectively. Finely divided silver was suspended in similar solutions of the two alkaline iodides; on adding iodine, the silver was rapidly dissolved to form silver iodide. The heat evolution per mole of silver iodide formed was 17220 cal for the potassium iodide solution and 16802 cal for the sodium iodide solution.

(i) Calculate the heat of formation of silver iodide from its elements at room temperature.

The free energy of formation at 298° C of silver iodide, evaluated from e.m.f. measurements, is −15745 cal. The entropies at 298° K of silver and silver iodide are 10·25 cal per gramme-atom and 26·8 cal per gramme-mole respectively.

(ii) Combining these data with the result of (i), calculate the entropy of solid iodine per gramme-atom at 298° K and compare your result with the calorimetric value of 13·95 obtained from the specific heat data of F. Lange (*Z. physik. Chem.*, **110**, 343, 1924).

NOTE: The second part of this problem may be regarded either as a method of measuring the entropy of iodine (concerning which there was some uncertainty at the time of the original paper) or as a test of the third law of thermodynamics upon which this indirect calculation of entropy depends.

66 * THE THERMODYNAMIC RELATIONS OF GREY AND WHITE TIN

J. N. Brönsted, *Z. physik. Chem.*, **88**, 479, 1914.

The transition point between white and grey tin is at $19°$ C. The heat of transformation was determined calorimetrically by comparing the heat required to raise equal masses of each modification from $0°$ C to temperatures between $45°$ and $58°$ C. In the case of white tin the heat corresponded to the specific heat of white tin; the corresponding quantity for grey tin included the heat transformation. The average of several concordant determinations led to a value of 532 cal per gramme-atom for the heat transformation at $0°$ C.

The specific heat of the two allotropes was measured between $80°$ and $288°$ K using the Nernst–Eucken technique in which a platinum spiral serves simultaneously as a thermo-meter as well as a source of heat. The following values are selected from their results:

T ($°K$)	C_p (white)	C_p (grey)
79·8	4·64	3·80
94·8	5·07	4·30
197·2	6·23	5·71
248·4	6·36	5·87
273·0	6·39	5·90
288·1	6·40	5·91

(i) Compare the difference between the specific heats with the following empirical equation devised by Brönsted:

$$C_p(\text{white}) - C_p(\text{grey}) = 0.49 + 3.25 \times 10^{-8}(300 - T)^3.$$

(ii) With the aid of the empirical equation, the heat of transformation at $0°$ C, and Kirchhoff's equation, derive an expression for the heat of transformation at constant pressure between $80°$ and $292°$ K.

(iii) With the aid of the Gibbs–Helmholtz equation derive an expression for the free energy change between the same temperatures.

(iv) Plot the course of ΔH and ΔF between 80° and 292° K.

NOTE: The measurements of Brönsted given in this problem are taken from a comprehensive study of the thermodynamics of a very simple condensed system. The problem involves the expression of heat-content and free energy changes in the form of expansions in ascending powers of T. Part (iii) necessitates the evaluation of the integration constant of the Gibbs–Helmholtz equation (cf. Problem 16).

67 THE HEAT OF FORMATION OF THE HYDROGEN BOND FROM THE DEGREE OF DIMERIZATION OF ACETIC ACID

Undergraduate data from Physical Chemistry Laboratory, Oxford.

The apparent molecular weight of acetic acid was determined over the temperature range 150–250° C by Dumas' method. The weight of acid contained in the bulb was determined by breaking the bulb under water and titrating the resulting solution with standard 0·038 N baryta. A new bulb was used for each determination and its volume was found to ±0·5 ml, by filling it with water from a burette. The following experimental results were obtained.

T (°C)	P (mm)	Titre (in ml) with 0·038 N Ba(OH)$_2$	Volume of bulb (ml)
155	756·6	46·70	43·7
169	756·8	42·45	41·7
185	756·8	36·65	41·6
219	756·4	41·90	54·1
245	756·4	19·00	29·2
254	756·8	24·7	38·0

Calculate the apparent molecular weight of the acetic acid
at each temperature. Calculate the values of the equilibrium constants between unassociated and associated
species, assuming that the acetic acid is present only as
monomers and dimers. Thus find the heat of formation of
the hydrogen bond from the variation of the equilibrium
constant with temperature.

NOTE: Accurate measurements by means of a gas density balance of
the vapour density of acetic acid are described by E. W. Johnson and
L. K. Nash, *J. Am. Chem. Soc.*, **72**, 547, 1950. This more accurate work
shows that significant quantities of the acetic acid trimer are present
as well as of the dimer.

68 THE ISOMERIZATION EQUILIBRIUM OF CYCLOHEXANE AND METHYLCYCLOPENTANE IN THE LIQUID PHASE

D. P. Stevenson and J. H. Morgan, *J. Am. Chem. Soc.*, **70**,
2773, 1948.

In the course of a study of this isomerization equilibrium,
catalysed by aluminium chloride or bromide in the liquid phase,
Stevenson and Morgan measured the relative amounts of cyclohexane and methylcyclopentane present in the equilibrium
mixtures. Independent analyses carried out by mass spectro-
metry and by infra-red spectrophotometer were in fair agreement and below are tabulated average values at the three
temperatures used:

Temperature ($^\circ C$)	$K = \dfrac{methylcyclopentane}{cyclohexane}$
27	0·132
59	0·241
100	0·503

(i) Plot $\log_{10} K$ against the reciprocal of the absolute temperature and, by visual inspection, draw what seems to you the best straight line covering the three experimental points. From this line deduce the value of the coefficients in the equation

$$\log_{10} K = A - B/T.$$

(ii) Use the method of least squares to evaluate the coefficients A and B.

(iii) From the results of (ii) calculate the heat content change of the isomerization of cyclohexane to form methylcyclopentane at the average temperature of the measurements.

(iv) Assuming that the change of heat capacity upon isomerization is $+0 \cdot 6$ cal/mole °K and may be considered temperature-independent over the range of experiment, calculate the heat-content change and the entropy change of isomerization at 298° K. Calorimetric measurements by other workers lead to values of 3930 cal/mole and $10 \cdot 44$ entropy units respectively for these quantities.

NOTE: The methods of analysis of the equilibrium mixture are worth noting. The authors demonstrated the participation of a number of irreversible side reactions but gave reasons for supposing that these would have a negligible effect on the methylcyclopentane/cyclohexane ratio.

(ii) The method of least squares (see E. Bright Wilson, *An Introduction to Scientific Research* (McGraw-Hill, New York, 1952), pp. 217–19, or F. Daniels, J. W. William, P. Bender, R. Alberty, and C. D. Cornwell, *Experimental Physical Chemistry* (McGraw-Hill, New York, 1962), pp. 413–14) is a useful way of eliminating the subjective factor in curve fitting. Its helpfulness is much more obvious and more substantial when a larger number of experimental points is involved; it is introduced into this problem for illustrative purposes because the small number of experimental points reduces the computational labour involved in the method.

69 THE RELATION BETWEEN OSMOTIC PRESSURE AND VAPOUR-PRESSURE LOWERING IN CONCENTRATED SOLUTION

Lord Berkeley, E. G. J. Hartley, and C. V. Burton, *Phil. Trans. Roy. Soc.* A, **209**, 177, 1909.

The osmotic pressure, vapour-pressure lowering, and density of a series of concentrated aqueous solutions of calcium ferrocyanide were measured at 0° C with the following results:

g of salt per 1000 g of water	Density (Δ)	v.p. solvent / v.p. solution	Osmotic pressure (atmospheres)
499·7	1·3218	1·1071	130·66
472·2	1·3086	1·0917	112·84
428·9	1·2866	1·0702	87·09
395·0	1·2688	1·0571	70·84
313·9	1·2234	1·0332	41·22

Calculate from the vapour-pressure lowering of each solution the corresponding osmotic pressure, taking into account the variation of the density of the solution with concentration but neglecting the compressibility of the solution.

NOTE: The concordance of the calculated and observed osmotic pressures is a striking verification of the thermodynamic relationship between vapour-pressure lowering and osmotic pressure. This relation is applicable to concentrated solutions, since it is independent of all assumptions as to the nature of the relationship between osmotic pressure and concentration, although it assumes that the solvent vapour obeys the gas laws. The deviations from ideality of the solutions measured by Berkeley and his collaborators may be judged from the fact that the osmotic pressure is trebled by an increase in concentration of about 60 per cent. The equation neglects corrections for the compressibility of solvent and solution, but the more complicated equation (quoted in the original paper), which takes these into account, is in only slightly better agreement with the experimental results.

70 THE EINSTEIN EQUATION APPLIED TO THE SPECIFIC HEAT OF CHLORINE

A. Eucken and G. Hofmann, *Z. physik. Chem.* B, **5**, 442, 1929.

From spectroscopic data the fundamental frequency of the chlorine molecule is found to correspond to a wave number of 565 reciprocal centimetres.

(i) With the aid of the Einstein equation calculate the vibrational contribution to the molar heat capacity of chlorine at 270° and 452° K.

(ii) The experimentally observed molar heat capacity at atmospheric pressure at these two temperatures is 7·927 and 8·503 cal/mole respectively. What inferences may be drawn from a comparison of these values with the result of (i)?

(iii) What percentage of chlorine molecules will have zero and one quantum of vibrational energy respectively at 298° K and at 813° K?

NOTE: A diatomic gas molecule constitutes a good approximation to a harmonic oscillator relatively free from disturbing effect, and the Einstein equation may therefore be expected to account for the vibrational specific heat with fair precision. The fundamental frequency is now known with considerable accuracy from spectroscopic data.

The rotational energy may be regarded as 'classical' at the temperatures of the problem. See the comment on Problem 62 regarding tables of the Einstein function.

The percentage of molecules without vibrational energy at room temperature is significant from the point of view of absorption spectra. The half-quantum of zero-point energy is of course always present.

SECTION SIX

Electrical Conductivity and Miscellaneous Electrochemistry

71 ## THE CONDUCTIVITY OF TRIMETHYL TIN CHLORIDE IN ETHYL ALCOHOL

C. A. Kraus and C. C. Callis, *J. Am. Chem. Soc.*, **45**, 2624, 1923.

The specific conductivity of solutions of $(CH_3)_3SnCl$ in ethyl alcohol at 25° C are tabulated below:

Concentration ($mole/litre \times 10^3$)	Specific conductivity ($ohm^{-1} cm^{-1} \times 10^{-7}$)
0·1566	17·88
0·2600	24·18
0·6219	40·09
1·0441	53·36

Evaluate *graphically* Λ_0 (the equivalent conductivity at infinite dilution) and the dissociation constant of the salt.

NOTE: If $1/\Lambda_c$ is plotted against $C \times \Lambda_c$, both Λ_0 and K can be calculated from the two intercepts or, alternatively, from the slope and one of the intercepts. In evaluating K a little care is necessary with the powers of ten. This graphical method, which was developed by C. A. Kraus and W. C. Bray (*J. Am. Chem. Soc.*, **35**, 1315, 1913), is applicable to a rather limited category of electrolytes. For electrolytes of low ionization constant the extrapolation is too long to give reliable results; for electrolytes of high ionization constant the interionic forces, ignored in the Ostwald dilution law, produce curvature on the plot. The 120-page paper by Kraus and Bray, a determined effort to interpret the conductivity–concentration variation of electrolytes of all types ten years before the appearance of the classic work of Debye and Hückel, is instructive to look at for more reasons than one.

72 A TEST OF THE ONSAGER EQUATION FOR AQUEOUS SODIUM CHLORIDE

T. Shedlovsky, *J. Am. Chem. Soc.*, **54**, 1411, 1932.

One of the most rigorous tests of the Onsager equation in aqueous solution was made by Shedlovsky, who measured the conductivity of a series of uni-univalent electrolytes in water at 25° C. The following table is taken from his results for sodium chloride.

Concentration (equiv/litre) $\times 10^4$	Equivalent conductivity (Λ_c) $(cm^2\, ohm^{-1}\, equiv^{-1})$
0·59441	125·79
4·2677	124·58
13·448	123·31
21·253	122·51
31·862	121·70

(i) Find Λ_0 and the slope $d\Lambda_c/d\sqrt{c}$ graphically.

(ii) Evaluate Λ_0 with the aid of Shedlovsky's empirical extension of the Onsager equation.

(iii) Compare the observed slope with that predicted by the Onsager equation, which for 1–1 electrolytes in water at 25° C is:

$$\Lambda_c = \Lambda_0 - (0\cdot 2274\Lambda_0 + 59\cdot 79)\sqrt{c}.$$

NOTE: The empirical extension of the Onsager equation by Shedlovsky (*J. Am. Chem. Soc.*, **54**, 1405, 1932) has the form

$$\Lambda_0 = \frac{\Lambda_c + \beta\sqrt{c}}{1 - \alpha\sqrt{c}} - Bc,$$

and is of value both in calculating Λ_0 from conductivity data which do not extend to extreme dilutions and in revealing the abnormality of certain salts (such as the nitrates). Empirical developments of the equation relating equivalent conductance and concentration are discussed by G. Jones and H. S. Bickford (*J. Am. Chem. Soc.*, **56**, 602, 1934) and more recently by H. S. Harned and B. B. Owen, *The Physical Chemistry of Electrolytic Solutions* (Reinhold, New York, 1958), ch. 6, and by R. M. Fuoss and F. Accascina, *Electrolytic Conductance* (Interscience, New York, 1959), ch. XV. According to Fuoss and Accascina the validity of Shedlovsky's empirical equation up to concentrations as high as 0·1 M is due to a more or less fortuitous compensation of terms.

An examination of the graph in Shedlovsky's paper will show that his experiments offer more substantial confirmation of the Onsager equation as a limiting law than is suggested by the necessarily limited selection of his data incorporated in this problem.

73 THE HYDROLYSIS OF AQUEOUS SOLUTIONS OF IODINE FROM CONDUCTIVITY MEASUREMENTS

G. Jones and M. L. Hartmann, *J. Am. Chem. Soc.*, **37**, 241, 1915.

The solubility of iodine in water was found to be 0·0006383 moles/litre at 0° C. The specific conductivity of the solution was $0·6 \times 10^{-6}$ ohm^{-1} cm^{-1} greater than that of pure water. The equilibrium constant $[I'][I_2]/[I'_3]$ is $7·07 \times 10^{-4}$ mole/litre^{-1} at 0° C and the equivalent ionic conductivities of the ions concerned at the same temperature are:

$$H^+ = 240$$
$$I' = 43·4$$
$$I'_3 = 22·8.$$

Estimate the hydrolysis constant of iodine in aqueous solution, viz.

$$\frac{[HIO][H^+][I']}{[I_2]}.$$

NOTE: As a first approximation it is necessary to begin this calculation by identifying the concentration $[I_2]$ with the solubility of iodine, that is by assuming that the fall in concentration due to hydrolysis is negligible. The result of the calculation will show whether a second approximation is necessary. The restriction introduced by the necessity for electrical neutrality provides one of the equations required for the solution.

Problem 47 is based on an investigation of the same equilibrium system by spectrophotometry.

74 THE SOLUBILITY OF SILVER CHLORIDE IN WATER BY CONDUCTANCE MEASUREMENTS

J. A. Gledhill and G. McP. Malan, *Trans. Faraday Soc.*, **48**, 258, 1952.

Gledhill and Malan measured the specific conductance of saturated solutions of silver chloride in carefully purified water at 25° C. Purified air was passed through the cell during the attainment of saturation. It was found that the resistance of the cell rose to a maximum (attained in about 4 hours), then fell and ultimately reached values that fell slowly and uniformly with time. The initial rise in resistance was attributed to the removal of dissolved carbon dioxide and ammonia; by the time that the 'steady state' was reached it was assumed that saturation equilibrium with respect to silver chloride had been reached and that the slow linear fall of resistance that continued was due to solution of the Pyrex glass of the conductance cell. This latter was found to correspond to an increase of specific conductance of

$$0.3 \times 10^{-9} \text{ ohm}^{-1} \text{ cm}^{-1} \text{ hour}^{-1}.$$

The specific conductance of the solution was measured at the beginning of the steady state. In a typical experiment a specific conductance of $1926 \times 10^{-9} \text{ ohm}^{-1} \text{ cm}^{-1}$ was observed after 12 hours of saturation; the water used showed a specific conductance of $82 \times 10^{-9} \text{ ohm}^{-1} \text{ cm}^{-1}$.

The ionic conductances of the silver and chloride ions are 61.92 and 76.34 at infinite dilution and the Onsager equation for the equivalent conductance of silver chloride at 25° C is:

$$\Lambda_c = 138.26 - 91.72 \sqrt{c}.$$

The limiting equation for the activity coefficient for a 1–1 electrolyte in water at 25° is:

$$-\log_{10} f = 0.506 \sqrt{c}.$$

(i) Calculate the specific conductance of silver chloride

corrected for (a) the conductance of the solvent, (b) the conductance due to the glass dissolved during saturation.

(ii) Calculate the solubility of silver chloride in water, making allowance for the influence of interionic attraction on the speeds of the ions.

(iii) Calculate the thermodynamic solubility product (in molality units), if the density of the saturated solution is 0·9970.

NOTE: The correction for the influence of interionic attraction on the equivalent conductance is small in such a dilute solution but exceeds the experimental error of the measurements. As an intermediate step the solubility should first be calculated ignoring this correction. The results obtained in this paper are in good agreement with those obtained from e.m.f. measurements.

75 THE CONDUCTIVITY OF SALTS IN SOLVENTS OF LOW DIELECTRIC CONSTANT

P. Walden, *Z. physik. Chem.*, **148**, 45, 1930.

Examine the conformity of the two electrolytes below with the Ostwald dilution law:

Lithium bromide in acetophenone ($D=18\cdot1$) at 25° C.

Dilution (litres mole^{-1}) .	2093	5255	8250	17700
Equivalent conductivity .	14·33	19·41	22·19	26·26

Tetraethylammonium picrate in chloroform ($D = 4\cdot95$) at 25° C.

Dilution (litres mole^{-1}) .	5852	24140	49620	95520
Equivalent conductivity .	0·424	0·936	1·628	2·213

In the second case Λ_0 may be evaluated from Walden's rule, taking the viscosity of chloroform as 0·00538 and the $\Lambda_0\eta$ product for tetraethylammonium picrate as 0·563.

NOTE: In the case of the first electrolyte the graphical method of Problem 41 may be used. For the second electrolyte the conductivity ratio (and hence the dissociation constant) may be calculated for each concentration by means of the Λ_0 value derived from Walden's rule. The notes on Problem 81 may be consulted for sources of more sophisticated discussion of the conductance of electrolytes showing much ionic association.

76 THE CONDUCTIVITY OF SILVER NITRATE IN BENZONITRILE AND ITS TRUE DEGREE OF DISSOCIATION

A. R. Martin, *J. Chem. Soc.*, 3270, 1928.

Below are tabulated the equivalent conductivities of solutions of silver nitrate in benzonitrile at various dilutions at 25° C:

Dilution (*litres per mole*) $v = 1/c$	Equivalent conductivity ($cm^2\ ohm^{-1}\ equiv^{-1}$) Λ_c
106·8	10·62
611·0	20·57
3276	34·72
11680	42·88
41278	47·28

(i) Plot the equivalent conductivity against the square root of the concentration and compare the result with the limiting slope of the Onsager equation, which for 1–1 electrolytes in benzonitrile at 25° C is:

$$\Lambda_c = \Lambda_0 - (0 \cdot 8475\Lambda_0 + 53 \cdot 14)\sqrt{2c}.$$

(ii) Find the 'true' degree of dissociation (corrected for the variation of ionic mobility with concentration) at $v = 11680$ and compare the result with the conductivity ratio Λ_c/Λ_0.

NOTE: The 'true' degree of dissociation may be found by a short series of successive approximations as described by C. W. Davies, *The Conductivity of Solutions* (Chapman & Hall, London, 1933), ch. vii. Problem 81 illustrates a more elaborate method of handling conductance data for electrolytes showing 'incomplete dissociation'; the notes appended to that problem provide references to recent discussions of the field.

77* THE TRANSPORT NUMBERS OF POTASSIUM CHLORIDE BY A MODERN APPLICATION OF HITTORF'S METHOD

D. A. MacInnes and M. Dole, *J. Am. Chem. Soc.*, **53**, 1357, 1931.

Potassium chloride was electrolysed in a modern form of Hittorf apparatus between a silver anode and a cathode of silver coated electrolytically with silver chloride. The transport apparatus was in series with two silver coulometers, and the solutions were analysed potentiometrically after electrolysis. The following table gives the results for the two extreme concentrations measured:

	I	*II*
Concentration (equiv/litre) (approximate) .	0·02	3·0
Amperage	0·002	0·044
Voltage applied	15	5
Time of electrolysis (hours) . .	23	16·5
Wt. of silver in coulometer (g) (1) . .	0·16024	2·7760
,, ,, ,, ,, ,, (2) . .	0·16043	2·7756
Wt. of anode portion (g) . . .	117·79	131·10
,, ,, cathode portion (g)	120·99	135·30
Per cent of KCl in anode portion . .	0·10339	19·205
,, ,, ,, ,, ,, ,, middle portion .	0·14932	19·777
,, ,, ,, ,, ,, middle portion .	0·14948	..
,, ,, ,, ,, ,, cathode middle portion .	0·14939	19·775
,, ,, ,, ,, ,, ,, portion . .	0·19404	20·328

Find (from the data for anolyte *or* catholyte) the transport number of the potassium ion at both concentrations.

NOTE: The data of this problem are taken from a modern determination by the classical Hittorf method in an apparatus incorporating a number of refinements with a view to obtaining the highest precision. The method of calculation is quite straightforward (cf. M. Dole, *Principles of Experimental and Theoretical Chemistry* (McGraw-Hill, New York, 1935), ch. ix). The concentrations quoted in the first line of the table are approximate; the exact concentration of the solution before electrolysis should be inferred from the compositions of the middle portions. B. J. Steel and R. H. Stokes (*J. Phys. Chem.*, **62**, 450, 1958) have employed conductivity measurements to determine the concentration changes during electrolysis.

N.B. Five-figure logarithms are necessary in this problem.

78* THE HYDRATION OF IONS

E. W. Washburn, *J. Am. Chem. Soc.*, **31**, 322, 1909.

A current of about 0·1 ampere was passed through a solution, containing approximately 1·28 moles of lithium chloride and 0·1 mole of raffinose per 1000 g of water, between a silver anode and a silver–silver chloride cathode for 13 hours. After electrolysis the solution was divided into an anode portion, a cathode portion, and three middle portions. The polarimetric estimation of raffinose and the gravimetric estimation of the halide in the anode, cathode, and one of the middle compartments led to the following results (the three middle portions being found to be identical in composition):

	Anode	*Middle*	*Cathode*
Weight of portion . .	104·4 g	. .	81·47 g
Per cent raffinose . .	4·806	4·730	4·619
Per cent lithium chloride .	4·440	4·939	5·565

The mean result from the two silver coulometers in series with the transport apparatus showed that 0·04643 equivalents of electricity had passed through the solution.

Calculate *either* from the anode *or* the cathode analyses

(i) the 'apparent' transport number of the lithium ion (uncorrected for hydration);

(ii) the 'true' transport number of the lithium ion;

(iii) the net transfer of water (in moles) per equivalent of electricity passed;

(iv) the number of molecules of water attached to each lithium ion if the chlorine carried x molecules.

NOTE: The concentration of the solution before electrolysis may be taken as equal to that of the middle compartment after electrolysis. The calculation of the *apparent* transport number is carried out as in the preceding problem; the calculations are referred to the same mass of (raffinose plus water) before and after electrolysis—that is to say both substances are treated as stationary. In calculating the *true* transport number only the raffinose is assumed to be stationary, calculations being referred to the same amount of raffinose before and after electrolysis.

It is now fairly clear (see, for example, L. G. Longsworth, *J. Am. Chem. Soc.*, **69**, 1288, 1947, and C. H. Hale and T. De Vries, ibid., **70**, 2473, 1948) that the assumption that the added non-electrolyte—in this case raffinose—is electrically inert is untrue. The net transfer of water computed on the basis of this assumption has not the simple meaning that Washburn attached to it.

79 THE TRANSPORT NUMBERS OF SODIUM CHLORIDE FROM MOVING BOUNDARY MEASUREMENTS

L. G. Longsworth, *J. Am. Chem. Soc.*, **54**, 2741, 1932.

The following data relate to the measurement of the transport numbers of 0·02 N sodium chloride at 25° C by the moving boundary method, using the highly developed technique of MacInnes and Longsworth. The anode (placed at the bottom of the electrolysis tube) was a cadmium disk and the rising boundary between the Cd·· and Na· ions was 'self-adjusting' and therefore always sharp; the cathode consisted of silver coated electrolytically with silver chloride. The current was kept constant by an automatic device and measured by the potential drop across a standard resistance in series with the electrolytic cell.

Current	0·0016001 ampere			
Cross-sectional area of electrolysis tube	0·1115 cm²			
Distance traversed by boundary (cm) .	0·0	2·0	7·0	10·0
Time (sec)	0	689	2414	3453

Calculate the mean transport number of sodium in 0·02 N sodium chloride.

NOTE: For a discussion of the moving boundary method see M. Dole, *Principles of Experimental and Theoretical Chemistry* (McGraw-Hill, New York, 1935), ch. ix, D. A. MacInnes, *Principles of Electrochemistry* (Dover, New York, 1951), ch. iv, or R. A. Robinson and R. H. Stokes, *Electrolyte Solutions* (Butterworth, London, 1959), ch. v. The original paper of Longsworth may be consulted for an account of two small corrections (the 'volume' and the 'solvent' correction) which increase the value obtained directly from the above data by 0·0006.

The principal difficulties have been experimental rather than theoretical; the method is now susceptible to such precision that the results can be compared with the predictions of the interionic attraction theory (Dole, ch. x) and can be used in calculating activity coefficients (cf. Problem 53). For later refinements of the technique see L. G. Longsworth, *J. Am. Chem. Soc.*, **65**, 1755, 1943, and **69**, 1288, 1947.

80* THE THERMODYNAMIC DISSOCIATION CONSTANT OF ACETIC ACID FROM CONDUCTIVITY MEASUREMENTS

D. A. MacInnes and T. Shedlovsky, *J. Am. Chem. Soc.*, **54**, 1429, 1932.

The equivalent conductivity of aqueous solutions of sodium acetate (containing a known small excess of acetic acid to repress hydrolysis) was measured at 25° C with the following results, to which a solvent correction for both water and excess acid has already been applied:

Concentration (equivs litre^{-1}) $\times 10^4$	Equivalent conductivity ($cm^2\ ohm^{-1}\ equiv^{-1}$)
1·8627	89·92
7·3205	88·90
15·256	87·95
27·973	86·96
43·016	86·07

(i) Plot the function $\dfrac{\Lambda + 59 \cdot 79 \sqrt{c}}{1 - 0 \cdot 2274 \sqrt{c}}$ against the concentration and thus evaluate Λ_0 and the constants of the Shedlovsky extension of Onsager's equation.

(ii) A similar analysis of the conductivity data for sodium

chloride and hydrochloric acid leads to the following equations for the two electrolytes:

$$\Lambda_{\text{NaCl}} = 126\cdot42 - 88\cdot53\sqrt{c} + 89\cdot5c(1 - 0\cdot2274\sqrt{c}),$$

$$\Lambda_{\text{HCl}} = 426\cdot04 - 156\cdot67\sqrt{c} + 165\cdot5c(1 - 0\cdot2274\sqrt{c}).$$

Assuming the independent migration of ions, write down the equation for the variation with ionic concentration of the sum of the mobilities of the ions of acetic acid (that is, the variation with concentration of the equivalent conductivity of the hypothetical completely dissociated acetic acid), and construct a graph from the equation for ionic concentrations up to 0·001 N.

The following conductivity data were obtained for aqueous solutions of acetic acid at 25° C:

Concentration $(equivs\ litre^{-1}) \times 10^4$	Equivalent conductivity $(cm^2\ ohm^{-1}\ equiv^{-1})$
0·28014	210·32
1·5321	112·02
10·2831	48·133
98·421	16·367
523·03	7·200

(iii) Calculate the 'Ostwald' dissociation constant for each concentration, neglecting the variation of mobilities with concentration.

(iv) Calculate the true degree of dissociation at each concentration, computing the ionic concentration in each case by a series of successive approximations and using the graph from part (ii) of the problem.

(v) Calculate from these true degrees of dissociation the dissociation constant (K') in terms of concentrations (as distinct from activities).

(vi) Plot the logarithm of these dissociation constants against the square root of the *ionic* concentration.

(vii) By extrapolation evaluate the thermodynamic dissociation constant and compare the slope of the graph with that to be expected from the Debye–Hückel limiting equation for activity coefficients. Compare the thermodynamic

120

dissociation constant with the value derived from e.m.f. measurements by Harned and Ehlers ($1 \cdot 754 \times 10^{-5}$ at $25°$ C; cf. Problem 43).

NOTE: The work upon which this problem is based constitutes one of the most accurate determinations of the dissociation constant of a weak electrolyte and takes account of the interionic forces not only in their effect on the mobility of the ions but also in so far as they alter the activities of the ions in the dissociation equilibrium. The Shedlovsky extension of Onsager's equation has already been commented upon (cf. Problem 72). In (iv) the true degree of dissociation is to be calculated by the method described by C. W. Davies, *The Conductivity of Solutions* (Chapman & Hall, London, 1933), ch. vii. The reasons for the deviations from linearity at the higher concentrations in the graph drawn in (vi) are discussed by MacInnes and Shedlovsky.

A later paper from the same laboratory by T. Shedlovsky and R. L. Kay (*J. Phys. Chem.*, **60**, 151, 1956) on the dissociation constant of acetic acid in methanol–water mixtures illustrates a different method of analysing the conductance data. A general survey of the study of incompletely dissociated electrolytes by conductivity is provided by C. B. Monk, *Electrolytic Dissociation* (Academic Press, London, 1961), ch. 8.

81* THE DISSOCIATION CONSTANT OF POTASSIUM IODIDE IN PYRIDINE FROM CONDUCTANCE MEASUREMENTS

D. S. Burgess and C. A. Kraus, *J. Am. Chem. Soc.*, **70**, 706, 1948.

Burgess and Kraus measured the equivalent conductance of a number of salts in pyridine at $25°$ C. The following data are selected from their measurements on potassium iodide:

Concentration (mole litre^{-1}) $\times 10^5$	Equivalent conductance (cm^2 ohm^{-1} equiv^{-1})
10·79	59·96
6·564	64·68
3·328	70·08

The dielectric constant of pyridine is $12 \cdot 01$ and its viscosity $0 \cdot 008824$ poise at $25°$ C.

(i) Plot the equivalent conductance against the square root of the molarity of the solution and determine the apparent equivalent conductance at zero concentration (Λ_0').

(ii) From Λ_0' calculate the apparent limiting slope from the Onsager equation

$$\Lambda_c = \Lambda_0' - \left(\frac{8 \cdot 203 \times 10^5}{(DT)^{3/2}} \Lambda_0' + \frac{82 \cdot 43}{\eta(DT)^{1/2}}\right) \sqrt{c}$$

and compare the result with the slope of the line passing through the three measurements.

(iii) Employing the extrapolation method of R. M. Fuoss and T. Shedlovsky (*J. Am. Chem. Soc.*, **71**, 1496, 1949) and using the apparent value of Λ_0 obtained in (i) calculate the true value of Λ_0 and the dissociation constant of the electrolyte.

NOTE: The variation of equivalent conductance with concentration of many dilute aqueous solutions of strong electrolytes is adequately represented by the Onsager equation. In solvents of low dielectric constant even uni-univalent salts at high dilutions still show marked deviation from the Onsager equation owing to the formation of ion pairs. In such cases the equivalent conductance at infinite dilution can therefore not be obtained accurately by extrapolation; furthermore the form of the conductance curve depends not only on the varying speed of the ions owing to interionic forces but also upon the dissociation equilibrium of the ion pairs, which is itself influenced by interionic forces.

The cooperation of these factors leads to a relation of conductance to concentration more complicated than that of Onsager. C. A. Kraus and R. M. Fuoss (*J. Am. Chem. Soc.*, **55**, 476, 1933) and, later and more simply, R. M. Fuoss and T. Shedlovsky (loc. cit.) have shown how conductance data at high dilution can be used to calculate both Λ_0 and K, the thermodynamic dissociation constant of the ion pairs for such weak electrolytes in solvents of low dielectric constant. The method assumes that Shedlovsky's empirical extension of the Onsager equation (see Problem 72) is valid using the concentration of free ions rather than the stoicheiometric concentration of the solution; it also assumes that the mass-action law holds for the dissociation of ion pairs, using activity coefficients calculated from the limiting Debye–Hückel law (again based on the concentration of free ions):

$$-\log_{10} f^2 = \frac{3 \cdot 649 \times 10^6}{(DT)^{3/2}} \sqrt{(\text{ionic concentration})}.$$

Although the underlying assumptions are straightforward, the computation involved can be rather complicated; Shedlovsky showed how it can be made relatively simple. The matter is discussed by H. S. Harned and B. B. Owen, *The Physical Chemistry of Electrolytic Solutions* (Reinhold, New York, 1958), pp. 286–91. Ch. 14 of R. A. Robinson and R. H. Stokes, *Electrolyte Solutions* (Butterworth, London, 1959), may also be consulted.

(iii) It is convenient to begin by computing for pyridine the two numerical coefficients of the Onsager equation and that relating log (activity coefficient) to $\sqrt{}$ (ionic concentration). It will be sufficiently accurate to approximate S to the value of $1+\mathbf{Z}$ (in the notation of the Shedlovsky paper). The successive stages of computation for the three solutions are best arranged in tabular form; suitable successive column headings might, for example, be

$$c, \quad \sqrt{c}, \quad \Lambda, \quad \sqrt{(c\Lambda)}, \quad S, \quad cS\Lambda/\Lambda_0', \quad \sqrt{(cS\Lambda/\Lambda_0')},$$
$$-\log f^2, \quad f^2, \quad \Lambda S, \quad 1/\Lambda S, \quad c\Lambda Sf^2.$$

In all these calculations the provisional value of Λ_0 obtained by simple linear extrapolation should be used. The intercept of the final plot of $1/\Lambda S'$ against $c\Lambda S'f^2$ gives the reciprocal of the true Λ_0; the dissociation constant is then readily derived from the slope.

A discussion of 'Interaction in Ionic Solutions' (*Discussions of the Faraday Society* No. 24, 1957) provides further insight into the tangled question of 'ion-association' or 'incomplete dissociation'.

Further discussion of the conductance of electrolytes showing ion-association is provided by two papers by C. A. Kraus (*J. Phys. Chem.*, **58**, 673, 1954, and **60**, 129, 1956), by C. B. Monk, *Electrolytic Dissociation* (Academic Press, London, 1961), and by R. M. Fuoss and F. Accascina, *Electrolytic Conductance* (Interscience, New York, 1959). K. H. Stern and E. S. Amis (*Chem. Rev.*, **59**, 1, 1959) and R. L. Kay (*J. Am. Chem. Soc.*, **82**, 2099, 1960) may also be consulted for the trend of recent work on ion-pair association; Kay's paper describes the application of a high-speed digital computer to the analysis of conductance data.

N.B. Five-figure logarithms are necessary in this problem.

82 THE HEAT OF SOLVATION OF IONS

E. Lange, *Fortschr. Chem. Phys.*, 1928, Band 19, Heft 6; N. Bjerrum, *Z. physik. Chem.*, **127**, 358, 1927.

The lattice energy of potassium iodide, calculated from the attractive and repulsive forces between the ions by the Born theory, is 148 kcal per mole. The heat of solution in water at infinite dilution is $+4\cdot9$ kcal per mole at 25° C.

(i) Calculate the sum of the heats of hydration of anion and cation at infinite dilution.

(ii) Compare this result with that calculated from the Born–Bjerrum equation (which is based on a purely electrostatic picture of solvation):

$$\Delta H = -\frac{N\epsilon^2 z^2}{2r}\left(1 - \frac{1}{D} - \frac{T}{D^2}\frac{dD}{dT}\right),$$

where ΔH is the heat of solvation (in ergs) of an ion of charge $z\epsilon$ and radius r in a solvent of dielectric constant D at absolute temperature T. D and dD/dT for water may be taken as 83 and -0.38 respectively; the lattice radii of the potassium and iodide ions are 1·33 and 2·20 Å respectively.

NOTE: This problem illustrates the magnitude of the ion-solvent forces which are responsible for the solubility of salts in polar solvents in spite of the large cohesive forces present in electro-valent crystals. There can be little doubt, however, that the Born–Bjerrum model of the ion as a charged sphere immersed in a continuous dielectric is greatly over-simplified; the intense field of force round the ion must polarize the molecules in the vicinity very drastically (see, for example, F. A. Askew *et al.*, *J. Chem. Soc.*, 1368, 1934). Discussion No. 24 of the Faraday Society (1957) on 'Interaction in Ionic Solutions' illustrates the imperfections in our understanding of the matter; the general introduction by R. P. Bell (pp. 17–19) to that discussion is helpful in providing perspective. Ch. 4 of J. O'M. Bockris, *Modern Aspects of Electrochemistry* (Butterworth, London, 1954), reviews ionic solvation from various sides.

The temperature coefficient of the dielectric constant of water is rather uncertain (cf. E. Lange, *Z. Elektrochem.*, **36**, 772, 1930).

The negative sign of the heat of solvation corresponds to heat *evolved*.

83 STANDARD ELECTRODE POTENTIALS IN METHANOL

P. S. Buckley and H. B. Hartley, *Phil. Mag.*, **8**, 320, 1929 (cf. G. Nonhebel and H. B. Hartley, ibid., **50**, 729, 1925; J. W. Woolcock and H. B. Hartley, ibid., **5**, 1133, 1928).

The e.m.f. at 25° C of the cell

Ag.AgCl | NaCl in MeOH | NaClO$_4$ in MeOH | AgClO$_4$ in MeOH | Ag
0·01 M   0·01 M   0·01 M

is 0·5243 volt, of which 0·0033 volt is (by calculation) due to the liquid junction potentials. The concentrations are expressed in moles per 1000 g of solvent. In *these* concentration units (cf. Nonhebel and Hartley, loc. cit.; Woolcock and Hartley, loc. cit.) the e.m.f. of the cell

$$\text{Ag.AgCl} \mid \underset{\text{(unit activity)}}{\text{HCl in MeOH}} \mid \text{H}_2$$

at 25° C is 0·0082 volt. The activity coefficient in the same concentration units of all completely dissociated 1–1 electrolytes in methanol at 0·01 M may be assumed to be the same as that of 0·01 M HCl, namely, 0·745.

Calculate:

(i) the standard electrode potential of silver in methanol on the standard hydrogen scale;

(ii) the solubility (activity) product of silver chloride in methanol;

(iii) the standard potential of chlorine in methanol if the cell

$$\text{Ag} \mid \underset{\text{(saturated)}}{\text{AgCl aq.}} \mid \text{Cl}_2$$

has an e.m.f. of 1·1362 volts at 25° C.

NOTE: The dependence of activity coefficients on concentration units is dealt with briefly in the paper of Woolcock and Hartley quoted; a more detailed treatment will be found in H. S. Harned and B. B. Owen, *The Physical Chemistry of Electrolytic Solutions* (Reinhold, New York, 1958), ch. i.

Conventions of sign must be carefully observed in solving this problem; the cells are written with the right-hand electrode as the positive pole, that is to say, positive electricity will move through the cell from left to right when the cell gives current. In deducing an unknown e.m.f. by combining known e.m.f.s it sometimes saves confusion to arrange the potentials in order along a qualitative vertical scale so as to visualize the necessary additions and subtractions geometrically. The electrode potentials should be expressed in terms of the sign convention described in Note 10 on p. xvi.

Part (iii) depends on the fact that the free energy of formation of solid silver chloride from its elements is independent of the solvent from which it is precipitated.

84 AN EXPERIMENTAL TEST OF THE INTERIONIC ATTRACTION THEORY APPLIED TO HEATS OF DILUTION

E. Lange and P. A. Leighton, *Z. Elektrochem.*, **34**, 566, 1928.

According to the interionic attraction theory the integral heat of dilution of a binary strong electrolyte at high dilutions is given by the equation

$$V_c = +\frac{N\epsilon^2 z^2}{JD}\left(\frac{8\pi z^2 \epsilon^2 N}{1000 DkT}\right)^{\frac{1}{2}}\left(1+\frac{T}{D}\frac{dD}{dT}\right)\sqrt{c},$$

where V_c is the integral heat of dilution in calories per mole (i.e. the heat *absorbed* when $1/c$ litres of solution of concentration c are added to an infinite amount of water), N is the Avogadro number, ϵ the electronic charge, z the valency of the ions, J is the mechanical equivalent of heat in ergs per calorie, k is Boltzmann's constant, D is the dielectric constant of the solvent, T the absolute temperature, and c is the initial concentration in moles per litre. For water at $25°$ C D may be taken as 83 and dD/dT probably lies between $-0\cdot349$ and $-0\cdot385$.

Using a very sensitive differential (or 'twin') calorimeter Lange and Leighton obtained the results tabulated below for aqueous solutions of potassium chloride at $25°$ C. In one half of the calorimeter 93 cm³ of solution of concentration c_1 were diluted down to concentration c_2; in the blank half of the calorimeter a similar volume of water was simultaneously 'diluted' with water. A multiple junction thermocouple and galvanometer recorded the temperature difference thereby set up between the two halves of the calorimeter. The heat capacity of the calorimeter was estimated by passing known amounts of electrical energy through a resistance heater in one half and measuring the galvanometer deflexion produced; the average value was 86×10^{-5} cal/mm galv. deflexion. In the asterisked experiments a small quantity of electrical energy (specified in column 4) was passed into the blank half of the calorimeter to cut down the galvanometer deflexion and the heat leakage between the two halves.

Initial concentration, c_1	Final concentration, c_2	Galvanometer deflexion (mm)	Compensation heating (cal)
0·00303	0·000326	4·5	. .
0·00606	0·000653	12·0	. .
0·0202	0·00218	16·0	0·0442*
0·060	0·00648	122·0	0·109*

(i) Calculate the values of A in the theoretical equation

$$V_c = A \sqrt{c}$$

corresponding to the two extreme values of dD/dT.

(ii) Calculate from the experimental results the heat of dilution per mole in each of the four dilution experiments.

(iii) Compare these experimental values with the corresponding theoretical values of $V_{c_1 c_2} (= V_{c_1} - V_{c_2})$.

NOTE: The data of this problem are taken from the researches of Lange and his collaborators in high-precision calorimetry of electrolytes; the experimental technique and theoretical implications of the work are summarized by E. Lange and A. L. Robinson (*Chem. Rev.*, **9**, 89, 1931); a shorter account with less experimental detail will be found in the *Ann. Repts. on Progr. Chem., Chem. Soc., London*, **29**, 29, 1932.

For obvious reasons V_c is not itself directly measurable, but $(V_{c_1} - V_{c_2})$ can be directly determined, and it is this quantity that is most readily compared with theoretical predictions.

J. M. Sturtevant gives a useful review of methods of chemical calorimetry in Part 1, ch. 10 of *Physical Methods of Organic Chemistry* (Interscience, New York, 1959).

85 THE KINETICS OF THE ELECTROLYTIC DISCHARGE OF HYDROGEN AND OXYGEN FROM AQUEOUS SOLUTIONS

F. P. Bowden, *Proc. Roy. Soc.* A, **126**, 107, 1930.

Bowden measured the potential at which hydrogen is discharged at a mercury cathode from N/5 sulphuric acid at varying current densities and temperatures; similar experiments were also carried out for the discharge of oxygen at a platinum anode from the same electrolyte. The following results are derived from the graphs in Bowden's paper:

Hydrogen discharge at mercury

Current density (amp/cm^2)	Potential on saturated calomel scale (volt)
273° K	
$1{\cdot}71 \times 10^{-6}$	$-1{\cdot}010$
$5{\cdot}15$	$-1{\cdot}064$
$20{\cdot}6$	$-1{\cdot}128$
$41{\cdot}1$	$-1{\cdot}166$
345° K	
$12{\cdot}9 \times 10^{-6}$	$-0{\cdot}914$
$41{\cdot}1$	$-0{\cdot}985$
$91{\cdot}0$	$-1{\cdot}044$
367	$-1{\cdot}120$

Oxygen discharge at platinum

Current density (amp/cm^2)	Potential on saturated calomel scale (volt)
273° K	
$1{\cdot}30 \times 10^{-6}$	$+1{\cdot}501$
$3{\cdot}98$	$+1{\cdot}500$
$40{\cdot}6$	$+1{\cdot}640$
424	$+1{\cdot}749$
354° K	
$14{\cdot}4 \times 10^{-6}$	$+1{\cdot}320$
123	$+1{\cdot}454$
1000	$+1{\cdot}600$

The reversible potentials of the hydrogen and oxygen electrodes on the saturated calomel scale are about $-0\cdot3$ volt and $+0\cdot9$ volt respectively.

What inferences may be drawn as to the relationship between current density, potential, and temperature for the two discharge processes?

NOTE: The kinetics and mechanism of electrode processes constitute an area of investigation whose complexities are still largely unresolved. Ch. 7 and 9 in J. A. V. Butler, *Electrical Phenomena at Interfaces* (Methuen, London, 1951), may be consulted for perspective.

86 THE ELECTROLYTIC SEPARATION OF DEUTERIUM

Experimental data taken from results obtained in Oxford.

The preferential discharge of the lighter isotope of hydrogen when aqueous solutions are electrolysed proceeds according to the equation

$$d \ln H = \alpha d \ln D,$$

where H and D represent the relative numbers of atoms of hydrogen and deuterium present in the electrolyte, and α is a constant (apparently very sensitive to the conditions of electrolysis) called the electrolytic separation coefficient.

$51\cdot16$ g of a solution made up by dissolving $1\cdot16$ g of sodium hydroxide in deuterium-enriched water of specific gravity $1\cdot001120$ were electrolysed between a nickel anode and an iron cathode until the solution was reduced in weight to $14\cdot36$ g. The final solution was saturated with carbon dioxide (to facilitate distillation and—approximately—to restore the isotope ratio of the oxygen in the solution) and distilled. The specific gravity of the distillate, as measured by the temperature at which a small glass bulb just floated in it, was $1\cdot003605$. The specific gravity of pure deuterium oxide is $1\cdot1074$, and the specific gravity of water may be assumed to vary linearly with its deuterium content, the specific gravity of deuterium-free water being $0\cdot999981$.

129

Neglecting errors due to loss by evaporation and spray, which were minimized by cooling the electrolytic cell and the use of a reflux condenser for the electrolytic gas, calculate the value of α at an iron cathode under the conditions of experiment.

H. C. Urey and G. K. Teal, *Rev. Mod. Phys.*, **7**, 34, 1935; A. Farkas, *Light and Heavy Hydrogen* (Cambridge, 1935), Part II, ch. ii.

N O T E : The deuterium content of the original D-rich water should first be calculated from its specific gravity and then corrected for the addition of the sodium hydroxide (whose deuterium content may be neglected). The result combined with the deuterium content of the final product and the loss in weight by electrolysis may be substituted in the integrated form (see the note on Problem 87) of the equation defining the separation coefficient to calculate the latter.

87 THE DEUTERIUM CONTENT OF ORDINARY WATER AND THE ELECTROLYTIC SEPARATION OF THE OXYGEN ISOTOPES

H. L. Johnston, *J. Am. Chem. Soc.*, **57**, 484, 2737, 1935.

Fifty litres of water were reduced by five successive stages of fractional electrolysis to a final *light* fraction of 45 cm³. Iron electrodes were employed and at each stage of the electrolysis 25 per cent of the electrolyte was decomposed; the electrolytic gases thus produced were dried and recombined, and the 25 per cent of 'light water' from each stage served for the preparation of the electrolyte for the subsequent stage.

The gradual fall in specific gravity is recorded in the following table:

Product of stage	Fall in specific gravity (parts per million)
1	16·7
2	22·1
3	23·9
4	25·4
5	27·4

(i) If the electrolytic separation coefficient for deuterium of the iron cathodes used in the experiment may be taken as 8, and if 1/4000 may be taken as the *maximum* plausible value for the D/H ratio in ordinary water, what is the maximum value of the D/H ratio in the product of the third stage of electrolysis?

(ii) What increment in specific gravity would such a deuterium content produce in pure protium oxide, assuming the same molecular volume for all the varieties of water molecule made possible by the isotopy of its constituent elements?

(iii) If the fall in specific gravity after the third stage may be attributed exclusively to the accumulation of O^{16} at the expense of O^{18} (the presence of O^{17} being neglected), estimate by graphical extrapolation the specific gravity of water free from deuterium but containing the normal proportion of oxygen isotopes, and hence calculate the D/H ratio in ordinary water.

(iv) With the same assumptions, and adopting the value of 514 for the ratio O^{16}/O^{18} in ordinary water, calculate the value of the electrolytic separation coefficient of these two isotopes of oxygen at an iron anode.

(v) From the last result, calculate the volume of water which must be electrolysed in order to produce one cubic centimetre of water with double the normal concentration of the heavy isotope of oxygen.

NOTE: (i) For the definition of the electrolytic separation coefficient see the preceding problem. It is most useful in its integrated form: $\left(\dfrac{D_{\text{initial}}}{D_{\text{final}}}\right)^{a} = \left(\dfrac{H_{\text{initial}}}{H_{\text{final}}}\right)$, where the symbols relate to the composition of the *electrolyte*.

(ii) The variation of specific gravity with deuterium content may be taken as linear.

(iii) For the purpose of this extrapolation, the fall in specific gravity may be plotted against the number of electrolyses.

(iv) In calculating the oxygen enrichment from density changes it may be assumed that $H_2^1 O^{16}$ has the same molecular volume as $H_2^1 O^{18}$.

The separation coefficient is readily calculated by means of the expression

$$\left(\frac{O^{18}_{initial}}{O^{18}_{final}}\right)^{\alpha-1} = \left(\frac{O^{16}_{initial}}{O^{18}_{initial}}\right) \bigg/ \left(\frac{O^{16}_{final}}{O^{18}_{final}}\right),$$

where the symbols relate to the composition of the *electrolyte*, bearing in mind that for a low separation coefficient, such as that of oxygen, $\frac{O^{18}_{initial}}{O^{18}_{final}}$ is virtually the same as the ratio of the initial and final weights of water.

Kinetics and Photochemistry

88 THE MOLECULAR STATISTICS OF THE CATALYTIC DECOMPOSITION OF OZONE

R. J. Strutt, *Proc. Roy. Soc.* A, **87**, 302, 1912.

In one of the earliest applications of molecular statistics to chemical kinetics Strutt investigated the catalytic decomposition of ozone by a silver oxide surface. When air at a pressure of a few millimetres is passed through an electric discharge, the issuing gas emits a yellowish glow due to the interaction of the ozone and nitric oxide formed. The luminosity is completely extinguished by passage through an oxidized silver gauze which destroys the ozone. Strutt passed air successively through a discharge tube and an oxidized silver gauze and adjusted the rate of flow until the glow was just destroyed by the gauze. In two experiments with a piece of gauze 0·0369 cm² in surface area he found that with a rate of flow of 264 cm³ per sec at 3·5 mm pressure the glow was reduced to about a quarter of its former intensity, whereas at 141 cm³ per sec and 3 mm pressure the glow was completely extinguished.

From the kinetic theory it is known that the mass of gas striking an area A in one second is $\frac{3}{13}\rho\bar{u}A$, where ρ is the density of the gas and $\bar{u}$ is its root mean square molecular velocity.

Taking the temperature of the experiment as 290° K, estimate the ratio of the number of collisions of ozone molecules with the gauze to the number of ozone molecules destroyed.

NOTE: The ozone concentration may be regarded as proportional to the glow intensity; the ratio to be calculated involves no information as to the initial concentration of ozone. In the original paper the area of the gauze is misprinted.

89 THE RATE OF A RAPID REACTION BY A STEADY STATE METHOD

R. G. Pearson and L. H. Piette, *J. Am. Chem. Soc.*, **76**, 3087, 1954; J. A. Young and R. J. Zeto, *J. Chem. Ed.*, **35**, 146, 1958. (Supplementary experimental observations supplied from the M.S. thesis of L. H. Piette, Northwestern University, 1954, by the courtesy of Dr. R. G. Pearson.)

The reaction between nitroethane and the hydroxide ion in aqueous solution:

$$C_2H_5NO_2 + OH^- \rightarrow C_2H_4NO_2^- + H_2O$$

is rapid at room temperature. Pearson and Piette showed that it could be measured by generating hydroxide ions cathodically with a constant known current in a solution of known nitroethane concentration and measuring electrometrically the pH of the solution in the rapidly attained equilibrium state at which the rate of electrolytic generation of hydroxide ion was equal to its rate of reaction with nitroethane.

A platinum gauze cathode was used; the platinum wire anode was segregated in a cylindrical compartment filled with the sodium form of a cation exchange resin so as to replace the anodically generated hydrions by sodium as they were formed. In addition to these two electrodes the reaction vessel contained a magnetic stirrer and the indicating electrodes of the pH meter.

In one experiment the electrolyte consisted of 250 ml. of 0·1 M potassium chloride solution containing 2·0313 g of nitroethane. The following observations of time, pH, and current were carried out at 25° C:

Time (min)	Current (amp)	pH
0	0	5·08

Current switched on at 0 min

1	0·100	8·80
2·5	0·100	8·80

Current switched off at 2·5 min
and on again at 3·5 min

4·5	0·200	9·09
6·0	0·200	9·09

Current switched off at 6·0 min
and on again at 6·5 min

7·5	0·055	8·55
8·5	0·055	8·58

(i) Calculate the rate constant for the reaction at each of the three values of the current, neglecting the drop in nitroethane concentration during the course of the experiment.

(ii) Estimate the error involved in ignoring the depletion in nitroethane during the experiment and compare it with that arising from an error of 0·05 in the equilibrium pH value.

(iii) Using the rate constant computed in (i) for 0·100 amp calculate the time necessary for the pH value of the system to rise to 8·75 during the initial period of electrolysis at 0·100 amp.

NOTE: (ii) In estimating the error involved in neglecting the depletion in nitroethane it will be sufficient to calculate the effect at its maximum, namely that operating at the end of a series of electrolyses, on the rate constant computed from the equilibrium pH at the end of 8·5 minutes. The analysis of the relative importance of different sources of error is discussed by Young and Zeto.

(iii) The calculation of the rate of approach to equilibrium in this case involves a very simple integration.

90 THE DISTRIBUTION OF ENERGY IN BIMOLECULAR COLLISIONS

C. N. Hinshelwood, *Kinetics of Chemical Change* (Clarendon Press, Oxford, 1940), ch. i and iii.

The energy of activation of a thermal reaction is 44000 calories.

(i) Calculate the proportion of bimolecular collisions at 600° K in which the energy of 'head-on' collision (i.e. distributed between one degree of freedom of translational motion in each molecule) exceeds the energy of activation.

(ii) Calculate the proportion of bimolecular collisions at 600° K in which the energy in one vibrational degree of freedom in one molecule exceeds E_1 and that in the other exceeds E_2, where $E_1+E_2 = 44000$ cal.

(iii) Calculate the proportion of bimolecular collisions at 600° K in which the vibrational energy shared between one degree of freedom in each molecule exceeds 44000 cal *irrespective* of the way in which it is distributed (i.e. with a contribution from zero upwards from either molecule).

(iv) Calculate the proportion of bimolecular collisions at 600° K possessing energy greater than 44000 cal distributed between 6, 12, and 18 quadratic terms respectively.

NOTE: The proportion of bimolecular collisions fulfilling certain energy conditions is a fundamental consideration in the collision theory of chemical kinetics. This proportion varies according to the assumptions that are made as to the way in which the energy must be distributed between the various degrees of freedom of the colliding molecules. This problem includes the various possibilities which may be significant in kinetics. These possibilities are discussed in the two chapters of Hinshelwood cited. It should be realized that the expression used where a large number of quadratic terms is concerned is an approximation obtained by taking only the first term of a series. F. H. McDougall, *Physical Chemistry* (Macmillan, New York, 1952), pp. 451–9, and A. A. Frost and R. G. Pearson, *Kinetics and Mechanism* (Wiley, New York, 1961), ch. 4, provide helpful discussions of this aspect of the collision approach to reaction rates.

91 THE THERMAL DECOMPOSITION OF NITROUS OXIDE IN THE GASEOUS PHASE

C. N. Hinshelwood and R. E. Burk, *Proc. Roy. Soc.* A, **106**, 284, 1924.

The thermal decomposition of nitrous oxide was measured manometrically and shown to be independent of the volume/surface ratio of the reaction vessel.

The following table gives the time of half-change at 1030° K and various initial pressures:

Initial pressure (mm)	Half-life (sec)
52·5	860
139	470
296	255
360	212

The next table gives the variation of half-life with temperature:

Temperature (°K)	Initial pressure (mm)	Half-life (sec)
1085	345	53
1030	360	212
967	294	1520

(i) What is the order of the reaction?

(ii) Calculate the velocity constant in $1 \text{ mole}^{-1} \text{ sec}^{-1}$ units at each temperature.

(iii) Evaluate graphically the energy of activation corrected for the variation of molecular velocity with temperature.

(iv) Compare the energy of activation, thus obtained, with that derived by the application to the observed velocity constant at 1030° K of the equation:

No. of molecules reacting

$$= \text{No. of molecules colliding} \times e^{-E/RT},$$

where E is the energy of activation.

The diameter of the nitrous oxide molecule is found from viscosity measurements to be 3·32 Å.

NOTE: Since this reaction proceeds at a relatively high temperature the correction for the variation of molecular velocity (and therefore of collision rate) with temperature must be applied to the heat of activation. The equation quoted in (iv) is the simplest possible expression for the reaction velocity; a number of real examples are fairly well expressed by it.

That the thermal decomposition of nitrous oxide is less simple than was originally supposed is illustrated by plotting the reciprocal of the half-life against the initial pressure and extrapolating back to zero pressure. As with many other gas reactions, later investigations have revealed progressive stages of complexity. Thus, for example, F. F. Musgrave and C. N. Hinshelwood (*Proc. Roy. Soc.* A, **135**, 23, 1932, and **137**, 25), showed catalysis of the reaction by nitric oxide and halogens; they and also E. Hunter (ibid., **144**, 386, 1934) have shown from curves representing the variation of half-life with pressure that there must be several distinct modes of activation. A review by H. S. Johnston (*J. Chem. Phys.*, **19**, 663, 1951) shows the reaction to be unimolecular.

92 THE CIS–TRANS ISOMERIZATION OF METHYL CINNAMATE IN THE GASEOUS PHASE

G. B. Kistiakowsky and W. R. Smith, *J. Am. Chem. Soc.*, **57**, 269, 1935.

The kinetics of the isomerization of *cis*-methyl cinnamate was studied in the gaseous state, the extent of conversion into the *trans*-form being determined by the melting-point of the product. The following are selected results:

Temperature (°K)	Pressure (mm)	Time (sec)	Percentage trans- formation
635	565	4660	59·6
635·5	308	3210	51·6
637	72	4170	60·4
635·5	71	3798	59·4*
601·0	69	10170	28·0*
564·5	80	89580	26·2

The experiments marked * were made in a bulb packed so as to increase the surface six-fold.

Make all the inferences you can from these data as to the qualitative and quantitative characteristics of the reaction.

NOTE: The cryoscopic method of following the course of this reaction is somewhat unusual in the study of the kinetics of gas reactions. From the data it may be inferred whether the reaction is homogeneous or heterogeneous, what is its order and heat of activation.

The quantitative characteristics of the reaction are most concisely expressed by an equation of the form

$$\text{velocity constant} = Ae^{-E/RT}.$$

93 THE THERMAL DECOMPOSITION OF NITROUS OXIDE ON GOLD

C. N. Hinshelwood and C. R. Prichard, *Proc. Roy. Soc.* A, **108**, 211, 1925.

The decomposition of nitrous oxide at the surface of an electrically heated gold wire was measured manometrically with the following results:

Temperature	Initial pressure (mm)	Time (min)	Percentage decomposition
990° C	200	30	32
,,	,,	53	50
,,	,,	100	73

At the same temperature and at an initial pressure of 400 mm the time of half-change was 52 min.

The average velocity constant at three temperatures is given below:

Temperature (°C)	Velocity constant (sec⁻¹)
834	0·0000428
938	0·000123
990	0·000221

Find (i) the order of reaction, and (ii) the mean energy of activation; compare them with the corresponding quantities for the homogeneous reaction (cf. Problem 91).

NOTE: The kinetics of the decomposition on a gold surface may be contrasted with the behaviour on platinum. (C. N. Hinshelwood and C. R. Prichard, *J. Chem. Soc.*, **127**, 327, 1925.) K. J. Laidler, *Chemical Kinetics* (McGraw-Hill, New York, 1950), pp. 166–9, may be consulted for another approach to this reaction.

94 THE THERMAL DECOMPOSITION OF AMMONIA ON TUNGSTEN AND PLATINUM

C. N. Hinshelwood and R. E. Burk, *J. Chem. Soc.*, **127**, 1105, 1925.

Tungsten

The following figures relate to the decomposition of ammonia on an electrically heated tungsten wire at 856° C.

Initial composition of mixture	100 mm NH_3	100 mm NH_3 100 mm H_2	200 mm NH_3
Time (sec)	*mm of ammonia decomposed*		
100	13·5	14	14
200	23·5	24·5	27
300	33·5	34·5	38
400	42·5	44	48·5
500	51	52·5	59

Platinum

The following figures relate to similar experiments with an electrically heated platinum wire at 1138° C.

(*a*) Initial composition: 200 mm NH_3.

Time (sec) . . .	10	60	120	240	360	720
mm NH_3 decomposed .	28	56	72	89	100	120

(b) With 100 mm initial pressure of ammonia, 50 mm decomposed in 180 sec.

(c) When excess hydrogen was admitted initially to 100 mm of ammonia, the pressure of ammonia decomposed in 120 sec with varying pressures of hydrogen was as follows:

p_{H_2} (mm)	50	75	100
p_{NH_3} decomposed in 120 sec .	33	27	16

What conclusions can be drawn as to the mechanism of the decomposition of ammonia at the surface of the two metals?

NOTE: The contrast between the kinetics at the two metal surfaces is characteristic of heterogeneous catalysis; a further contrast is provided by comparing the above data for a tungsten surface with those obtained by W. Frankenburger and A. Hodler (*Trans. Faraday Soc.*, **28**, 229, 1932) with 'active' tungsten at lower temperatures.

95 THE KINETICS OF THE REACTION BETWEEN NITRIC OXIDE AND HYDROGEN

C. N. Hinshelwood and T. E. Green, *J. Chem. Soc.*, 730, 1926.

Nitric oxide reacts with hydrogen in the region of 1100° K, the *ultimate* result of the interaction being expressed by the equation:

$$2NO + 2H_2 = N_2 + 2H_2O.$$

The reaction may be followed manometrically and was investigated in a silica bulb with the following results.

Equimolecular amounts of nitric oxide and hydrogen

The time of half-change ($t^{\frac{1}{2}}$) at various initial pressures (a) of each gas was measured at 826° C with the following results:

a ($mm_{H_2} = mm_{NO}$)	$t_{\frac{1}{2}}$ (sec)
354	81
340·5	102
288	140
202	224

(i) Calculate the order of the reaction.

Influence of pressure of the separate gases

The initial rate of reaction for varying proportions of the two reactants was found by plotting reaction curves and drawing tangents. These experiments also relate to 826° C:

p_{H_2} (mm)	p_{NO} (mm)	Rate of reaction (mm/100 sec)
400	359	150
400	300	103
400	152	25
289	400	160
205	400	110
147	400	79

(ii) Calculate the order of the reaction with respect to each reactant.

(iii) Calculate the average velocity constant in mm/sec units from the data for equimolecular proportions.

(iv) Calculate the velocity constant in the same units from the following data:

p_{NO} (mm)	p_{H_2} (mm)	$t_{\frac{1}{2}}$ (sec)
402	201	46
232	313	152

(v) Can the deviation from a whole number of the total order of reaction found in (i) be connected with the fact that the addition of powdered silica to the bulb caused a slight increase in the reaction velocity?

The velocity constant (in mole/litre/sec units) at a series of temperatures was as follows:

T (°C) . . .	826	788	751	711
k	476	275	130	59

(vi) Calculate the heat of activation. Compare your results

142

with the value of 60000 cal which would be expected for a bimolecular reaction proceeding with the same speed at the same temperature.

NOTE: A reinvestigation of this reaction, together with the analogous reaction with deuterium, by C. N. Hinshelwood and J. W. Mitchell (*J. Chem. Soc.*, 378, 1936) has shown a number of complexities previously unsuspected. Some of the problems raised by termolecular reactions are discussed by C. N. Hinshelwood, *The Structure of Physical Chemistry* (Oxford, 1951), pp. 417–20, by A. F. Trotman-Dickenson, *Gas Kinetics* (Butterworth, London, 1955), pp. 262–72, and by S. W. Benson, *The Foundations of Chemical Kinetics* (McGraw-Hill, New York, 1960), pp. 306–16.

96 THE KINETICS OF THE PARA → ORTHO-HYDROGEN CONVERSION

A. Farkas, *Orthohydrogen, Parahydrogen and Heavy Hydrogen* (Cambridge, 1935), Part i, ch. iv.

Between 600° C and 800° C para-hydrogen is converted into the equilibrium mixture of ortho- and para-forms at a rate independent of the surface–volume ratio of the silica reaction vessel. A. Farkas investigated the kinetics of the reaction by measuring the thermal conductivity of the gas at intervals.

At a given pressure the rate of conversion may be expressed by the equation

$$u_t = u_0 \, e^{-kt},$$

where u_0 and u_t represent the percentage excesses of para-hydrogen over the equilibrium percentage (25 per cent) at the beginning of the conversion and at time t respectively. At 923° K the following values of k were obtained at a series of pressures:

Pressure (mm)	k (reciprocal second units)
50	0·00106
100	0·00153
200	0·00217
400	0·00310

143

(i) Calculate the order of the reaction. What mechanism does the order suggest?

$k*$ is the quotient obtained by dividing k by the atomic hydrogen concentration, calculated from thermodynamic data; for this quantity Farkas obtained the following values over a temperature range:

T $(°K)$	$k*$ $(mole/litre/sec$ $units)$
873	$1·37 \times 10^9$
973	$2·00 \times 10^9$
1023	$2·38 \times 10^9$

(ii) Calculate the heat of activation of the process

$$H + p\text{-}H_2 \rightarrow o\text{-}H_2 + H$$

correcting your result for the variation of molecular velocity with temperature.

Cf. A. Farkas, *Z. physik Chem.* B, **10**, 419, 1930.

NOTE: The kinetic data of this problem provide unequivocal evidence of the mechanism of the para $\rightarrow$ ortho-hydrogen conversion, which is a reaction of great theoretical interest (see Farkas's book, ch. iv); in particular it was the subject of one of the earliest *a priori* calculations of reaction velocity by H. Eyring and M. Polanyi. A discussion of the reaction together with sources of further experimental data will be found in A. F. Trotman-Dickenson, *Gas Kinetics* (Butterworth, London, 1955), ch. 4.

97 * THE STATISTICS OF THE REACTION OF ATOMIC CHLORINE WITH HYDROGEN

W. H. Rodebush and W. C. Klingelhoefer, *J. Am. Chem. Soc.*, **55**, 130, 1933.

Chlorine was passed through a high-frequency electrodeless discharge and the partially dissociated gas was mixed with hydrogen and streamed through a thermostated reaction bulb. At the far end of the bulb a piece of silver foil stopped the reaction by its very effective catalysis of the recombination of chlorine atoms. The degree of dissociation of the chlorine from the discharge tube was measured by means of a Wrede diffusion gauge. The products of reaction were analysed by freezing out the chlorine and hydrogen chloride in liquid-air traps and titrating with standard thiosulphate and alkali respectively. The following data relate to a typical run:

Volume of reaction bulb	. .	10 cm³
Pressure in reaction bulb	. .	0·340 mm
Temperature of reaction bulb	.	0° C
Rate of hydrogen flow .	. .	6·3 cm³/min
Rate of chlorine flow (calculated as Cl₂).		9·1 cm³/min
Percentage dissociation of chlorine		11 per cent
Length of run	. . . .	10 min
Thiosulphate titre of product	.	36·5 cm³ of 0·20 N solution
Alkali titre of product .	. .	9·1 cm³ of 0·10 N solution

Rate of hydrogen flow . . . 6·3 cm³/min ⎫ calculated for gases
Rate of chlorine flow (calculated as ⎬ at n.t.p.
Cl₂). . . . . . 9·1 cm³/min ⎭

Assuming that the reaction $Cl+H_2 = HCl+H$ is always followed by the much faster reaction $H+Cl_2 = HCl+Cl$, and that the diameters of atomic chlorine and molecular hydrogen are 2·97 Å (= the diameter of the argon atom) and 2·39 Å respectively, calculate:

(i) the average number of molecules of hydrogen chloride formed for each chlorine atom introduced;

(ii) the average number of collisions with hydrogen undergone by each chlorine atom in the reaction vessel;

(iii) the probability of a collision between a chlorine atom and a hydrogen molecule resulting in reaction.

NOTE: Since the rate of flow of chlorine is expressed as cubic centimetres of molecular chlorine, correction must be made for its 11 per cent dissociation in calculating both the time spent by the gases in the reaction bulb and the partial pressures of the gases in the bulb. There is an error in the table at the top of p. 137 of the original paper, since the alkali titration must refer to the total run and cannot refer to one minute of it. The change of the concentration of hydrogen during reaction is to be neglected.

The original paper may be consulted for other observations, such as the (very small) effect of added moisture and oxygen, which are of importance in connexion with the general problem of the hydrogen–chlorine combination. The lesser fruitfulness of the collision process of chlorine atoms with deuterium molecules is of interest (cf. A. Farkas, *Orthohydrogen, Parahydrogen and Heavy Hydrogen*, Cambridge, 1935, Part ii, ch. iv, or H. C. Urey and G. K. Teal, *Rev. Mod. Phys.*, **7**, 34,

1935). A. F. Trotman-Dickenson, *Gas Kinetics* (Butterworth, London, 1955), pp. 181–8, discusses a number of ways of studying the rate of reaction between chlorine atoms and hydrogen molecules; there is a fair degree of harmony among results obtained by quite different methods.

98 THE ACID HYDROLYSIS OF METHYL ACETATE

W. B. S. Newling and C. N. Hinshelwood, *J. Chem. Soc.*, 1357, 1936.

The rate of hydrolysis of esters in the presence of strong acids, which is readily followed by titration, is reversible and proceeds according to the differential equation:

$$\frac{dx}{dt} = k_1 \,[\text{Acid}]\,(a-x) - k_2\,[\text{Acid}]\,(x)^2,$$

where $(a-x)$ is the concentration of ester and x that of each of the reaction products at time t; [Acid] is the concentration of strong acid present.

In aqueous acetone at $80\cdot2°$ C methyl acetate initially $0\cdot05$ M was $90\cdot0$ per cent hydrolysed at equilibrium. The following results were obtained for the rate of hydrolysis in the presence of $0\cdot05$ M HCl:

Time (sec)	Percentage hydrolysis
1350	21·2
2070	30·7
3060	43·4
5340	59·5
7740	73·45

(i) Integrate the differential equation so as to obtain an expression for the velocity constant of the forward reaction k_1 in terms of the equilibrium constant K, the initial concentration of ester a, the concentration of hydrochloric acid, and the value of x at time t.

(ii) Hence evaluate a series of values of k_1 in mole/litre/ sec units.

146

NOTE: This is a simple example of the analysis of the kinetic data of a reversible reaction. When the kinetic equation is rearranged for integration it will be found to correspond to a well-known standard form of integral. The integration constant is evaluated, as usual, by inserting the condition that $x = 0$ when $t = 0$. I am indebted to Professor Hinshelwood for the detailed data of the problem.

99 THE EFFECT OF AROMATIC SUBSTITUTION ON REACTION VELOCITY

E. G. Williams and C. N. Hinshelwood, *J. Chem. Soc.*, 1079, 1934.

While investigating whether the effect of substituents on the velocity of organic reactions is due primarily to a change in the energy of activation or to other factors, Hinshelwood and Williams measured the rate of reaction between aniline and benzoyl chloride in benzene solution and also the corresponding rates between substituted anilines and substituted benzoyl chlorides. The following table gives the velocity constants in mole/litre/sec units for various pairs of reactants at various temperatures:

Reactants	$k_{5°C}$	$k_{40°C}$	$k_{100°C}$
Aniline + p-nitro-benzoyl chloride .	0·286	0·871	..
Aniline + benzoyl chloride . .	0·0308	0·122	..
p-nitraniline + benzoyl chloride .	..	0·000110	0·00253

(i) Find the energy of activation of each reaction.

(ii) Compare the observed rate of reaction at 40° C with the number of collisions having the necessary energy of activation; for the purpose of this calculation the mean diameter of all the molecules may be taken as, say, 6 Å.

(iii) Do the experimental results suggest that substituents affect the rate of reaction by changing the heat of activation or by changing other factors which are not involved in the exponential term?

147

NOTE: The velocity constant, k, of a bimolecular reaction may be expressed in the form

$$10^3 Nk = P . Z_{AB} . e^{-E/RT},$$

where N is the Avogadro number, the exponential term has its usual significance, Z_{AB} is the collision number per litre between the two kinds of molecule, and P is the quantity sometimes called the phase-factor and is regarded as being determined by orientation conditions, quantum-mechanical restrictions, and other temperature-independent quantities. If different pairs of reactants are considered at the same temperature, the collision number will be inversely proportional to the square root of the reduced mass (M) of the reactants (since the collision diameter will vary little from one pair of substituted reactants to another) and we may therefore write

$$2 \cdot 303 \log_{10} k . M^{\frac{1}{2}} = \log_{10} P + \text{constant} - E/RT.$$

If P does not vary much from one pair of reactants to another we should expect to find that

$$2 \cdot 303 \log_{10} k . M^{\frac{1}{2}} = \text{constant} - E/RT.$$

A graph of E against $\log_{10} k . M^{\frac{1}{2}}$ at a single selected temperature therefore suggests itself as a possible way of answering the question raised in (iii).

The particular relation between P and E obtaining in this group of reactions is not to be regarded as generally valid. There seems to be a growing body of evidence which suggests that P and E are probably functionally related. For a general discussion of 'P factors' see Hinshelwood (*J. Chem. Soc.*, 1111, 1935), Hinshelwood and Winkler (ibid., 371, 1936), and Fairclough and Hinshelwood (ibid., 538, 1937). The graphical survey provided by Figs. 1 and 2 of the paper of Hinshelwood and Winkler places the results of the present problem in a truer perspective. The paper of C. N. Hinshelwood, K. J. Laidler, and E. W. Timm (*J. Chem. Soc.*, 848, 1938) is also of interest.

It is nowadays more usual to discuss the influence of solvent and structure on reaction rates in terms of the transition-state approach to kinetics (see, for example, K. J. Laidler, *Chemical Kinetics* (McGraw-Hill, New York, 1950), or E. S. Gould, *Mechanism and Structure in Organic Chemistry* (Holt, Reinhart & Wilson, New York, 1959). A lecture by R. P. Bell (*J. Chem. Soc.*, 629, 1943) helps to provide perspective for alternative approaches to the theory of reaction kinetics in solution.

100 A TEST OF THE PRIMARY SALT EFFECT IN DILUTE SOLUTION

V. K. La Mer, *J. Am. Chem. Soc.*, **51**, 3341, 1929.

The reaction

$$BrCH_2COO^- + S_2O_3^= = S_2O_3CH_2COO^= + Br^-$$

is particularly suitable for the examination of the primary salt effect because it is free from side reactions, can be studied at high dilution, and proceeds without change of the ionic strength of the solution. The reaction was followed by adding an excess of iodine and back-titrating with standard thiosulphate solution; the initial normality of the two reactants was identical.

The following detailed experimental data were obtained in Run 27. Three flasks were filled with 50·03 cm³ of each of the two sodium salts at 0·002 N together with 100·06 cm³ of boiled water. After time t, excess of iodine solution was added to each flask and the solution was back-titrated. The initial titre in terms of the iodine solution was 99·21 cm³.

Flask	Time t (min)	Iodine used up (cm³)
1	2112	75·58
2	3356	66·02
3	3559	64·80

(i) Calculate the velocity constant for each flask in equivalent/litre/minute units.

Similar experiments at other concentrations led to the following values:

Normality of reactants	Velocity constant
0·000666	0·304
0·00100	0·317
0·00250	0·354
0·005	0·385

(ii) Plot the logarithm of the velocity constant against the

149

square root of the ionic strength and draw on the same graph a straight line having the slope predicted by the Brönsted theory.

NOTE: The experiments upon which this problem is based constitute one of the earlier tests of the Brönsted theory of the primary salt effect. In this theory the idea of a transition state made its debut in kinetics. R. P. Bell (*Ann. Repts. on Prog. Chem., Chem. Soc. London*, **31**, 67, 1934) and A. A. Frost and R. G. Pearson, *Kinetics and Mechanism* (Wiley, New York, 1961), ch. 7, may be consulted for perspective.

Conversion to the appropriate concentration units should not be overlooked. In calculating the ionic strength it must be remembered that the normality of the sodium thiosulphate solution relates to its reaction with iodine; for this solution 'normal' = 'molar' (see the correction by La Mer, *J. Am. Chem. Soc.*, **51**, 3678, 1929).

101 THE MUTA-ROTATION OF GLUCOSE

J. N. Brönsted and E. A. Guggenheim, *J. Am. Chem. Soc.*, **49**, 2554, 1927.

The muta-rotation of glucose in the presence of a buffer of o-toluic acid and sodium o-toluate was measured in a dilatometer with the results tabulated below. V and V' are the volume readings (in arbitrary units) after times t and $(t+120)$ minutes respectively.

t	V	V'
0	4·395	6·50
6	4·615	6·545
15	4·91	6·60
40	5·53	6·72
82	6·18	6·835

Verify that the reaction is first order, and calculate the velocity constant in reciprocal minutes.

NOTE: The experimental data lend themselves to the application of Guggenheim's method (*Phil. Mag.*, **2**, 538, 1926) for the evaluation of the velocity constant; this method obviates the necessity of knowing either the starting-point or the end-point of the reaction. The method is described by A. A. Frost and R. G. Pearson, *Kinetics and Mechanism* (Wiley, New York, 1961), pp. 49–50.

102 THE DETERMINATION OF THE CATALYTIC COEFFICIENTS OF ACIDS AND BASES IN THE MUTA-ROTATION OF GLUCOSE

J. N. Brönsted and E. A. Guggenheim, *J. Am. Chem. Soc.*, **49**, 2554, 1927 (cf. Problem No. 101).

The muta-rotation of glucose takes place slowly and spontaneously in pure water, is slightly catalysed by hydrogen ions, and very strongly catalysed by hydroxyl ions. The velocity constant is approximately given by the equation:

$$K = K_0 + k_{H_3O^+}[H_3O^+] + k_{OH^-}[OH^-],$$

where K is given in reciprocal minute units, K_0 is the rate of spontaneous reaction, and $k_{H_3O^+}$ and k_{OH^-} are the catalytic coefficients of the hydrion and hydroxyl-ion respectively. Since $k_{H_3O^+}$ is of the order of 0.1 while k_{OH^-} is of the order of several thousand, the rate of spontaneous reaction is most reliably measured in faintly acid solution. Between pH values of 4 and 6 neither hydrion nor hydroxyl-ion exerts an appreciable catalytic effect, and in this range of hydrion concentration the reaction is therefore particularly suitable for measuring the feeble catalytic effect of weak bases such as the anions of organic acids and weak acids like the acid molecules themselves.

To this end Brönsted and Guggenheim made a series of muta-rotation measurements in solutions sufficiently dilute to eliminate all appreciable neutral salt effects. The data overleaf are selected from their results.

(i) Evaluate K_0, the velocity constant of the spontaneous reaction.

(ii) Evaluate $k_{H_3O^+}$.

	Solution	$K \times 10^3$
(a)	$HCl \times 10^{-4}$ N	5·29
	$HClO_4 \times 10^{-5}$ N	5·23
	$HClO_4 \times 10^{-4}$ N + 0·1 N KNO_3	5·40
	$HClO_4 \times 10^{-4}$ N + 0·025 N $Ba(NO_3)_2$	5·30
(b)	$HClO_4 \times 0·0048$ N	6·00
	$HClO_4 \times 0·0325$ N + 0·2 N KNO_3	10·02
	$HClO_4 \times 0·0247$ N	8·92

(c)	Sodium mandelate normality	Mandelic acid normality	$K \times 10^3$
	0·050	0·001	5·80
	0·100	0·001	6·38
	0·125	0·001	6·66
	0·100	0·050	6·70
	0·100	0·100	7·04

(d)	Pyridine normality	Pyridine perchlorate normality	
	0·025	0·025	7·46
	0·050	0·050	9·29
	0·050	0·100	9·63
	0·050	0·200	9·39

(iii) Estimate the catalytic coefficients of the mandelate ion and the pyridine molecule (basic catalysts), those of mandelic acid and the pyridinium ion (acid catalysts) and also that of the water molecule (which may be regarded as the catalyst determining the spontaneous rate).

(iv) Plot the logarithm of the catalytic coefficients of the various species involved against the logarithm of their dissociation constants (as defined by Brönsted).

NOTE: The concentration of water in all the reaction mixtures may be taken as $1000/18$ mole litre^{-1}; its acid dissociation constant, by Brönsted's definition, will be $\dfrac{K_W \times 18}{1000}$; the basic dissociation constant of the conjugate base [OH$^-$] will be $\dfrac{1000}{K_W \times 18}$. For the oxonium ion the acid dissociation constant is $\dfrac{1000}{18}$ and the basic dissociation constant of the conjugate base, water, will be $\dfrac{18}{1000}$. Under the same convention the acid dissociation constants of the mandelic acid molecules and the pyridinium ion are $4·3 \times 10^{-4}$ and $3·5 \times 10^{-6}$ respectively.

The exponential (or logarithmic) relationship between catalytic con-

152

stant and dissociation constant, often called the Brönsted relation, is discussed by R. P. Bell, *The Proton in Chemistry* (Cornell U.P., Ithaca, 1959), ch. 10. A. A. Frost and R. G. Pearson, *Kinetics and Mechanism* (Wiley, New York, 1961), ch. 9, also provides useful perspective for this problem.

103 THE QUANTUM EFFICIENCY OF THE FERRIOXALATE ACTINOMETER

C. A. Parker, *Proc. Roy. Soc.* A, **220**, 104, 1953; C. G. Hatchard and C. A. Parker, ibid., **235**, 518, 1956.

On exposure to light of wave-lengths below 4900 Å the ferrioxalate ion undergoes decomposition in accordance with the equation:

$$2Fe(C_2O_4)_3^{---} \longrightarrow 2FeC_2O_4 + 3C_2O_4^{--} + 2CO_2$$

Any precipitation of the ferrous oxalate formed can be prevented by an appropriate concentration of sulphuric acid and the amount of ferrous salt formed by photolysis can be measured by converting the ferrous iron into the intensely coloured complex with 1 : 10 phenanthroline and estimating its concentration by spectrophotometer. Parker has shown that these circumstances combine to make the photolysis of potassium ferrioxalate the basis of a simple, precise, and sensitive actinometer. The measurements recorded below are taken from the two papers establishing the effectiveness of the actinometer, supplemented by additional experimental detail kindly provided by the authors.

(i) *Estimation of ferrous iron by phenanthroline*

Below are tabulated the optical densities (in a 1 cm cell) at 5100 Å of mixtures of varying proportions of acid ferrous sulphate solution treated with constant volumes of phenanthroline solution and an acetate buffer. Every mixture was made up to a total volume of 20 ml and allowed to stand for half an hour until the optical density was constant. Each value of the optical density has been corrected for the optical density of each mixture without the addition of the ferrous salt.

Micro-moles of ferrous ion in the 20 ml sample	Optical density per cm at 5100 Å
0·5	0·277
1·2	0·661
2·0	1·103

(i) From the above data calculate an average value for the conversion factor required to compute the ferrous ion content of an unknown solution from the optical density of the mixture obtained by treating the unknown solution by the procedure used in obtaining the figures tabulated. Express your result as the number of micro-moles of ferrous iron in a 20 ml sample needed to produce an optical density of unity in a 1 cm cell.

(ii) *The quantum efficiency of the actinometer over a range of wavelengths*

In the following measurements 15 ml of 0·006 M $K_3Fe(C_2O_4)_3$ in 0·01 N H_2SO_4 were irradiated by light from a mercury lamp passed through appropriate filters. The optical depth of the cell was 15 mm and the area of cell face exposed was 0·785 cm². The intensity of the incident light was measured by an 18-junction thermopile, which calibration showed to develop one microvolt for 17·778 microwatts/cm² of incident radiation. The fractions of light absorbed by the solution in the 15 mm cell were 0·5977 at 4360 Å, 0·9624 at 4050 Å, and 1·000 at 3660 Å respectively. After irradiation at each wave-length a 10 ml aliquot of the solution was taken, treated with phenanthroline and acetate buffer and made up to a total volume of 20 ml; the ferrous iron content was then measured spectrophotometrically in a 1 cm cell at 5100 Å as in part (i).

The table of results on the opposite page includes the correction factor to be applied for the transmission by the cell face, whose incompleteness meant that not all the incident radiation reached the actinometer solution.

Calculate the quantum efficiency (moles of ferrous iron formed per Einstein absorbed) at each wave-length.

154

Wave-length ($\mathring{A}$) . . .	4360	4050	3660
Mean thermopile response (microvolts)	25·81	5·37	11·53
Time of exposure (min) . .	30	45	20
Transmission of cell face . .	0·9568	0·9516	0·9336
Optical density of aliquot after treatment with phenanthroline and buffer	0·568	0·267	0·257

NOTE: The intensity of most sources of monochromatic radiation is so low that the amount of chemical change produced is very small unless the quantum efficiency is enhanced by a chain reaction. The ferrioxalate actinometer circumvents this difficulty by the use of an extremely sensitive spectrophotometric procedure for estimating the ferrous ion produced. The sensitivity attained is about one thousand times greater than that of the well-known uranyl oxalate actinometer. Small rapid fluctuations of the light source as well as a steady decrease in light intensity were corrected for by deflecting a small proportion of the light on to a phototube by means of a clear glass plate inclined at 45° to the beam. The thermopile readings quoted are corrected for this source of error.

The incident light, as measured by the thermopile, must be corrected for the area of cell face exposed, for the fraction of light transmitted by the front cell face, and for the fraction of light reaching the solution that was absorbed by the actinometer solution.

104 THE ISOMERIZATION OF ORTHO-NITRO-BENZALDEHYDE BY LIGHT

F. Weigert and L. Brodmann, *Trans. Faraday Soc.*, **21**, 453, 1925.

In ultra-violet light ortho-nitro-benzaldehyde isomerizes to ortho-nitroso-benzoic acid; the course of the reaction in acetone solution may be followed by conductivity measurements. Weigert and Brodmann followed the change in monochromatic light of wave-length 366 mμ from a mercury lamp. The intensity of radiation was measured by a bolometer which had been calibrated against a Hefner candle. In the experiments outlined below *all* the incident radiation was absorbed by the reactant mixture.

Volume of reaction vessel (cm^3)	Radiated surface (cm^2)	Incident radiation per cm^2 $\left(\dfrac{cal}{sec} \times 10^5\right)$	Time of illumination (hr min)		Initial conc. of aldehyde $(g/100$ $cm^3)$	Conc. of acid formed $(g/100$ $cm^3)$
15	15	2·72	1	0	0·5	0·0097
15	15	2·64	3	40	0·2	0·0381

Calculate the quantum efficiency of the reaction.

NOTE: There is slight confusion in the original paper regarding the tabulation of the experimental data. Concentrations which must be grammes per 100 cm³ are described as 'grammes per cent'.

105 THE PHOTOCHEMICAL OXIDATION OF PHOSGENE

G. K. Rollefson and C. W. Montgomery, *J. Am. Chem. Soc.*, **55**, 142, and 4025, 1933.

Rollefson and Montgomery studied the direct photochemical oxidation of phosgene by oxygen in the light of the quartz mercury arc. The net reaction is

$$2COCl_2 + O_2 = 2CO_2 + 2Cl_2$$

and its course may be followed manometrically. They showed that the rate of reaction was directly proportional to the phosgene concentration and to the light intensity. At high oxygen pressures the rate was independent of the oxygen concentration, but at lower pressures the rate fell off gradually with the oxygen pressure. Experiments with varying initial pressures of oxygen and chlorine showed that the rate was a function of the chlorine/oxygen ratio and that all the kinetic data were adequately represented by the equation

$$\frac{d(CO_2)}{dt} = \frac{kI_0(COCl_2)}{1 + k'(Cl_2/O_2)},$$

where I_0 is the intensity of the incident radiation, which was only feebly absorbed under the conditions of experiment. In the second paper it was shown that the quantum efficiency was two.

Show that the experimental results may be accounted for by the following mechanism:

$$COCl_2 + h\nu \quad = COCl + Cl \qquad (1)$$
$$COCl + O_2 \quad = CO_2 + ClO \qquad (2)$$
$$COCl_2 + ClO = CO_2 + Cl_2 + Cl \qquad (3)$$
$$COCl + Cl_2 \quad = COCl_2 + Cl \qquad (4)$$
$$Cl + Cl + M \quad = Cl_2 + M \qquad (5)$$

NOTE: The kinetic equation is readily derived by writing down the conditions that the concentrations of the two intermediate active radicals ClO and COCl do not vary with time, together with the equation for the rate of formation of carbon dioxide. Since the absorption is feeble, the proportion of incident light absorbed will vary directly with the phosgene concentration.

For further work on the photochemistry of phosgene see, for example, F. Almasy and T. Wagner-Jauregg (*Z. physik. Chem.* B, **19**, 405, 1932) and C. W. Montgomery and G. K. Rollefson (*J. Am. Chem. Soc.*, **56**, 1089, 1934). This reaction with other aspects of the photochemistry of phosgene is discussed by G. K. Rollefson and M. Burton, *Photochemistry* (Prentice-Hall, New York, 1939), pp. 313–19.

106 THE IODINE-SENSITIZED PHOTOCHEMICAL DECOMPOSITION OF ETHYLENE IODIDE IN CARBON TETRACHLORIDE SOLUTION

H. J. Schumacher and E. O. Wiig, *Z. physik. Chem.* B, **11**, 45, 1930.

A solution of ethylene iodide and iodine in carbon tetrachloride is decomposed at 100° C by light from a mercury vapour lamp which has been filtered so as to exclude all light but that of longer wave-length than 3800 Å. The net result of the reaction is

$$C_2H_4I_2 = C_2H_4 + I_2.$$

No appreciable decomposition takes place at room temperature nor in the absence of iodine; ethylene iodide alone shows no appreciable absorption at wave-lengths above 3800 Å; iodine shows continuous absorption below 4995 Å. The back reaction may be neglected under the conditions of experiment; there is, however, a certain amount of thermal (or 'dark') reaction which can be separately measured and allowed for. The reaction may be followed by titrating the solution with standard thiosulphate before and after irradiation.

Influence of ethylene iodide concentration and iodine concentration at constant light intensity

Ethylene iodide concentration ($g/100\ cm^3$)	$N/200$ Thiosulphate titre of 5 cm³ of solution before irradiation	Time of irradiation (min)	Iodine formed (expressed in cm³ thio. per 5 cm³ solution)	Iodine formed (corrected for thermal reaction)
5·00	29·40	20	8·97	8·04
5·00	23·99	10	5·05	4·57
2·46	24·52	20	4·47	4·04
2·50	22·83	20	5·03	4·60
2·50	77·38	20	5·54	4·24

Deviations of the order of 10 per cent are to be attributed to fluctuations in light intensity; under the conditions of the above experiments the light absorption was almost complete.

(i) What inferences may be drawn from these figures as to the dependence of rate on the initial concentrations of ethylene iodide and iodine?

Influence of light intensity

Cutting down the light intensity in the proportion 16·43 : 7·64 by means of a copper gauze reduced the rate of reaction in the proportion 9·43 : 6·42.

(ii) From this information and the result of (i), formulate an equation for the rate of disappearance of ethylene iodide in terms of light intensity and the concentrations of reactants.

Quantum yield

In the experiments on quantum yield the light from the mercury vapour lamp was passed successively through three filters which transmitted only light between 3800 and 4800 Å; under these circumstances the effective radiation is almost exclusively that of the 4047 and 4358 Å lines of the mercury arc. Of these the latter is more intense so that the effective wavelength may be taken as 4240 Å.

With these filters irradiation experiments were carried out on two solutions, each 55 cm^3 in total volume; the results are tabulated below, using the same column headings as above:

2·46	29·84	20	4·19	3·74
2·43	28·93	20	3·77	3·32

A Moll thermopile, which had been calibrated against a standard filament lamp, showed that the radiation incident on the reaction vessel, which was almost completely absorbed, amounted to $9·15 \times 10^3$ ergs/sec.

(iii) Calculate the quantum yield under these conditions of light intensity and concentration.

(iv) Show how the observed facts may be explained by the following reaction mechanism:

$$I_2 + h\nu = I + I$$
$$I + C_2H_4I_2 = C_2H_4I + I_2$$
$$C_2H_4I = C_2H_4 + I$$
$$I + I = I_2$$
$$C_2H_4 + I = C_2H_4I$$

NOTE: The deduction of the kinetic equation from the postulated mechanism is made by writing down the conditions for the stationary concentrations of the two active radicals C_2H_4I and I and combining them with the equation for the rate of formation of iodine.

The original paper also includes a correlation of the photochemical results with the data for the thermal reaction, together with some deductions as to the molecular statistics of the process

$$I + C_2H_4I_2 \longrightarrow C_2H_4I + I_2.$$

The decomposition has also been studied in the region of discontinuous absorption by iodine (R. G. Dickinson and N. P. Nies, *J. Am. Chem. Soc.*, **57**, 2382, 1935). This paper illustrates how misleading a simple comparison of quantum efficiencies at different wave-lengths may be for a reaction whose rate is proportional to the square root of the light intensity. For such reactions the 'quantum efficiency' is too dependent on light intensity, concentrations, and temperature to be a significant quantity.

Two later papers (R. E. DeRight and E. O. Wiig, *J. Am. Chem. Soc.*, **57**, 2411, 1936, and W. H. Janneck and E. O. Wiig, *J. Am. Chem. Soc.*, **62**, 1877, 1940) round out the picture of the photochemistry of ethylene iodide by describing the photolysis in carbon tetrachloride solution in the absence of iodine (at shorter wave-lengths) and the decomposition in the vapour phase (both thermal and photochemical).

107 * THE PHOTOCHEMICAL DECOMPOSITION OF NITROGEN PEROXIDE

R. G. W. Norrish, *J. Chem. Soc.*, 1158, 1929.

Nitrogen peroxide is decomposed by ultra-violet light into nitric oxide and oxygen, the decomposition products recombining thermally until an equilibrium is set up:

$$2NO_2 \underset{\text{dark}}{\overset{\text{light}}{\rightleftharpoons}} 2NO + O_2.$$

On illuminating a vessel containing nitrogen peroxide an increase in pressure occurs whose magnitude has been shown to be in agreement with the hypothesis that the photochemical reaction results from the collision of a photochemically activated molecule with a normal molecule, while the reverse 'dark' reaction proceeds in a termolecular manner with a velocity constant which is well known.

Norrish measured the quantum efficiency of the photochemical reaction at 25° C and various wave-lengths by measuring the pressure increase at equilibrium under radiation of known intensity and combining the result with the known velocity data for the 'dark' reaction.

The following are the experimental data upon which his results are based:

(a) *The* $N_2O_4 \rightleftharpoons 2NO$ *equilibrium*

The equilibrium constant $\dfrac{p_{NO_2}^2}{p_{N_2O_4}} = 108$ at 25° C in mm units.

(b) *The termolecular recombination velocity constant*

$$\frac{d[2NO_2]}{dt} = k[2NO]^2[O_2].$$

k is $1 \cdot 66 \times 10^6$ litre^2 mole^{-2} min^{-1} at 25° C.

(c) *Calibration of instruments for measuring radiation.* A thermopile was calibrated by means of a Leslie cube and shown to give one centimetre galvanometer deflexion when absorbing 460 ergs/sec. The sodium photoelectric cell used in the photochemical measurements was calibrated against the thermopile for the wave-lengths studied with the following results:

Wave-length ($\mathring{A}$)	Thermopile galvanometer reading (cm)	Photo-cell galvanometer reading (cm)
4360	5·80	9·10
4050	3·32	9·02
3650	3·60	21·08

(d) *Photochemical measurements.* The quartz reaction vessel had a volume of 30·3 cm^3; the source of radiation was a mercury lamp used with various colour filters to isolate individual wave-lengths.

Wave-length ($\mathring{A}$)	Initial pressure of peroxide (mm)	Galvanometer deflexion		Pressure increase at equilibrium (mm)
		Reaction cell empty (cm)	With reaction cell filled (cm)	
4360	100	12·9	0·3	0·00
4050	100	10·2	0·3	2·06
3650	100	21·8	0·3	2·85

In order to correct for loss of light by reflection in calculating the absorbed radiation, the difference between the two galvanometer readings ($\propto$ incident — transmitted radiation) must be multiplied by 1·17.

Calculate the quantum efficiency at each wave-length.

NOTE: Norrish's paper gives a particularly clear picture of the photochemical apparatus and techniques of the period.

It is convenient to begin by calculating the factor for converting galvanometer deflexions into quanta/second at each wave-length; in calculating absorptions these figures must be multiplied by 1·17 as indicated in the problem.

The next stage is the calculation of x, the partial pressure of the oxygen at photochemical equilibrium. This is complicated by the association equilibrium of the nitrogen peroxide and leads to a quadratic equation for x in terms of the initial pressure (P) and the pressure increase (p). This equation, whose deduction should be verified, is

$$x^2 + x\{20\cdot25 - p - \sqrt{(729 + 27P)}\} + p\{\tfrac{1}{4}p - 6\cdot75 + \tfrac{1}{2}\sqrt{(729 + 27P)}\} = 0.$$

(In the original paper 729 is replaced by 730; this seems to be a numerical slip, but one which is quite without practical significance.)

The partial pressure of oxygen at photochemical equilibrium (and hence, by inference, the partial pressure of nitric oxide) having been determined, the rate of thermal formation and therefore of photochemical decomposition of nitrogen peroxide is readily calculated. When this is expressed as the number of molecules decomposing per second in the reaction vessel and compared with the radiation absorbed, the quantum efficiency is obtained.

A later paper by H. H. Holmes and F. Daniels (*J. Am. Chem. Soc.*, **56**, 630, 1934) contains confirmation of Norrish's mechanism for this reaction as well as further information and references regarding the photochemistry of the oxides of nitrogen. The photochemistry of nitrogen peroxide is reviewed by G. K. Rollefson and M. Burton, *Photochemistry* (Prentice-Hall, New York, 1939), pp. 160–4, and W. A. Noyes, jr., and P. A. Leighton, *The Photochemistry of Gases* (Reinhold, New York, 1941), pp. 400–3.

108 HEATS AND ENTROPIES OF ACTIVATION FOR REACTIONS IN SOLUTION

K. J. Laidler and D. Chen, *Trans. Faraday Soc.*, **54**, 1026, 1958.

The hydrolyses of common esters in alkaline solution are second-order reactions, the rates being proportional to the concentration of the ester and of the hydroxide ions. Laidler and Chen measured the rates of alkaline hydrolysis of methyl and ethyl acetates in aqueous solution at four temperatures, and obtained the following rate constants (in litre mole^{-1} sec^{-1}):

Temperature ($°C$)	Methyl acetate	Ethyl acetate
4·0	0·0343	0·0258
10·0	0·0573	0·0410
18·0	0·0982	0·0680
25·0	0·158	0·1080

For each ester

(i) plot log k against the reciprocal of the Kelvin temperature, find the best value of the slope by the method of least squares and hence calculate the Arrhenius energy of activation, E, in kcal per mole.

(ii) calculate the heat (enthalpy) of activation $\Delta H^{\ddagger}$ at 25° C.

(iii) calculate the entropy of activation, $\Delta S^{\ddagger}$ from $k_{25°C}$ and either E or $\Delta H^{\ddagger}$.

(iv) convert the rate constants into the units cm^3 mole^{-1} sec^{-1}, and again calculate the entropy of activation. Why does the choice of units affect the value of the entropy of activation? Is this the case for reactions of all orders?

NOTE: The 'Arrhenius' or 'experimental' energy of activation, E, is defined by the Arrhenius equation

$$k = A\, e^{-E/RT} \tag{1}$$

where A is sometimes called the frequency or pre-exponential factor.

The absolute rate equation expressed in terms of thermodynamical quantities is (W. F. K. Wynne-Jones and H. Eyring, *J. Chem. Phys.*, **3**, 492, 1935)

$$k = \frac{\mathbf{k}T}{h} e^{-\Delta G^{\ddagger}/RT} \tag{2}$$

$$= \frac{\mathbf{k}T}{h} e^{-\Delta S^{\ddagger}/R} e^{-\Delta H^{\ddagger}/RT} \tag{3}$$

where $\Delta G^{\ddagger}$, $\Delta S^{\ddagger}$, and $\Delta H^{\ddagger}$ are respectively the free energy of activation, the entropy of activation, and the heat (enthalpy) of activation; $\mathbf{k}$ is the Boltzmann constant and h Planck's constant. For reactions in solution it can be shown (S. Glasstone, K. J. Laidler, and H. Eyring, *The Theory of Rate Processes*, McGraw-Hill, New York, 1941, pp. 197–9) that $\Delta H^{\ddagger}$ is related to the experimental energy of activation by

$$E = \Delta H^{\ddagger} + RT \tag{4}$$

From equations (3) and (4) it follows that

$$k = e\frac{\mathbf{k}T}{h} e^{\Delta S^{\ddagger}/R} e^{-E/RT} \tag{5}$$

The entropy of activation can be calculated using either (3) or (5).

109 THE INFLUENCE OF PRESSURE ON REACTION RATES IN SOLUTION

D. Chen and K. J. Laidler, *Canadian J. Chem.*, **37**, 599, 1959.

The fading of bromphenol blue in alkaline solution is a second-order reaction between hydroxide ions and the quinoid form of the dye:

quinoid form (blue)   carbinol form (colourless)

164

The following results show the variation of the second-order rate constant k (in litres mole^{-1} sec^{-1}) with the hydrostatic pressure p (in lb in.$^{-2}$) at 25° C:

Pressure	Rate constant
14·7	$9·30 \times 10^{-4}$
4000	$11·13 \times 10^{-4}$
8000	$13·1 \times 10^{-4}$
12000	$15·3 \times 10^{-4}$
16000	$17·9 \times 10^{-4}$

Calculate the volume of activation, $\Delta V^{\ddagger}$, for the reaction.

NOTE: The variation of rate constant with pressure is given by the van't Hoff equation

$$\left(\frac{\partial \ln k}{\partial p}\right)_T = -\frac{\Delta V^{\ddagger}}{RT}$$

If, therefore, $\ln k$ is plotted against p the slope at any point is equal to $-\Delta V^{\ddagger}/RT$ at the corresponding pressure. In the present example the plot is close to a linear one, so that $\Delta V^{\ddagger}$ is independent of pressure over the range of the investigation.

Care must be taken with the units in this problem; $\Delta V^{\ddagger}$ should be obtained in cm^3 mole^{-1}.

The influence of pressure on reaction rates and the relation of the volume of activation to the nature of the transition state are discussed by S. W. Benson, *The Foundations of Chemical Kinetics* (McGraw-Hill, New York, 1960), pp. 510–17.

110* THE PHOTOLYSIS OF ACETONE

A. F. Trotman-Dickenson and E. W. R. Steacie, *J. Chem. Phys.*, **18**, 1097, 1950; R. E. Dodd and E. W. R. Steacie, *Proc. Roy. Soc.* A, **223**, 283, 1954.

The following reaction scheme has been suggested for the photolysis of acetone between 100° C and 250° C, and at pressures above 10 mm:

$$CH_3COCH_3 + h\nu \longrightarrow 2CH_3 + CO \qquad (1)$$
$$CH_3 + CH_3 \longrightarrow C_2H_6 \qquad (2)$$
$$CH_3 + CH_3COCH_3 \longrightarrow CH_4 + CH_2COCH_3 \qquad (3)$$
$$CH_3 + CH_2COCH_3 \longrightarrow C_2H_5COCH_3 \qquad (4)$$
$$2CH_2COCH_3 \longrightarrow (CH_2COCH_3)_2 \qquad (5)$$

It will be noted that chains are not set up under this reaction scheme. A quantum yield of unity for carbon monoxide formation is well established under the experimental conditions specified. The present problem is concerned exclusively with steps (2) and (3), the reactions of free methyl radicals produced in the primary process to form ethane and methane respectively.

Trotman-Dickenson and Steacie studied the photolysis by passing light from a mercury arc through acetone vapour in a cylindrical quartz reaction vessel, 195 cm^3 in volume, whose temperature was controlled by enclosure in an aluminium block furnace. The reaction products were analysed by low-temperature fractionation and combustion on copper oxide. The following observations are selected from their results:

Run	Tem-perature ($°K$)	Acetone pressure (mm)	Time (sec)	Products (micromoles)		
				CO	CH$_4$	C$_2$H$_6$
26	543	45·9	5100	13·17	15·20	1·70
27	423	93·6	2760	17·68	5·67	12·80
29	471	96·5	2400	15·67	11·20	6·30
30	544	96·8	2400	15·13	19·70	1·47
158	422	96·3	15420	9·85	8·05	3·68
160	422	96·3	29250	5·79	6·56	1·66

(i) Write down rate equations for steps (2) and (3) in the reaction scheme and by eliminating the concentration of methyl radicles show how the rates of methane (R_{CH_4}) and ethane ($R_{C_2H_6}$) production must be related to the acetone concentration, if the reaction scheme is to be valid.

(ii) Calculate the rates of production of each hydrocarbon in molecules per cm^3 per second (R) and the initial concentration of acetone in molecules per cm^3 [A] for each run.

(iii) For each run calculate the value of the function

$$F = R_{\text{methane}}/[R_{\text{ethane}}^{\frac{1}{2}} \times [A]].$$

(iv) Assuming a quantum efficiency of unity for carbon monoxide production, calculate in quanta per second the light absorbed in runs 27, 158, and 160 and hence infer the effect of light intensity on the value of F.

(v) From the value of F in runs 26 and 30, what tentative conclusion can be drawn as to the influence of acetone concentration on its magnitude?

(vi) From a plot of $\log_{10} F$ against reciprocal temperature for runs 27, 29, and 30, together with the assumption that the activation energy of step (2) is negligible, calculate the activation energy of step (3).

There is reason to think that the combinations of free atoms and some simple radicals do not take place as bimolecular reactions but require a third molecule (of any kind) to remove the excess energy evolved by the combination; this is sometimes called 'the third body restriction'. The constancy of F at two different acetone pressures disclosed by the results of (v) tends to suggest that this restriction is not operative at acetone pressures of 45 mm upwards. There was however some suggestion of a rise in F, corresponding to a drop in ethane formation, in experiments by Trotman-Dickenson and Steacie at lower pressures. The kinetics of the photolysis were accordingly studied by Dodd and Steacie at still lower pressures of acetone (20–0·2 mm).

The experimental arrangements were broadly similar to those of the earlier paper except that (a) to provide sufficient products for analysis without exceeding 5 per cent acetone photolysis at low pressures it was necessary to circulate the reactant by means of a mercury diffusion pump through an extra volume of one litre for pressures below 3 mm and of six litres for pressures below 0·4 mm, (b) analyses were confirmed by mass-spectrometry. The volume of the reaction vessel was 1185 cm³.

The observations in the table overleaf are extracted from the results of Dodd and Steacie at 520°K.

Ignoring steps (4) and (5) in the reaction scheme, which play no part in the formation of methane and ethane, the third-body restriction can be introduced by re-writing the reaction scheme:

$$CH_3COCH_3 + h\nu \longrightarrow 2CH_3 + CO \qquad (1)$$
$$CH_3 + CH_3 \longrightarrow C_2H_6{}^* \qquad (2)$$
$$CH_3 + CH_3COCH_3 \longrightarrow CH_4 + CH_2COCH_3 \qquad (3)$$

Run	Acetone pressure (mm)	Rate of formation of products (molecules/cm³/sec × 10⁻¹¹)		
		CO	CH₄	C₂H₆
101B	0·271	5·68	2·17	2·63
97B	0·885	21·6	7·83	11·9
100B	2·99	77·1	39·3	41·2
104B	11·0	271	207	131
103B	19·8	386	357	126

$$C_2H_6{}^* \quad\;\; \to CH_3 + CH_3 \qquad (6)$$
$$C_2H_6{}^* + M \to C_2H_6 + M \qquad (7)$$

where $C_2H_6{}^*$ is the energy-rich ethane molecule formed by the union of two methyl radicals and M can be any molecule but under the conditions of the experiments will be most likely to be an acetone molecule. This scheme covers the possibility of the excited ethane molecule reforming methyl radicals unless its excess energy is removed by a third body.

(vii) Assuming that $R_{methane}$ and R_{ethane} are determined by the rates of steps (3) and (7) respectively and also that M is acetone, apply the stationary state method to compute values of F (defined in (iii) above) and

$$G = R_{methane}/(R_{ethane}^{\frac{1}{2}} \times [A]^{\frac{1}{2}})$$

in terms of the rate constants of steps (2), (3), (6), and (7) above and of the concentration of acetone.

(viii) Calculate the values of F and G (in molecule, cubic centimetre, second units) for each of the five runs carried out at low pressures.

(ix) Plot the values of F and G against the logarithm of the acetone pressure and compare the form of the curves with the conclusions arrived at in (vii).

NOTE: The photolysis of acetone has been investigated in detail by a large number of investigators and found very useful in elucidating the behaviour of free radicals in general and methyl radicals in particular. The formation of carbon monoxide (with a quantum yield of unity) provides a convenient 'internal actinometer' and check on the number of methyl radicals formed. The data quoted relate to less than 5 per cent reaction and can be treated as initial rates.

(ii) The pressure of acetone quoted in the first table is that exerted at the temperature of photolysis.

(iii) Differences in the value of F of up to 5 per cent (or even perhaps 10 per cent) are reasonably attributable to experimental uncertainties, including the errors inherent in the analysis of the small quantities of photolytic products.

(v) The results of Trotman-Dickenson and Steacie show a significant rise in F at pressures of acetone below 24 mm (see parts (vii) and (ix)).

(ix) The paper of Dodd and Steacie should be consulted for a discussion of the subtler details of the reaction; among other things they examined the relative effectiveness of other molecules besides acetone in removing energy from excited ethane molecules. The photolysis of acetone is also discussed in detail by E. W. R. Steacie, *Atomic and Free Radical Reactions* (Reinhold, New York, 1954), where pp. 330–40 and 538–50 are particularly relevant to the present problem, and by S. W. Benson, *The Foundations of Chemical Kinetics* (McGraw-Hill, New York, 1960), pp. 370–9.

111 THE PHOTOLYSIS OF AZOMETHANE

M. H. Jones and E. W. R. Steacie, *J. Chem. Phys.*, **21**, 1018, 1953.

The decomposition of azomethane, both photochemical and thermal, with nitrogen, ethane, and methane as the principal products has been extensively investigated largely because of the role probably played by methyl radicals in the reaction. Jones and Steacie studied the photochemical reaction over a temperature range where the thermal reaction made no appreciable contribution and analysed the products by mass-spectrometry. The light source was a mercury arc and filters were used so that the predominant radiation absorbed by the azomethane vapour was at 3660 Å. Measurements were confined to the initial stages of the reaction (less than 6 per cent decomposition); under these conditions the rates of formation of nitrogen, methane, and ethane were virtually independent of the amount of decomposition. The uranyl oxalate actinometer was used in the measurements of quantum yield.

The following results are taken from a much larger body of data obtained by Jones and Steacie under the experimental conditions described:

	1	2	3	4
Temperature . .	294° K	294° K	294° K	436 ° K
Initial pressure of azomethane (mm) .	94·4	100·7	42·5	97·5
Light absorbed (quanta/min $\times 10^{-16}$) .	1·17	0·40	4·91	1·88
Rate of formation of products (cm^3 at n.t.p./min $\times 10^5$)				
N_2	40·7	13·8	160·7	66·1
CH_4 . . .	5·01	2·71	4·63	Not measured
C_2H_6 . . .	29·3	7·19	142·3	,, ,,

Using the above limited sample of information draw whatever tentative inferences you can as to:

(i) The influence of the intensity of absorbed light on the rate of nitrogen production.

(ii) The quantum yield of nitrogen and its temperature dependence.

(iii) The form of the relationship connecting the rates of formation of the two alkanes and the initial pressure of azomethane at the lower temperature.

Jones and Steacie propose the reaction scheme

$$CH_3N{=}NCH_3 + h\nu \rightarrow N_2 + 2CH_3 \qquad (1)$$
$$CH_3 + CH_3N{=}NCH_3 \rightarrow CH_4 + CH_2N{=}NCH_3 \qquad (2)$$
$$CH_3 + CH_3 \rightarrow C_2H_6 \qquad (3)$$

(iv) Examine the compatibility of this scheme with the inferences you have drawn in (i), (ii), and (iii).

From a series of photolyses at different temperatures but otherwise similar conditions Jones and Steacie obtained the following values of the function $R_{CH_4}/(R_{C_2H_6}^{\frac{1}{2}} \times [\text{azomethane}])$, where R_X signifies the rate of formation of X in the units of the first table:

T (°K)	362	424	449
Function $\times 10^{-2}$ . .	43·0	194	308

From a plot of the logarithm of the function against the reciprocal temperature, together with the assumption that step (3) in the reaction scheme has zero activation energy, (v) estimate the activation energy of step (2).

NOTE: The mass-spectrometric analysis of the decomposition products at high temperatures showed peaks that could be plausibly attributed to methyl ethyl di-imide and tetramethylhydrazine; Jones and Steacie in the original paper explain how these might originate from alternative reactions of the radicals produced in their scheme—reactions that were favoured by higher temperatures and an increased percentage decomposition of azomethane.

112* THE PHOTO-BROMINATION OF METHANE

G. B. Kistiakowsky and E. R. Van Artsdalen, *J. Chem. Phys.*, **12**, 469, 1944.

In a study of the photochemical and thermal bromination of methane Kistiakowsky and Van Artsdalen followed the progress of the reaction by measuring photometrically the rate of disappearance of bromine in the reaction vessel. An accuracy of 0·1 mm was achieved in the measurement of bromine pressures by frequent calibration of the photometric system with known pressures of bromine vapour. In order to eliminate the effect of reaction products on the rate of reaction (including the production of poly-bromo-methanes), the measurements of partial pressure of bromine during the progress of reaction were extrapolated back to zero time to give the initial rate of disappearance of bromine. Constant light intensity was maintained by amperage control of the lamp circuit. At the temperature of the measurements recorded below, the thermal bromination reaction may be neglected and it may also be assumed that the extinction coefficient of bromine vapour is temperature-independent.

(i) In one series of measurements at 503° K the following results were obtained:

Initial pressures (mm at 503° K)		Initial rate of disappearance of bromine (mm/sec)
CH_4	Br_2	
555	41·1	0·105
284	40·5	0·0723
497	16·3	0·0646

Find the values of the exponents a, b, and c in the equation

$$-dp_{Br_2}/dt = k' \, p_{CH_4}^a p_{Br_2}^b p_{total}^c$$

that fit in best with the data; values of ± 1, $\pm\frac{1}{2}$, and 0 for the exponents are the only ones that need consideration. (ii) Similar measurements over a range of temperatures were carried out after modifying the optical system (so that the rate constants here are not numerically comparable with those of part (i)):

Temperature (°K)	p_{CH_4} (mm)	p_{Br_2} (mm)	$-dp_{Br_2}/dt$ (mm/sec)
483	483	44·1	0·0397
453	419	51·1	0·0113
423	400	44·9	0·00235

Assuming the kinetic equation arrived at in part (i), use the observations quoted to evaluate k' at the three temperatures and hence the activation energy of the reaction.

(iii) The influence of light intensity was examined by interposing between light source and reaction vessel a screen which intercepted 55·5 per cent of the incident radiation. This was found to cut down the rate of bromination to 68·3 per cent of its value before the interposition of the screen. How does the reaction rate vary with the intensity of incident radiation?

(iv) Rate measurements carried out with hydrogen bromide added to the reaction mixture beforehand showed that

under these conditions the initial rate of disappearance of
bromine obeyed the following rate equation:

$$-dp_{Br_2}/dt = \frac{k' \, p_{CH_4} p_{Br_2}^{\frac{1}{2}} p_{total}^{-\frac{1}{2}}}{1 + \dfrac{k_4}{k_3} \dfrac{p_{HBr}}{p_{Br_2}}}$$

In one set of measurements under these conditions the
following results were obtained at $483°$ K:

p_{CH_4} (mm)	p_{Br_2} (mm)	p_{HBr} (mm)	$-dp_{Br_2}/dt$ (mm/sec)
363	46·6	121	0·0197

What value of k_4/k_3 will account for these results when
combined with the value of k' for $483°$ K obtained in
part (ii)?

(v) Show how all the experimental results cited can be
accounted for by the following reaction mechanism:

$$Br_2 + photon \rightarrow Br + Br \tag{1}$$
$$Br + CH_4 \quad \rightarrow CH_3 + HBr \tag{2}$$
$$CH_3 + Br_2 \quad \rightarrow CH_3Br + Br \tag{3}$$
$$CH_3 + HBr \quad \rightarrow CH_4 + Br \tag{4}$$
$$Br + Br + M \rightarrow Br_2 + M \tag{5}$$

where M represents any molecule able to remove energy
liberated by the re-combination of bromine atoms. The
geometry of the apparatus was such that the number of
quanta absorbed by the bromine molecules per second was
proportional to the product of the incident light intensity
and the partial pressure of bromine.

NOTE: The reaction is discussed by E. W. R. Steacie, *Atomic and Free
Radical Reactions* (Reinhold, New York, 1954), pp. 707–8. It is interesting to compare the characteristics of this reaction with the kinetics of the
photochemical and thermal formation of hydrogen bromide from the
elements, which have been so intensively investigated.

113 THE MECHANISM OF CHAIN TERMINATION IN FREE RADICAL POLYMERIZATION

J. C. Bevington, H. W. Melville, and R. P. Taylor, *J. Polymer Sci.*, **12**, 449, 1954.

The principal features of the kinetics of many vinyl polymerizations can be accounted for by the following mechanism:

(1) $R\cdot + CH_2 = CHX \rightarrow R—CH_2—CHX\cdot$ (Chain initiation)

(2) $R—CH_2—CHX\cdot + CH_2 = CHX \rightarrow$
$$R—CH_2—CHX—CH_2—CHX\cdot$$
(Chain propagation, repeated many times)

(3a) $2R—(CH_2—CHX)_n^\cdot \rightarrow$
$$R—(CH_2—CHX)_n—(CHX—CH_2)_n—R$$
(Chain termination by combination)

or (3b) $2R—(CH_2—CHX)_n^\cdot \rightarrow$
$$R—(CH_2—CHX)_{n-1}CH = CHX$$
$$+ R(CH_2—CHX)_{n-1}CH_2—CH_2X$$
(Chain termination by disproportionation)

In the first step $R\cdot$ represents a free radical formed from an 'initiator' by thermal or photochemical means. The equations representing the alternative methods of chain termination are obvious over-simplifications since the two chain radicals involved in the two types of bimolecular process leading to chain termination need not and indeed normally will not be of identical lengths.

As a result of chain termination by combination each polymer molecule will contain two fragments of the initiator molecule; chain termination by disproportionation will, on the other hand, lead to one initiator fragment per polymer molecule.

Bevington, Melville, and Taylor examined the contributions of combination and disproportionation to chain termination in the polymerization of methyl methacrylate and of styrene by a radiochemical determination of the number of initiator fragments per polymer molecule in each case. As initiator they used azo-bi-isobutyronitrile labelled with C-14; this initiator dissociates photochemically into two free radicals with the formula $(CH_3)_2C(CN)\cdot$ and gaseous nitrogen.

A mixture of monomer, initiator, and solvent (when used) was irradiated at 25° by ultra-violet light from a mercury vapour lamp until a suitable degree of polymerization (as indicated by the amount of contraction in volume) had taken place. The polymer was freed from monomer and initiator by two precipitations and washings with methanol. The molecular weight of the polymer was measured by osmotic pressure determination in benzene solution, using a gel cellophane membrane and extrapolating the osmotic pressure/concentration ratio to infinite dilution.

The radioactivity of the labelled initiator and of the polymer were measured by oxidation to carbon dioxide, which was used to fill a Geiger counter. Geiger counts were corrected for background and reduced to a standard pressure of carbon dioxide; counts per minute accordingly relate to the same amount of total carbon.

Typical results for methyl methacrylate and styrene were as follows:

Solvent	Monomer	Molecular weight of polymer	Counts/min of polymer
Benzene . .	Methyl methacrylate	147000	60·5
None . . .	Styrene	114000	89·5

The counts/minute for the initiator were 96500.

(i) Calculate the average number of initiator fragments per polymer molecule in each case.

(ii) What conclusions can be drawn for each polymerization as to method of chain termination?

NOTE: The ratio of the specific activity of the polymer to that of the initiator is clearly related to the proportion of carbon atoms in each polymer molecule derived from the initiator. With a knowledge of the

175

number of carbon atoms per molecule of monomer and of initiator and the molecular weight of the polymer this relation provides the answer to (i). The original paper may be consulted for a discussion of the nature of and justification for the simplifying assumptions on which the method is based.

114 THE KINETICS OF A SIMPLE CONDENSATION POLYMERIZATION REACTION

P. J. Flory, *J. Am. Chem. Soc.*, **61**, 3334, 1939.

When diethylene glycol [HO—$(CH_2)_2$—O—$(CH_2)_2OH$] and adipic acid are heated together, with a slow stream of nitrogen passed through the mixture to remove the water formed in the reaction, 'polyesterification' occurs and linear condensation polymer molecules are formed consisting of alternate glycol and acid residues in chains of progressively increasing length. The progress of the polymerization may be followed by titrating weighed samples from time to time with alcoholic potassium hydroxide solution.

Using a vapour bath of boiling phenetole at 166° C to jacket the reaction mixture, and starting with an equimolecular mixture, Flory obtained the following results:

Time (min)	Neutralization equivalent of reaction mixture (g)
170	532
321	832
488	1072
793	1404
1008	1569

(i) Calculate the proportion of carboxyl groups that have been esterified in the successive samples.

(ii) Examine the compatibility of the results of (i) with the hypothesis that the rate is proportional to the product of the concentration of the hydroxyl groups in the mixture and the square of the concentration of the carboxyl groups and that it is unaffected by the progressive increase in molecular size or the concomitant rise in viscosity of the mixture.

NOTE: The paper on which this problem is based was one of the earliest to show that the rate of certain types of polymerization reaction could be accounted for by a quite simple reaction mechanism. The conclusion that the primary reaction between the various molecular species is that of reaction between functional groups and is independent, except near the beginning, of the nature and length of the chain to which the functional group is attached has been of great importance in the further study of polymerization kinetics.

(i) In an equimolecular mixture of dihydric alcohol and dibasic acid such as we have here the number of free carboxyl groups will equal the total number of molecules in the system at any stage of poly-esterification. A simple relationship can accordingly be derived connecting the neutralization equivalent of the mixture, the molecular weights of water and of the recurring structural unit of the chain, and the proportion (p) of carboxyl groups in the mixture that has been esterified.

(ii) The concentration of free carboxyl and free hydroxyl groups in the mixture will be proportional to $(1-p)$ at any given time.

The carboxyl group concentration enters the rate expression to the second power because in the absence of a strong acid a second molecule of the carboxylic acid undergoing esterification must function as a catalyst.

Spectroscopy and Molecular Structure

---

115 THE DIPOLE MOMENT OF GASEOUS HYDROGEN CHLORIDE

C. T. Zahn, *Phys. Rev.*, **24**, 400, 1924.

The dielectric constant of gaseous hydrogen chloride measured by a heterodyne beat method at atmospheric pressure over a range of temperatures is tabulated below:

Temperature (°K) T	(Dielectric Constant -1), corrected to atmos. pressure $\epsilon - 1$	Specific volume of gas relative to n.t.p. v
201·4	0·007452	0·733
294·2	0·003792	1·079
433·9	0·001948	1·594
588·8	0·001182	2·162

(i) Plot $(\epsilon - 1)vT$ against T and hence calculate the dipole moment of the hydrogen chloride molecule.

(ii) Compare the result with the product of the electronic charge and the internuclear distance as calculated from the moment of inertia of the molecule derived from the far infra-red absorption spectrum (cf. Problem 118). The spectroscopic data give a moment of inertia of $2·68 \times 10^{-40}$ c.g.s. units.

NOTE: These data are taken from one of the earlier measurements of dipole moment; the graph suggested treats the denominator of

$\dfrac{\epsilon-1}{\epsilon+2}$ as constant. Arithmetical labour is saved by using the numerical value $1 \cdot 27 \times 10^{-20}$ for $\sqrt{\left(\dfrac{9k}{4\pi N}\right)}$.

The temperature variation of the dielectric constant of a substance in the vapour phase represents a reliable method of measuring dipole moments. The experimental difficulties are considerable, however, and relatively little work of this kind has been done. Most dipole moments have been measured in solution, but the methods used involve many systematic errors which are difficult to avoid. See, for example, L. E. Sutton, *Determination of Organic Structures by Physical Methods*, ed. by E. A. Braude and F. C. Nachod (Academic Press, New York, 1955), ch. 9. The most accurate and reliable values of dipole moments come from microwave spectroscopy. See, for example, C. H. Townes and A. L. Shawlow, *Microwave Spectroscopy* (McGraw-Hill, New York, 1955), W. Gordy, W. V. Smith, and R. F. Trambarulo, *Microwave Spectroscopy* (Wiley, New York, 1953).

116 FORCE CONSTANTS OF DIATOMIC MOLECULES

The fundamental vibration frequencies (cm^{-1}) of some diatomic molecules are:

F_2^{19} 891·8,	Cl_2^{35} 564·9,	$Br^{79}Br^{81}$ 323·2,	I_2^{127} 214·36
HF 4141·305,	HCl^{35} 2988·95,	HBr^{81} 2649·67,	
HI^{127} 2309·5,	H_2 4405·3		

Calculate the force constants and comment on their values.

Use

$$
\begin{aligned}
H &= 1 \cdot 00813 \\
F &= 19 \cdot 00454 \\
Cl^{35} &= 34 \cdot 97867 \\
Br^{81} &= 80 \cdot 926 \\
Br^{79} &= 78 \cdot 929 \\
I^{127} &= 126 \cdot 932
\end{aligned}
$$

NOTE: Although these values are known with great accuracy, it is sufficient to use four-figure logs to illustrate the point of this problem.

117 FORCE CONSTANTS FROM RAMAN SPECTRA

A. Petrikaln and J. Hochberg, *Z. physik. Chem.* B, **4**, 299, 1929; L. A. Woodward, *Phil. Mag.*, **18**, 823, 1934.

When illuminated by the two mercury lines 4358·3 and 4046·6 Å, concentrated aqueous solutions of potassium cyanide give a Raman spectrum consisting of two lines of wave-lengths 4793·5 and 4419·2 Å respectively.

(i) Calculate the force-constant for the carbon–nitrogen link.

The Raman spectrum of acetylene consists of a strong line with a frequency displacement of 1960 cm^{-1}. This line is attributed to the vibration of the carbon–carbon linkage.

(ii) Calculate the force constant of the acetylenic linkage.

When using the mercury line 4358·3 Å as the exciting line, a strong aqueous solution of mercurous nitrate gave a Raman spectrum as follows—4326·2; 4390·5; 4500·2; 4566·1 Å. The vibration frequencies of 723 and 1044 cm^{-1} are characteristic of the nitrate ion.

(iii) Calculate the force constant of the Hg_2^{++} ion.

NOTE: In this problem it is assumed that these two stretching vibrations are localized in the multiple bonds. In these cases this approximation is a good one.

J. A. Hibben, *The Raman Effect and its Application* (Reinhold, New York, 1939); L. A. Woodward, *Quart. Rev.*, **10**, 185, 1956; G. Herzberg, *Infra-red and Raman Spectra of Polyatomic Molecules* (Van Nostrand, New York, 1945).

118 THE DIMENSIONS OF THE HYDROGEN CHLORIDE MOLECULE FROM ITS ROTATION SPECTRUM

M. Czerny, *Z. Physik.*, **34**, 227, 1925.

The rotation spectrum of hydrogen chloride consists of a series of lines in the far infra-red of which the lowest wave-numbers observed were:

$$124{\cdot}30 \text{ cm}^{-1}$$
$$145{\cdot}03 \quad ,,$$
$$165{\cdot}51 \quad ,,$$

Calculate the moment of inertia of the molecule, and hence the internuclear distance.

NOTE: The collision diameter of the hydrogen chloride molecule derived from viscosity measurements is $2{\cdot}86$ Å. Cf. Problems 119 and 120.

119 MICROWAVE SPECTRA OF CAESIUM CHLORIDE VAPOUR

A. Honig, M. L. Stitch, and M. Mandel, *Phys. Rev.*, **92**, 901, 1953.

At 715° C caesium chloride has a large enough vapour pressure to give microwave absorption. The low vibration frequency allows enough molecules to occupy excited vibrational levels at this temperature to permit rotational lines to be observed in the excited states.

The table gives the frequencies of the $J = 5 \longrightarrow 6$ pure rotational transitions in various vibrational levels, v.

v	$CsCl^{35}$ (Mc/sec)	v	$CsCl^{37}$ (Mc/sec)
0	25873·11	0	24767·86
1	25752·16	1	24654·26

v	CsCl³⁵ (Mc/sec)	v	CsCl³⁷ (Mc/sec)
2	25631·58	2	24541·40
3	25511·25		
4	25390·36		
5	25270·00		
6	25150·1		
7	25031·0		
8	24911·2		

(i) Find B_0, B_e, and r_e for these two molecules.

(ii) Calculate r_0, r_4, r_8 for CsCl³⁵ and compare these values with r_e.

$$\text{Use } Cl^{35} = 34\cdot98$$
$$Cl^{37} = 36\cdot98$$
$$Cs = 132\cdot91$$

NOTE: The frequencies of microwave absorption lines can be measured very accurately. For polyatomic molecules it is usually necessary to use the moments of inertia of isotopic species to calculate all the molecular parameters. The values of r_e of isotopic molecules are the same for a given bond but the values of r_0 are significantly different, as illustrated in this problem. CsCl is a particularly favourable case for observing rotational spectra in excited vibrational states; this is often not possible in other molecules and so the accuracy of the molecular parameters is limited by the availability of r_0 values only.

It is desirable to carry the calculation to five figures.

120 VIBRATION–ROTATION SPECTRUM OF HCL AND DCL

I. M. Mills, H. W. Thompson, and R. L. Williams, *Proc. Roy. Soc.* A, **218**, 29, 1953; J. Pickworth and H. W. Thompson, ibid., **218**, 37, 1953.

The frequencies of some of the vibration–rotation lines of these molecules are given in the table.

HCl³⁵ (cm⁻¹)	DCl³⁵ (cm⁻¹)
2998·05	2150·93
2981·05	2141·53
2963·35	2131·91
2944·99	2122·05
2925·92	2111·94
2906·25	2101·60

HCl^{35} (cm^{-1})	DCl^{35} (cm^{-1})
2865·14	2080·26
2843·63	2069·24
2821·59	2058·02
2799·00	2046·58
2775·77	2034·95
2752·01	2023·12
2727·75	2011·03

(i) Find the origins of the two bands and the fundamental vibration frequencies of HCl^{35} and DCl^{35}. The overtone vibrations of these molecules occur at 5668 and 8347 cm^{-1} and 4125·5 and 6108·5 cm^{-1} respectively. Calculate the force constant of the HCl link and the anharmonicity constants for HCl and DCl.

(ii) Assign the rotational lines to the P and R branches.

(iii) Obtain B_0 and B_1 for HCl^{35} and for DCl^{35}.

(iv) Find B_e from B_0 and B_1 for each molecule and calculate the equilibrium internuclear distance.

(v) Calculate r_0 and r_e for HCl^{35} and DCl^{35} and comment on their values.

NOTE: Use H = 1·008, D = 2·015, Cl^{35} = 34·98.

The simple difference plot of $R(J-1)-P(J+1)$ against $(J+\frac{1}{2})$ does not give a perfectly straight line because of centrifugal stretching of the molecule in the higher rotational levels. It is therefore necessary to use the equation

$$\Delta_2 F(J) = (4B-6D)(J+\tfrac{1}{2})-8D(J+\tfrac{1}{2})^3$$

where $\Delta_2 F(J)$ is $R(J-1)-P(J+1)$ or $R(J)-P(J)$, and D is the centrifugal stretching constant.

One then plots $\dfrac{\Delta_2 F(J)}{(J+\frac{1}{2})}$ against $(J+\frac{1}{2})^2$ for the two sets of differences and so obtains B_0, D_0, B_1, and D_1.

This is a laborious procedure and the student can obtain an approximate answer for B_0 and B_1 by using only the first rotational lines (for example $R(0)-P(2)$) where centrifugal stretching is very small.

$$\frac{4\pi^2 c^2}{N} = 5·8901 \times 10^{-2}$$

$$\frac{Nh}{8\pi^2} = 5·0536 \times 10^{-5}$$

References: G. Herzberg, *Molecular Spectra: vol. i. Diatomic Molecules* (Van Nostrand, New York, 1950).

121^* THE ROTATION–VIBRATION SPECTRUM OF HF

D. E. Kirkpatrick and E. O. Salant, *Phys. Rev.*, **48**, 945, 1935.

The wave-numbers (cm^{-1}, *in vacuo*) of *consecutive* lines in the absorption spectrum of HF vapour in the photographic infra-red and red regions of the spectrum are as follows:

11534·75	11409·45	14951·70
535·72	331·78	947·05
531·81	286·24	936·02
523·15	236·27	918·99
509·78	182·00	895·94
491·70	123·43	866·79
468·95	060·21	790·62
441·52		743·59
		690·70
		632·03
		567·70

(i) Assign vibrational and rotational quantum numbers by inspection.

(ii) Check your analysis of the two bands by the combination principle.

(iii) Determine the rotational constants in the ground vibrational level and in the other two levels.

(iv) Find the vibration frequency and the anharmonic constant.

(v) Obtain the equilibrium internuclear distance and the force constant.

(vi) Estimate the energy of dissociation.

NOTE: Plot $\dfrac{\Delta_2 F(J)}{(J+\frac{1}{2})}$ against $(J+\frac{1}{2})^2$ as indicated in the note to problem 120, and hence find B_v and D_v for the three vibrational levels.

Express $R(J-1)+P(J)$ in terms of ν_0, B', B'', D' and D'' and plot $R(J-1)+P(J)+2(B'-B'')J^2$ against $J^2(J^2+1)$, and hence obtain ν_0. It is desirable to carry the calculations to five figures. The methods are fully described in G. Herzberg, *Molecular Spectra: vol. i. Diatomic Molecules* (Van Nostrand, New York, 1950). On page 106 it is shown that $D = 4B^3/\omega^2$.

122
THE HEAT OF DISSOCIATION OF CHLORINE FROM ITS ABSORPTION SPECTRUM

H. Kuhn, *Z. Physik.*, **39**, 77, 1926.

The beginning of the continuum in the visible absorption spectrum of chlorine is at 4785 Å. One of the atoms produced has an energy of excitation estimated by L. A. Turner (*Phys. Rev.*, **27**, 397, 1926) from the arc spectrum of the gas as 0·109 volts.

Calculate the heat of dissociation of chlorine into normal atoms (i) in volts; (ii) in kilocalories per mole.

NOTE: Heats of dissociation are sometimes expressed in units more strictly applicable to critical potentials; a molecule is said to have a heat of dissociation of x volts when the energy required to dissociate a single molecule is x electron-volts. Interconversion with the other units commonly used (calories/mole and reciprocal centimetres) is readily performed with the aid of the factors in the table of constants at the end of the book.

123
THE HEAT OF DISSOCIATION OF THE DIATOMIC SODIUM MOLECULE FROM SPECTROSCOPIC DATA

W. Jevons, *Band Spectra of Diatomic Molecules* (Cambridge, 1932), ch. ix.

Sodium vapour has a system of absorption bands in the green, the origin of the 0,0 band being at $20302 \cdot 6$ cm^{-1}. The vibration levels in the upper state can be followed to very near the convergence point leading to a value of 0·35 volts for the dissociation energy in the upper state, the product of the dissociation being a normal atom and an atom excited to the level of the well-known D-line (5893 Å).

Find the heat of dissociation of the Na$_2$ molecule in the ground state.

NOTE: This problem is readily visualized if a diagram of the potential energy curves of the two states of the molecule is sketched and the various energy differences are referred to this diagram.

124 THE HEAT OF DISSOCIATION OF CARBON MONOXIDE FROM ITS VIBRATIONAL ENERGY LEVELS

R. T. Birge and H. Sponer, *Phys. Rev.*, **28**, 259, 1926.

The so-called 'fourth positive group of carbon', a series of absorption bands now known to be due to the carbon monoxide molecule, leads on analysis to the following equation for the vibrational energy levels in the ground state:

$$G_v = 2167 \cdot 4(v + \tfrac{1}{2}) - 12 \cdot 70(v + \tfrac{1}{2})^2,$$

where G_v is the vibrational energy term (in wave-number units) for the vibrational quantum number v, as derived from the measurement of lines ranging from $v = 0$ to $v = 25$.

Calculate the heat of dissociation of carbon monoxide.

NOTE: This method of calculating the heat of dissociation is liable to error, since it necessarily assumes that the equation for the vibrational energy level, based on the measurement of lines up to a vibration quantum number of 25, is equally valid up to the much higher quantum number corresponding to the convergence limit. In the case of carbon monoxide the error on this account is probably small.

The heat of dissociation of CO has been subjected to a very searching examination, as it had an important bearing on the heat of sublimation of carbon. For a discussion of this important problem see A. G. Gaydon, *Dissociation Energies and Spectra of Diatomic Molecules* (Chapman & Hall, London, 1953); T. E. Brackett, *J. Chem. Phys.*, **24**, 1103, 1956; L. Brewer and A. Searcy, *Ann. Rev. Phys. Chem.*, **7**, 259, 1956; D. M. Kern, *J. Chem. Ed.*, **33**, 272, 1956.

125 DISSOCIATION ENERGY OF OXYGEN

P. Brix and G. Herzberg, *Can. J. Phys.*, **32**, 110, 1954.

Brix and Herzberg studied the Schumann–Runge absorption bands of oxygen and obtained the frequencies of transitions from the lowest level of the ground state ($^3\Sigma_g^-$) to the vibrational levels (v') of the ($^3\Sigma_u^-$) excited state.

v'	ν_0 (cm^{-1})
0	49357·6
1	50045·6
2	50710·7
3	51352·2
4	51969·8
5	52561·6
6	53122·8
7	53656·8
8	54158·9
9	54624·4
10	55053·3
11	55441·5
12	55784·6
13	56085·5
14	56340·5
15	56550·5
16	56719·5
17	56852·4
18	56954·5
19	57030·2
20	57082·8
21	57114·8

(i) Plot the values of $\Delta G'_{v+\frac{1}{2}}$ against $v' + \frac{1}{2}$, where $\Delta G'$ is the spacing between adjacent vibrational levels of the upper state and v' is the vibrational quantum number of the upper state. Find the dissociation energies, D_0 and D_e of the $^3\Sigma_u^-$ state.

A weaker absorption band system was also observed in the near ultra-violet which is due to a $^3\Sigma_u^+ \longleftarrow {}^3\Sigma_g^-$ transition. The $^3\Sigma_u^+$ state has a dissociation limit at 41259 cm^{-1}. The lowest atomic energy levels of oxygen are:

^3P ground state; ^1D 1·967 eV; ^1S 4·190 eV

According to the Wigner–Witmer rules two singlet atoms cannot give rise to a triplet molecular state.

(ii) From the convergence limit you have found for the $^3\Sigma_u^-$ state, and that given for the $^3\Sigma_u^+$ state, identify the dissociation products of the $^3\Sigma_u^-$ state.

(iii) Obtain D_0 for the $^3\Sigma_g^-$ (ground) state of oxygen.

NOTE: This is a simple example of the determination of accurate energies of dissociation from spectroscopic measurements. The methods used in more complicated cases are described in G. Herzberg, *Molecular Spectra: Diatomic Molecules* (Van Nostrand, New York, 1950), ch. 7.

The potential energy curves for these states of oxygen are shown in this chapter.

126 INFRA-RED AND RAMAN SPECTRA OF SIMPLE MOLECULES

G. Herzberg, *Infra-red and Raman Spectra of Polyatomic Molecules* (Van Nostrand, New York, 1945); L. A. Woodward, *Quarterly Reviews,* **10**, 185, 1956.

The vibration frequencies of simple molecules can be found from infra-red and from Raman spectra. The selection rules which control the activity of a vibrational mode in these spectra depend on the symmetry of the molecule.

Sometimes the physical properties of the substance do not permit both the infra-red and the Raman spectrum to be observed, sometimes a line is so weak as not to be observed in the Raman effect, and sometimes extra lines appear as overtones, combination frequencies, or as a result of Fermi resonance. In spite of these difficulties the shapes of simple molecules can often be established from the presence or absence of vibrational frequencies. The following examples provide simple exercises of this kind.

Deduce the shapes of the following molecules from the fundamental frequencies observed.

	i.r. (cm^{-1})	Raman (cm^{-1})
CO_2 . . .	680, 2350	1283
N_2O . . .	588, 1285, 2223	not observed, 1286p, 2223dp
$ZnCl_2$ in non-aqueous solution . .	not studied	305, i.a., i.a.
$ZnBr_2$ in non-aqueous solution . .	,, ,,	208, i.a., i.a.
ZnI_2 in non-aqueous solution . .	,, ,,	163, i.a., i.a.
SCl_2 liquid . .		208p, 514p, 535dp
NO_2^- . . .		813p, 1240 dp, 1331·3p
NO_3^- . . .	830, 678, 1350	720, 1050, 1360
NF_3 . . .	497, 642, 907, 1031	515, 667, 905, 1050

In the table, p means that the Raman line remains polarized, dp means that it is depolarized, i.a. means that the vibration is inactive.

SECTION NINE

Crystal Structure

(by Professor D. Hodgkin)

The following textbooks may be found useful in connexion with problems in this section:

W. J. Moore, *Physical Chemistry* (Prentice-Hall, Englewood Cliffs, 1962).
C. W. Bunn, *Chemical Crystallography* (Oxford, 1961).
K. Lonsdale, *Crystals and Atoms* (G. Bell & Sons, London, 1948).
W. L. Bragg, *The Crystalline State*, Part I (G. Bell & Sons, London, 1933).

---

127 THE WAVE-LENGTH OF PALLADIUM K_a X-RADIATION

W. H. Bragg, *Proc. Roy. Soc.* A, **89**, 246, 430, 1913;
W. L. Bragg, ibid., **89**, 248, 1913.

The structure of the unit cube of sodium chloride is shown in the diagram:

● chlorine.
○ sodium.

The unit cell of sodium chloride

(i) What is the molecular weight of NaCl associated with this cube?

(ii) Given that the density (ρ) of sodium chloride is 2·17, calculate the side of the unit cell (a) from the relation

$$\rho = \frac{Mm}{V},$$

190

where M is the mol. wt. of NaCl in the cell, m is the mass of the hydrogen atom $= 1 \cdot 662 \times 10^{-24}$ g, and V is the volume of the unit cell $= a^3$.

(iii) The observed angle θ, at which X-rays are first reflected from the cube face of sodium chloride (100) is $6° \, 1'$ for Pd K_a radiation.

Calculate the wave-length of the X-rays from Bragg's law

$$n\lambda = 2d \sin \theta,$$

n being the order of the reflection (2 in this case),[1] λ the wave-length of the X-rays, and d the spacing of the plane (equal here to a).

128* THE ATOMIC SCATTERING CURVES OF SODIUM, CHLORINE, AND FLUORINE

W. L. Bragg, R. W. James, and C. S. Bosanquet, *Phil. Mag.*, **41**, 309, 1921; **42**, 1, 1921; R. Havighurst, *Phys. Rev.*, **28**, 869, 1926.

For the rock salt type of structure the geometrical structure factor for any reflecting plane simplifies to one or other of the two forms $f_A + f_B$ or $f_A - f_B$, where f_A and f_B are the scattering factors of the two contributing atoms at the angle of reflection.

The table gives the experimentally observed structure factors, $F_{\mathrm{obs.}}$, for reflections from planes of sodium chloride and sodium fluoride. Plot these values for NaCl and NaF against the half-spacing $\sin \theta / \lambda$. From the curves for $f_{\mathrm{Cl}} + f_{\mathrm{Na}}$, $f_{\mathrm{Cl}} - f_{\mathrm{Na}}$ and of $f_{\mathrm{Na}} + f_{\mathrm{F}}$, $f_{\mathrm{Na}} - f_{\mathrm{F}}$, determine by addition and subtraction of the corresponding ordinates the values of $f_{\mathrm{Cl}}, f_{\mathrm{Na}}, f_{\mathrm{F}}$ at values of $\sin \theta / \lambda = 0 \cdot 1, \, 0 \cdot 2, \, 0 \cdot 3$, &c. Compare the values of f_{Na} derived from the two compounds.

---

[1] Owing to the arrangement of the atoms in sodium chloride no first-order reflection occurs.

	NaCl			NaF	
Spectrum	$\dfrac{\sin\theta}{\lambda}$	$F_{\text{obs.}}$	Spectrum	$\dfrac{\sin\theta}{\lambda}$	$F_{\text{obs.}}$
111	0·154	4·54	111	0·188	1·27
200	0·178	20·65	200	0·217	14·25
220	0·253	15·62	220	0·306	10·80
311	0·295	2·44	311	0·359	1·38
222	0·307	13·18	222	0·375	8·39
400	0·355	11·60	400	0·432	6·59
333	0·462	2·28	331	0·472	1·46
511	0·462	2·32	420	0·483	5·51
440	0·502	7·46	422	0·531	4·75
600	0·533	6·89	511+333	0·562	1·06
444	0·614	5·28	440	0·610	3·46
711	0·633	2·03	600+244	0·648	3·04
800	0·711	4·04	620	0·684	2·55
660	0·755	3·34	622	0·718	2·38
555	0·770	1·53	642	0·810	1·86
933	0·883	1·12	553+731	0·831	0·39
1000	0·888	2·22	820+644	0·894	1·41
880	1·01	1·55	822+660	0·918	1·33
1200	1·07	1·12	840	0·968	1·22
777	1·08	0·56	842	0·993	1·03
1244	1·18	0·70	664	1·015	0·92

129 THE MOLECULAR WEIGHT AND SYMMETRY OF NICKEL PHTHALOCYANINE

J. M. Robertson, R. P. Linstead, and C. E. Dent, *Nature*, **135**, 506, 1935; J. M. Robertson, *J. Chem. Soc.*, 615, 1935; 1195, 1936; 219, 1937.

Write down the general form of the structure factor for crystal structures in which there are the three following symmetry operations taken separately:

(i) A centre of symmetry (i.e. for every atom at x, y, z there is one at $\bar{x}$, $\bar{y}$, $\bar{z}$).

(ii) A diad screw axis of symmetry (i.e. for every atom at x, y, z there is one at $\bar{x}$, $y+\frac{1}{2}$, $\bar{z}$ where b is the screw axis).

(iii) A glide plane of symmetry (i.e. for every atom at x, y, z there is one at $x+\frac{1}{2}$, $\bar{y}$, z, where the reflection plane is b (010) and the glide is parallel to the a axis).

(iv) In which cases do simplifications result for planes of the type $0k0$ with k odd, and of the type $h0l$ with h odd?

(v) Draw a projection on the b plane of a crystal unit cell showing the symmetry operations of (ii) and (iii) combined. Mark the three additional positions in the cell that must be occupied if one atom is placed at x, y, z (the 'general' positions corresponding to these symmetry operations). With this combination an additional symmetry operation, that of a centre of symmetry, appears. What are the coordinates of the centres of symmetry in your projection?

The unit cell dimensions of nickel phthalocyanine are $a = 19\cdot9$, $b = 4\cdot71$, $c = 14\cdot9$ Å, $\beta = 121\cdot9°$, and the density found is $1\cdot63$. The percentage of nickel is $10\cdot5$ per cent.

(vi) Calculate the molecular weight of phthalocyanine present in the unit cell and the number of nickel atoms. (The volume of the cell is $abc \sin \beta$.)

It is found that all $h0l$ reflections are absent for which h is odd and all $0k0$ reflections for which k is odd. (Space group P $2_1/a$.)

(vii) Calculate the maximum molecular weight of the phthalocyanine molecule from the crystallographic data, and compare it with the minimum molecular weight indicated by the chemical analysis.

(viii) Hence deduce the minimum molecular symmetry and the positions of the nickel atoms in the cell.

130* THE FOURIER REPRESENTATION OF THE DEPENDENCE OF ATOMIC VIBRATION ON TEMPERATURE IN SODIUM CHLORIDE

R. W. James and E. M. Firth, *Proc. Roy. Soc.* A, **117**, 62, 1928; cf. W. H. Bragg, *Phil. Trans.* A, **215**, 253, 1915; W. L. Bragg, *Proc. Roy. Soc.* A, **123**, 537, 1929.

The electron density in sheets parallel to a given crystal plane can be expressed as the sum of a Fourier series in which the observed F values for orders of reflections from the plane are introduced as coefficients of the terms.

$$\rho_x = \frac{1}{d} \sum_{-\infty}^{\infty} F_n \cos 2\pi n \frac{x}{d},$$

or

$$\rho_x = \frac{Z_0}{d} + \frac{2}{d} \sum_{n=1}^{n=\infty} F_n \cos 2\pi n \frac{x}{d},$$

where ρ_x is the electron density at a distance x from the origin and Z_0, the number of electrons in the cell, is the contribution of the first term of the series, F_{000}.

F observed. Rock salt

	$T = 86° K$	$T = 290° K$	$T = 900° K$
111	4·61	4·54	4·11
222	14·45	13·18	8·98
333	2·60	2·30	0·93
444	7·18	5·28	1·09
555	2·22	1·53	0·12
666	4·12	2·00	0·05
777	1·19	0·56	0·004
888	1·90	0·50	. .
999	0·30	0·01	. .
10, 10, 10	0·32	. .	. .

The table above gives the F values ($f_{Cl} + f_{Na}$ or $f_{Cl} - f_{Na}$) observed by James and Firth for reflections from the (111) plane of rock salt at three different temperatures, 86° K, 290° K, and 900° K. Calculate the electron density normal to (111) at intervals of $2\pi x/d = 10°$, using the table of cosines given on p. 259. Plot this against x/d for each of the three temperatures and compare the three curves. Take $d = 3\cdot25$ Å and $Z_0 = 11+17$ or 28.

131* THE CRYSTAL STRUCTURE OF IRON PYRITES

W. L. Bragg, *Proc. Roy. Soc.* A, **88**, 428, 1913; **89**, 468, 1914; P. P. Ewald and W. Friedrich, *Ann. d. Physik.*, **44**, 1183, 1914; H. M. Parker and W. J. Whitehouse, *Phil. Mag.*, **14**, 939, 1932.

Iron pyrites crystallizes in the cubic space group $Pa\,3$; the side of the unit cell is 5·405 Å and this unit contains 4 FeS_2. From these conditions it follows that the parameters of the atoms must be

Fe: $\frac{1}{2}$, 0, 0; 0, $\frac{1}{2}$, 0; 0, 0, $\frac{1}{2}$; $\frac{1}{2}$, $\frac{1}{2}$, $\frac{1}{2}$.

S: $\pm(u,\,u,\,u)$; $\pm(\frac{1}{2}+u,\,\frac{1}{2}-u,\,u)$;

$\pm(u,\,\frac{1}{2}+u,\,\frac{1}{2}-u)$; $\pm(\frac{1}{2}-u,\,u,\,\frac{1}{2}+u)$.

(i) Write down the structure factor for the general reflections of the type hkl. Show that for reflections of the type $h00$ when h is even it reduces to the form

$$4(f_{Fe}+2f_S \cos 2\pi hu).$$

(ii) Plot curves to show the variation of the structure factors of the planes 200, 400, 600, 800, 1000, with values of u from 0 to 0·25.

Atomic scattering factors calculated for iron and sulphur at the angle of reflection for each of these planes are given in the table overleaf. From the observed F values also recorded deduce the most probable value for u. These F values are given equal to $f_{Fe}+2f_S \cos 2\pi hu$. A table of values of $\cos 2\pi n(x/d)$ for a series of values of n and x/d is given on p. 259.

Plane	200	400	600	800	1000
f_{Fe}	19·5	14·0	10·8	8·6	7·0
f_S	10·7	7·9	6·2	4·95	3·8
$F_{obs.}$	22·4	1·3	5·8	16·0	9·3

(iii) Using the values of u found, calculate F values and compare these with the observed F values. Evaluate R, the discrepancy factor or mean residual,

$$R = \frac{\Sigma \left[| F_{obs.} | - | F_{calc.} | \right]}{\Sigma \left[| F_{obs.} | \right]}.$$

(iv) Your calculation in (iii) will indicate the phase constants to be attached to each observed reflection; these are 0 or 180° since the structure is centrosymmetric, and appear as positive or negative signs attached to the calculated F values. Calculate the electron density distribution, ρ_x, in sheets parallel with the (100) planes in pyrites ($d = 5·405$ Å) by evaluating the Fourier series

$$\rho_x = \frac{1}{d}\left\{ F_{000} + 2 \sum_{0}^{h} F_{h00} \left(\cos 2\pi h x/d \right) \right\}.$$

F_{000} is the number of electrons in the unit cell corresponding with the composition 4 FeS_2, F_{h00}, the observed F values of the table in (ii), multiplied by 4, with the signs found by calculation in (iii); you may carry out the calculation for $\rho_x/4$ using F_{obs} as given, and F_{000} corresponding with FeS_2. Compare the value of u indicated by the electron density distribution with that obtained by trial.

(v) Calculate the Patterson distribution

$$P_x = \sum_{0}^{h} F_{h00}^2 \cos 2\pi h x/d$$

from the observed F_{h00} values squared and compare this with the electron distribution in (iv). (It is usual to calculate this series in this form from F^2 values derived directly from the measured intensities, often on an arbitrary scale, without the addition of the F_{000}^2 term or division by $1/d$). The peaks in this series should correspond with the vector

196

distances between atoms in the crystal; they provide an alternative route for the solution of the structure to the trial process of (ii). Derive the positions to be expected from your structure analysis for the Fe–Fe, Fe–S, and S–S vector distances, projected from the origin normal to (100), and compare these with the peak positions in P_x.

(vi) Using your preferred value of u, and the coordinates and cell size given above, calculate the distances of nearest approach, Fe–S and S–S. Compare these with the sum of the ionic and covalent radii:

$$Fe^{++} = 0.83, \quad S^{--} = 1.84, \quad Fe = 1.23, \quad S = 1.04 \text{ Å}.$$

132 THE CRYSTAL STRUCTURE OF PENTABORANE, B₅H₉

W. J. Dulmage and W. N. Lipscomb, *Acta Cryst.*, **5**, 260, 1952; A. L. Patterson, *Z. Krist.*, **90**, 517, 1935.

Pentaborane crystallizes in tetragonal crystals; the observed reflections show that the lattice is body centred and that there are mirror planes in the crystal parallel with the (100) and (010). The crystals are pyroelectric and therefore can have no centre of symmetry; the space group accordingly is I 4 mm. The unit cell dimensions, measured at $-115°$ C, are $a = 7.16 \pm 0.02$ Å, $c = 5.38 \pm 0.02$ Å; volume relations require that n, the number of molecules in the unit cell, is 2. From these observations, it follows that the molecule itself must have tetragonal symmetry.

(i) Consider possible ways of arranging the five boron atoms in space consistent with the presence in the pattern of a four-fold axis of symmetry. Sketch diagrammatic projections of your proposed structures (*a*) parallel with the four-fold axis (the *c* axis), (*b*) at right angles with this axis, parallel with a mirror plane in the structure.

(ii) Make a sketch of the vector distribution you would expect to see in the two projected views of your proposed structure. (These may be constructed graphically if desired, on tracing paper, setting the origin of the vector map on each atom in turn of the proposed structure and plotting around it the positions of the remaining atoms. The orientation of the molecular axes must be held parallel throughout in the projected structure and vector map.) Note that the vector map has a centre of symmetry, whether the structure has or not.

(iii) The figure fields 1 and 2 were calculated from the observed F^2 values for pentaborane by the relation

$$Pxy = \Sigma\, F_{hk0}^2 \cos\, 2\pi(hx+ky),$$

and
$$Pyz = \Sigma\, F_{0kl}^2 \cos\, 2\pi(ky+lz)$$

respectively. According to Patterson's relation, they should show peaks corresponding with the inter-atomic vectors in the crystal seen in projection along c and a. x, y, and z are here the fractional coordinates, at intervals of $\frac{1}{30}\, a$ and b and $\frac{1}{24}\, c$.

Plot the distributions on a grid drawn to a convenient scale (e.g. 2 cm or 1 in. = 1 Å) and sketch in contours at intervals such as 20. The figure fields correspond with $\frac{1}{8}$ of the unit cell and may be repeated over the whole projected area according to the symmetry elements of the crystal. (It is convenient to do this on tracing paper.) Compare the calculated plots with your theoretical diagrams. From observations on the stronger peaks alone derive the probable parameters of the boron atoms in the crystal. Owing to the limited experimental data obtained on the crystals the weaker peaks are a little confused by diffraction ripples as well as showing B–H vectors and the stronger peaks cannot be expected to have exactly the theoretical relative weights.

(iv) The figure fields 3 and 4 show the electron density projections, ρxy and ρyz, computed at the same intervals in a, b, and c from the observed F values and phase constants derived by Dulmage and Lipscomb. Plot the figure fields on the same scale as 1 and 2 and contour at intervals of 1 e/Å². Derive parameters for the boron atoms from the peak positions and compare these with the results of (iii). From the three-dimensional electron density distribution, Dulmage and Lipscomb give the parameters of the hydrogen atoms as follows:

	x	y	z
H_1 . . .	0·000	0·000	0·427
H_2 . . .	0·328 ± 0·006	0·000	0·092 ± 0·009†
H_3 . . .	0·136 ± 0·006	0·136 ± 0·006	−0·165 ± 0·009†

† and positions related by the four-fold axis.

Compare these with the peak positions in the projections. Calculate the B–B and B–H distances in pentaborane.

B_5H_9 1. *Patterson projection, Pxy*

	y $\tfrac{1}{2}$															0
	y 0															$\tfrac{1}{2}$
x x																
$\tfrac{1}{2}$ 0	150	113	46	21	46	64	41	3	$\overline{12}$	$\overline{5}$	4	$\overline{6}$	$\overline{18}$	$\overline{20}$	$\overline{14}$	$\overline{10}$
	113	83	29	13	36	49	23	$\overline{11}$	$\overline{19}$	$\overline{6}$	0	$\overline{10}$	$\overline{23}$	$\overline{24}$	$\overline{18}$	$\overline{14}$
	46	29	3	3	21	21	$\overline{7}$	$\overline{32}$	$\overline{28}$	$\overline{11}$	$\overline{8}$	$\overline{21}$	$\overline{33}$	$\overline{32}$	$\overline{24}$	$\overline{20}$
	21	13	3	10	21	13	$\overline{13}$	$\overline{30}$	$\overline{23}$	$\overline{11}$	$\overline{15}$	$\overline{30}$	$\overline{38}$	$\overline{33}$	$\overline{23}$	$\overline{18}$
	46	36	21	21	30	27	8	$\overline{7}$	$\overline{8}$	$\overline{7}$	$\overline{15}$	$\overline{27}$	$\overline{30}$	$\overline{21}$	$\overline{10}$	$\overline{6}$
	64	49	21	13	27	36	26	7	$\overline{4}$	$\overline{7}$	$\overline{10}$	$\overline{15}$	$\overline{15}$	7	0	4
	41	23	$\overline{7}$	$\overline{13}$	8	26	17	$\overline{8}$	$\overline{21}$	$\overline{17}$	$\overline{7}$	$\overline{7}$	$\overline{11}$	$\overline{11}$	$\overline{6}$	$\overline{5}$
$\tfrac{1}{4}$ $\tfrac{1}{4}$	3	$\overline{11}$	$\overline{32}$	$\overline{30}$	$\overline{7}$	7	$\overline{8}$	$\overline{33}$	$\overline{39}$	$\overline{21}$	$\overline{4}$	8	$\overline{23}$	$\overline{28}$	$\overline{19}$	$\overline{12}$

2. *Patterson projection, Pyz*

	y $\tfrac{1}{2}$															0
	y 0															$\tfrac{1}{2}$
z z																
$\tfrac{1}{2}$ 0	218	146	16	$\overline{25}$	49	124	104	116	$\overline{43}$	$\overline{31}$	5	16	$\overline{5}$	$\overline{29}$	$\overline{39}$	$\overline{39}$
	147	92	5	$\overline{16}$	37	79	50	$\overline{13}$	$\overline{37}$	$\overline{13}$	9	$\overline{3}$	$\overline{31}$	$\overline{39}$	$\overline{28}$	$\overline{16}$
	18	7	$\overline{5}$	6	21	6	$\overline{34}$	$\overline{50}$	$\overline{20}$	18	14	$\overline{28}$	$\overline{59}$	$\overline{45}$	$\overline{3}$	20
	$\overline{3}$	7	9	22	20	$\overline{5}$	$\overline{33}$	$\overline{32}$	$\overline{5}$	15	5	$\overline{22}$	$\overline{35}$	$\overline{24}$	$\overline{3}$	7
	59	47	23	10	15	26	26	12	$\overline{12}$	$\overline{29}$	$\overline{27}$	$\overline{5}$	12	0	$\overline{33}$	$\overline{51}$
	68	50	10	$\overline{15}$	$\overline{7}$	20	35	16	$\overline{27}$	$\overline{49}$	$\overline{50}$	$\overline{10}$	17	$\overline{1}$	$\overline{49}$	$\overline{74}$
$\tfrac{1}{4}$ $\tfrac{1}{4}$	$\overline{10}$	$\overline{8}$	$\overline{5}$	$\overline{10}$	$\overline{21}$	$\overline{27}$	$\overline{22}$	$\overline{14}$	$\overline{14}$	$\overline{22}$	$\overline{27}$	$\overline{21}$	$\overline{10}$	$\overline{5}$	$\overline{8}$	$\overline{10}$

B_5H_9.   3. *Electron density projection, ρxy*

Here and in 4, the figures give 10 e/Å²

	y $\tfrac{1}{2}$															0
	y 0															$\tfrac{1}{2}$
x x																
$\tfrac{1}{2}$ 0	59	49	30	27	39	48	40	24	13	10	10	7	5	3	3	3
	49	40	25	24	35	42	34	20	11	10	10	8	5	4	3	3
	30	25	17	18	26	28	20	11	8	9	9	7	5	4	3	3
	27	24	18	18	20	17	10	5	6	8	7	5	4	5	5	5
	39	35	26	20	16	12	7	6	7	7	5	4	5	7	8	7
	48	42	28	17	12	10	8	6	7	6	5	5	7	9	10	10
	40	34	20	10	7	8	6	4	3	5	6	7	8	9	10	10
$\tfrac{1}{4}$ $\tfrac{1}{4}$	24	20	11	5	6	6	4	0	0	3	7	7	6	8	11	13

4. *Electron density projection, ρyz*

y 0															$\frac{1}{2}$
z															
0	106	85	46	31	45	60	51	26	9	6	10	11	9	7	7	7
	88	72	41	29	40	49	40	21	9	9	11	11	9	7	6	5
	55	46	31	25	28	27	18	10	10	12	12	9	8	8	7	6
	44	38	28	22	20	16	9	7	10	13	10	9	10	10	7	4
	57	48	31	20	18	17	14	10	9	9	9	10	11	10	4	1
	62	50	28	14	14	18	15	9	5	5	8	9	10	8	5	3
	43	35	19	9	9	11	8	5	5	9	12	11	9	10	12	13
	18	16	12	9	7	5	3	4	9	16	19	18	15	16	20	22
	7	9	11	11	9	6	6	8	12	16	21	23	22	21	21	21
	10	11	11	10	8	9	11	11	10	13	19	24	24	22	21	21
	14	13	9	6	7	9	10	9	11	20	28	27	23	26	38	44
	12	11	8	7	8	9	7	8	20	39	48	38	26	38	68	84
$\frac{1}{2}$	7	7	7	9	11	10	6	9	26	51	60	45	31	46	85	106

NOTE: The 1 electron contour is not well defined and by a common crystallographer's convention might be shown dotted.

133 INTERATOMIC DISTANCES IN ZINC OXIDE

W. L. Bragg, *Phil. Mag.*, **39**, 647, 1920; V. M. Goldschmidt, *Trans. Faraday Soc.*, **25**, 253, 1929; L. Pauling and M. L. Huggins, *Z. Krist.*, **87**, 205, 1934.

Zinc oxide crystallizes in the hexagonal system with $a = 3 \cdot 24$ and $c = 5 \cdot 18$ Å. If the zinc and oxygen atoms are at 000 and $\frac{2}{3} \frac{1}{3} \frac{1}{8}$ respectively, find the interatomic distance. Given that the radii of the zinc and oxygen ions are $0 \cdot 80$ Å (Zn^{++}) and $1 \cdot 35$ Å (O^{--}) and that the covalent radii of the corresponding atoms are $1 \cdot 31$ Å and $0 \cdot 66$ Å respectively, do you consider the binding ionic or homopolar?

SECTION TEN

Radiochemistry

134 THE RADIOACTIVE CONSTANT OF THORIUM-X FROM IONIZATION MEASUREMENTS

E. Rutherford and F. Soddy, *J. Chem. Soc.*, **81**, 837, 1902.

Thorium nitrate was freed from thorium-X by several precipitations with ammonia. The ionizing power of the resulting 0·5 g of thorium-X-free thorium hydroxide was measured at intervals over a period of a month; the filtrate (containing thorium-X) was examined similarly, with the following results:

Time (days)	Activity of thorium (arbitrary units)	Activity of thorium-X (arbitrary units)
0	44	100
1	37	117
2	48	100
3	54	88
4	62	72
6	71	53
8	78	..
10	83	25·2
15	..	11·1
17	96·5	..
21	99	..
28	100	..

(i) Plot these results.

(ii) Disregarding the readings of the first two days, calculate (*a*) the half-life of thorium-X; (*b*) the radioactive constant of thorium-X.

(iii) Interpret the course of the curve during the first two days.

NOTE: These experiments of Rutherford and Soddy are historically important as the first quantitative study of the decay and regeneration of a radioactive element. Thorium-X ($_{88}$Ra^{224}) is not produced directly from thorium ($_{90}$Th^{232}) as was originally supposed; for information concerning the three intermediate elements see S. Meyer and E. Schwiedler, *Radioaktivität* (Teubner, Leipzig, 1927), pp. 492–524. Owing to the uncertainty as to the initial activity of the thorium hydroxide it is necessary to use a method such as that of Guggenheim (cf. Note on Problem 101) to calculate the disintegration constant from the regeneration curve.

The radioactive constant has been more accurately determined by F. Lerch (*Wien. Ber.*, **114**, 553, 1905) and H. N. McCoy and C. H. Viol (*Phil. Mag.*, **25**, 333, 1913). A somewhat simpler example of radioactive disintegration which may be studied by the ionization method is that of radium-F (polonium); see, for example, E. Schweidler (*Verh. d. Phys. Ges.*, **14**, 536, 1912).

G. Hevesy and F. A. Paneth, *Manual of Radioactivity* (Oxford, 1938), ch. 11, G. Friedlander and J. W. Kennedy, *Nuclear and Radiochemistry* (Wiley, New York, 1955), ch. 5, or S. Glasstone, *Source-book on Atomic Energy* (Van Nostrand, Princeton, 1958), ch. 5, may be consulted for the background of the observations on which this problem is based.

135 THE RADIOACTIVE CONSTANT OF RADIUM DETERMINED BY COUNTING THE ALPHA-PARTICLES EMITTED

E. Rutherford and H. Geiger, *Proc. Roy. Soc.* A, **81**, 141, 1908.

A quantity of radium-C, equal to that in equilibrium with 0·309 mg of radium, was emitting alpha-particles equally in all directions. An electrical detecting device with a circular aperture 1·23 mm in diameter and placed at 350 cm from the radioactive source registered an average number of 45 alpha-particles received every 10 minutes.

Calculate:

(i) the total number of alpha-particles expelled per second by the amount of radium-C which is in equilibrium with one gramme of radium;

(ii) the radioactive (or decay) constant of radium itself;

(iii) the half-life of radium (in years).

NOTE: The electrical detecting device used in this work consisted of a cylinder containing a central insulated wire at a different potential; an α-particle entering the cylinder caused multiple ionization and hence a readily detectable current. This was the forerunner of the 'Geiger counter' now so widely used for the detection of cosmic rays and fast particles in general.

The relation between the number of α-particles expelled by a given amount of radium-C ($_{83}Bi^{214}$) and that of those expelled by the amount of radium in equilibrium with it emerges directly from the nature of radioactive equilibrium.

Direct and indirect methods of measuring the number of particles emitted by one gramme of radium are discussed by E. Rutherford, J. Chadwick, and C. D. Ellis, *Radiations from Radioactive Substances* (Cambridge, 1930), pp. 60–4. G. Friedlander and J. W. Kennedy, *Nuclear and Radiochemistry* (Wiley, New York, 1955), ch. 10, sec. D, also discuss the techniques for measuring absolute disintegration rates.

136 THE PRODUCTION OF HELIUM BY RADIUM

B. B. Boltwood and E. Rutherford, *Phil. Mag.*, **22**, 586, 1911.

Boltwood and Rutherford measured the volume of helium evolved by 192 mg of radium, in the form of radium chloride, over a period of 83 days and found it to be 6·58 mm³. The radium chloride was originally free from radon; radon accumulated as the experiment proceeded together with the short-lived elements radium A, B, and C, each of which has a half-life of a few minutes; the half-life of radon is 3·8 days. The helium evolved was therefore jointly produced by the alpha-ray disintegration of radium, radon, radium-A, and radium-C, the decay of radium-B being a beta-ray change.

(i) Calculate the volume of helium produced per day by the radium present in the radioactive specimen.

(ii) Calculate the volume of helium produced per year by one gramme of radium in equilibrium with Rn, RaA, and RaC.

Rutherford and Geiger (cf. Problem 135) counted the alpha-particles emitted by a radium source and found that one gramme of radium in equilibrium with Rn, RaA, and RaC emits $13 \cdot 6 \times 10^{10}$ alpha-particles per second.

(iii) From this result and the result of (ii) calculate the Avogadro number.

NOTE: Allowance must be made in this calculation for the gradual formation of radon during the first few days; the half-lives of its successors are so short that they may be regarded as coming into radioactive equilibrium with the radon as soon as it is formed.

E. Rutherford, J. Chadwick, and C. D. Ellis, *Radiations from Radioactive Substances* (Cambridge, 1930), ch. i and ii, may be consulted for background.

137 THE SURFACE OF A PRECIPITATE MEASURED BY RADIOACTIVE INDICATOR

W. A. Koehler and J. H. Mathews, *J. Am. Chem. Soc.*, **46**, 1158, 1924.

Twenty cubic centimetres of a saturated solution of lead sulphate activated with thorium-B ($_{82}Pb^{212}$) was shaken with $0 \cdot 100$ g of dry precipitated lead sulphate for an hour. The mixture was then centrifuged; 5 cm³ of the clear supernatant liquid was evaporated to dryness and the activity of the residue measured with an electroscope; an average of several determinations showed that 32 sec were necessary for the electroscope leaf to pass over 10 divisions of the scale. 5 cm³ of the original activated solution when evaporated to dryness, without shaking with solid lead sulphate, caused the leaf to pass over

10 divisions in 22·9 sec. The natural leak of the electroscope was 10 divisions in 42·9 min. 100 cm³ of the saturated solution contained 0·0043 g of lead sulphate.

Calculate:

(i) the 'specific surface' of the precipitate (i.e. the proportion of the total number of lead atoms in the precipitate which are on its surface);

(ii) the surface area per gramme of precipitate, if its density is 6·3.

NOTE: The calculation involves the assumption, made reasonable by the earlier work of F. A. Paneth and W. Vorwerk (*Z. Physik. Chem.*, **101**, 445, 1922), that only the surface layer of the crystal participates in the exchange. It is to be noted that Koehler and Mathews define the 'specific surface' somewhat differently as the mass of lead on the surface of 1 g of lead sulphate. In order to calculate the surface area per gramme of precipitate it is necessary to know the surface occupied per ion-pair of lead sulphate in the surface; for the purposes of the calculation this may be taken as the two-thirds power of the volume of an ion-pair; i.e. the crystal may be imagined as built up of a series of cube-shaped ion-pairs. For a more recent application of this technique with some refinements I. M. Kolthoff and F. T. Eggertsen (*J. Am. Chem. Soc.*, **62**, 2125, 1940) may be consulted.

138 MASS-ENERGY EQUIVALENCE FOR NUCLEAR DISINTEGRATION

J. D. Cockcroft and E. T. S. Walton, *Proc. Roy. Soc.* A, **137**, 229, 1932.

When lithium is bombarded with protons accelerated through a potential gradient of more than 125 kilovolts, scintillations are observed with a range in air of 8·4 cm, and the characteristic appearance of alpha-particle scintillations. For an alpha-particle such a range corresponds to an energy of about 8·6 million electron-volts. The hypothesis put forward by Cockcroft and Walton to explain these scintillations is the process:

$$_3\mathrm{Li}^7 + {}_1\mathrm{H}^1 = {}_2\mathrm{He}^4 + {}_2\mathrm{He}^4.$$

The masses of the nuclei involved (on the 'physical' oxygen-16 scale) were then believed to be:

$$\text{Li}^7 = 7 \cdot 0104 \ (\pm 0 \cdot 003)$$
$$\text{H}^1 = 1 \cdot 0072$$
$$\text{He}^4 = 4 \cdot 0011$$

(i) Test the plausibility of the above hypothesis by using the mass-energy equation to determine the energy of the alpha-particles that would be produced in the nuclear reaction suggested and comparing the value obtained with the energy of the particles observed experimentally.

(ii) Examine the concordance obtained by using the following more recent values of the nuclear masses (also on the oxygen-16 scale):

$$\text{Li}^7 = 7 \cdot 0182$$
$$\text{H}^1 = 1 \cdot 0081$$
$$\text{He}^4 = 4 \cdot 0039$$

NOTE: The nuclear reaction studied by Cockcroft and Walton provided the first test of the Einstein equation for mass-energy conversion. Problem 7 is based on a more recent application of the principle of mass-energy equivalence.

Data from nuclear disintegration such as these led to an extensive revision of the masses of the lighter atoms; the values revised on this basis confirmed by subsequent mass-spectrograph measurements. (Cf. M. L. Oliphant, A. E. Kempton, and E. Rutherford, *Proc. Roy. Soc. A*, **150**, 241, 1935; F. W. Aston, *Nature*, **135**, 541, 1935; J. D. Cockcroft and W. B. Lewis, *Proc. Roy. Soc. A*, **154**, 261, 1936.

S. Glasstone, *Source-book of Atomic Energy* (Van Nostrand, Princeton, 1958), pp. 220–2, provides a general background for the problem.

139 THE ISOTOPE DILUTION ASSAY OF PENICILLINS

M. Gordon, A. J. Virgona, and P. Numerof, *Anal. Chem.*, **26**, 1208, 1954.

The isotope dilution method can be used to measure the concentration of penicillin in a fermentation broth by adding to it a penicillin salt, prepared by biosynthesis from inorganic sul-phate tagged with sulphur-35 and of known specific activity. The method is a measure of total penicillins since the diluted product is isolated as the N-ethylpiperidine salt and precipita-tion by N-ethylpiperidine is believed to cause no fractionation of the various penicillins.

The radioactive penicillin used in the assay described below was the potassium salt of benzyl-penicillin ('Penicillin G') tagged with sulphur-35; its molecular weight is 372·4. Its specific activity was measured by dissolving 10 mg of the salt in 2 ml of water and determining the beta-ray activity of an evaporated 0·025 ml aliquot of this solution on a glass plate in a gas-flow counter. The average of eight plates was 3100 counts per min, of which the background accounted for 60.

(i) Calculate the specific activity of the potassium salt in counts/min/mg.

To a 100 ml portion of a penicillin fermentation broth was added 20 mg of this tagged potassium salt. By a sequence of operations, consisting largely in alternate treatment with aqueous buffers and organic solvents and ending with precipita-tion with N-ethylpiperidine in chloroform solution, the peni-cillins in the mixture were obtained in the form of the salt of this base. The salt, whose molecular weight is 447·6, was puri-fied by re-crystallization. 10 mg of the purified salt were dis-solved in 2 ml of water and the beta-ray activity of an evapor-ated 0·025 ml aliquot was measured as before. The average of eight plates was 368 counts per min, of which the background again accounted for 60.

(ii) Calculate the specific activity of the N-ethylpiperidine salt and hence the specific activity of the corresponding potassium salt.

(iii) From the dilution factor derived from a comparison of the results of (i) and (ii) calculate the penicillin content of the original broth, expressed as mg of the potassium salt of penicillin G per ml.

The international penicillin unit is defined as that producing antibiotic effects equal to that of 0·0006 mg of a standard sample of the purified sodium salt of penicillin G, whose molecular weight is 356·3.

(iv) Calculate the penicillin concentration of the broth in terms of this unit, expressing your results in units/ml.

NOTE: The isotope dilution method is normally used for measuring the concentration of a single molecular species; in this case the total concentration of a group of closely related molecules is measured since it is known that under controlled conditions all the penicillins are precipitated without significant discrimination by N-ethylpiperidine. The different molecular weights of the three penicillin salts entering into the calculation must be allowed for in comparing their specific activities. The specific activities derived from the above figures are lower than those quoted in the original paper since the latter take into account the counting efficiency; this was about 45 per cent in this instance but, so long as it can be assumed constant, does not enter into the calculation. It may also be assumed that the specific activity data have been corrected for the decay of sulphur-35.

We are grateful to Dr. Gordon for providing supplementary details on experimental procedures and for helpful comments.

140 THE NATURAL ABUNDANCE OF TRITIUM

S. Kaufman and W. F. Libby, *Phys. Rev.*, **93**, 1337, 1954.

The existence of a minute amount of tritium in natural waters is now established; it has been called 'the rarest atomic species discovered in nature'. This tritium is believed to originate as a disintegration product of the bombardment of air by cosmic rays and it decays with a half-life of 12·5 years to form helium-3.

Kaufman and Libby measured the tritium–protium ratio in a large number of water samples in the following way. Tritium discharges even less readily than deuterium during electrolysis and is therefore concentrated in the residual electrolyte. The tritium assay of such a concentrate was carried out by converting the water into hydrogen by means of zinc dust and filling a Geiger counter with this tritium-containing hydrogen after mixing with ethylene and argon to improve counting characteristics. The tritium content of the concentrate combined with a knowledge of the isotopic fractionation during electrolysis then make it possible to calculate the tritium–protium ratio in the original water sample.

The electrolytic separation of the isotopes is governed by the equations:

$$d \ln p = \alpha d \ln d = \beta d \ln t$$

where p, d, and t are the number of gramme-atoms of protium, deuterium, and tritium in the electrolyte and α and β are the separation factors of deuterium and tritium, respectively, with respect to protium. Kaufman and Libby assumed that α and β are independent of isotopic concentrations. The deuterium content of water samples was determined by measuring the rate of fall of a drop of the sample of controlled size through an immiscible liquid of controlled density. A preliminary series of measurements was carried out in which both the deuterium content (by falling drop) and the tritium content (by Geiger counter) of a tritium-enriched water sample were followed through a series of electrolytic concentration stages; these showed that, although α fluctuates considerably in magnitude, the ratio β/α remains nearly constant at a value of about 2·1. The constancy of this ratio coupled with the measurement of deuterium content during electrolytic concentration makes it possible to compute the tritium enrichment factor for a specific sequence of electrolyses.

The following measurements were carried out to determine the tritium–protium ratio in a sample of Chicago rainwater, whose deuterium concentration may be taken as 0·0138 atom per cent. The rainwater was electrolysed (as 3 per cent sodium hydroxide solution) in two stages, with intermediate neutralization and distillation, until the volume of water was reduced by a factor of 3420. The deuterium content of the residue was found to be 17·5 atom per cent.

(i) Calculate the over-all value of α for this electrolytic concentration process.

(ii) Assuming that β/α is 2·1, calculate the tritium enrichment factor due to the electrolysis.

A sample of water from the concentrate was reduced quantitatively by zinc dust to hydrogen, mixed with ethylene and argon and used to fill a Geiger counter of 865 ml capacity at 25° C. The observed count, corrected for background and for the partial pressure of hydrogen in the counter, was 2·43 counts per min per cm of mercury pressure of hydrogen. This count must be multiplied by 1·035 to correct for those beta-particles which did not produce a discharge owing to the weaker field near the ends of the counter. The half-life of tritium is 12·5 years.

(iii) Calculate the number of atoms of tritium required to produce one disintegration per min.
(iv) Calculate the tritium–protium ratio of the hydrogen introduced into the counter.
(v) Calculate the tritium–protium ratio of the original rainwater from the results of (ii) and (iv).

NOTE: The half-life of tritium is such that it can be used like carbon-14 as a clock to establish the 'age' of water samples; the effective time scale is much shorter but the isotope is already being used in problems as diverse as the rate of circulation of world water supplies and the age of wines. A. G. Maddock and E. H. Willis (*Adv. Inorg. Chem. Radiochem.*, **3**, 287, 1961) discuss atmospheric activities and dating procedures, including those based on tritium.
(i) The molar volumes of H_2O and D_2O are so nearly identical that the volume reduction factor of 3240 may be taken as equal to the ratio of the number of hydrogen atoms (of all three kinds) present before electrolysis to the number remaining afterwards. The value of α arrived at here is not required in the later stages of the problem which depend only on the ratio β/α.
(iii) The desired figure is obviously the reciprocal of the radioactive decay constant of tritium in the appropriate time units.
We are indebted to Dr. Sheldon Kaufman for details of the Geiger counter that were not included in the original paper.

141 A TEST OF THE MECHANISM OF ALCOHOLIC FERMENTATION BY THE USE OF RADIOACTIVE TRACERS

D. E. Koshland, jr., and F. H. Westheimer, *J. Am. Chem. Soc.*, **72**, 3383, 1950.

According to the currently accepted mechanism of alcoholic fermentation by yeast all the carbon atoms originally present in the aldehyde group of the glucose should eventually appear in the methyl group of the ethanol produced. This mechanism can be tested by fermenting glucose labelled in the 1 position with C^{14} and determining the distribution of radioactivity in the fermentation products.

Glucose labelled in this way was fermented with yeast in a phosphate buffer to completion:

$$C_6H_{12}O_6O = 2C_2H_5OH + 2CO_2$$

The carbon dioxide evolved was precipitated as barium carbonate; the yeast cells were removed by centrifugation, washed and dried; the ethanol was distilled out of the solution and subjected to the series of chemical changes described in the next paragraph; the residues from the distillation were evaporated to dryness.

The ethanol was oxidized by potassium dichromate and sulphuric acid and the resultant acetic acid was neutralized with barium hydroxide. The barium acetate produced was pyrolysed to acetone which was then converted into its 2,4-dinitrophenylhydrazine derivative. Control experiments showed that all these processes were essentially quantitative under the experimental conditions and that in the process of pyrolysis no appreciable fraction of the carbon atoms in the methyl group appeared in the barium carbonate residue. Under these circumstances it is reasonable to suppose that the methyl groups in the ethanol produced by fermentation will appear as methyl groups of the acetone in its hydrazone.

In one of the experiments of Koshland and Westheimer 0·20 g of labelled glucose was fermented completely at 25° C for 70 hours with 0·68 g of yeast in a phosphate buffer (pH 5·2). The carbon dioxide liberated yielded 0·374 g of barium carbonate. The ethanol formed yielded 0·122 g of acetone 2,4-dinitrophenylhydrazone. 0·068 g of dry yeast and 15 ml of residual material (containing 0·48 g of dry solids) were also obtained from the fermentation mixture.

The radioactivity of the various products was measured on samples spread over an area of 5 cm² with an end-window Geiger counter. 0·40 g of the labelled glucose gave a count of 1950 counts per min. The total yield of hydrazone was diluted with 0·113 g of inactive hydrazone and 0·20 g of the diluted mixture gave a count of 653 counts per min. The barium carbonate (0·374 g) containing the carbon dioxide liberated during fermentation gave a count of 19 counts per min. The barium carbonate formed by pyrolysis of the barium acetate gave a counting rate of 15 counts per min for a sample of 0·112 g.

In order to compare the results obtained by counting different substances Koshland and Westheimer made the following measurements. A tagged sample of glucose was completely oxidized and the resultant carbon dioxide precipitated as barium carbonate; the counting rate of 0·40 g of the original glucose was found to be 5·58 times as great as that of 0·4 g of the barium carbonate produced. Since only two carbon atoms of glucose appear as carbon dioxide in fermentation, it can be inferred that the counting rate of 0·40 g of tagged glucose would be 5·58/3 or 1·86 times the counting rate of 0·40 g of barium carbonate derived from fermentation carbon dioxide *if* all the tagged atoms in the glucose were converted to carbon dioxide in fermentation. Difficulties in the complete oxidation of the hydrazone made it necessary to carry out the analogous comparison for the hydrazone by oxidizing not the hydrazone but its progenitor, barium acetate. A similar analysis of the data derived from the complete oxidation of tagged barium acetate to barium carbonate showed that the counting rate of 0·4 g of tagged glucose would be 1·5 times the counting rate of 0·20 g

212

of acetone 2,4-dinitrophenylhydrazone produced from the same glucose by the sequence of reactions described above *if* all the tagged carbon atoms in the glucose were converted into hydrazone *via* the ethanol produced by fermentation.

(i) Compare the activity of the hydrazone obtained from fermentation of ethanol with that to be expected on the assumption that the methyl group of the ethanol is derived exclusively from the aldehyde group of the glucose.

(ii) Compare the activity of the barium carbonate from fermentation of carbon dioxide with that to be expected on the assumption that the latter contains the carbon atoms of the aldehyde group of the glucose.

(iii) Compare the activity of the barium carbonate obtained by pyrolysis of barium acetate with that to be expected on the assumption that this carbonate contains the carbon atoms of the aldehyde group of the glucose.

NOTE: (*a*) The fermentation mechanism tested by these experiments, which involved the intermediate formation of phosphoric esters, is outlined in Koshland and Westheimer's paper.

(*b*) Before carrying out any calculations it is helpful to write down the equations representing the conversion of ethanol to the hydrazone.

(*c*) The thickness of the samples of barium carbonate counted were larger than the range of the soft beta radiation of C^{14} (20 mg of aluminium/cm^2) so that the count would be almost independent of sample thickness; the count obtained for each of the two samples of barium carbonate can be equated to the count for the 'standard sample' of 0·40 g of this substance without introducing serious error.

(*d*) The methods described for comparing counts of glucose, hydrazone, and barium carbonate are not applicable to the yeast and residual solids derived from the fermentation mixture. For these materials Koshland and Westheimer used equations (W. F. Libby, *Ind. and Eng. Chem. Anal. Edn.*, **19**, 2, 1947) which enable one to compute from a layer of known 'thickness' (expressed in mg/cm^2) the (larger) hypothetical count of the same amount of material in a layer of negligible thickness, where no self-absorption of beta-radiation would occur. Applying these equations to the experiment described in the problem, the yeast was found to contain 4·7 per cent and the residual solids 0·6 per cent of the total radioactivity present in the glucose before fermentation. The barium carbonate produced in the pyrolysis of the barium acetate was similarly shown to contain only 0·75 per cent of the total radioactivity present in the glucose before fermentation. The original paper may be consulted for details of these calculations, which involve the assumption that the yeast and the dry residue have the same counting characteristics as glucose.

We are indebted to Dr. Westheimer for amplifying some experimental details.

Miscellaneous

---

142 THE PRESSURE–VOLUME RELATIONS OF ETHYLENE COMPARED WITH THE VAN DER WAALS EQUATION

E. Cardoso and E. Arni, *J. Chim. Phys.*, **10**, 504, 1912; I. Masson and L. G. F. Dolley, *Proc. Roy. Soc.* A, **103**, 524, 1923.

Cardoso and Arni found the critical temperature and critical pressure of ethylene to be $9.5°$ C and 50.65 atmospheres respectively. Masson and Dolley found the volume of ethylene at 125 atmospheres pressure and $24.95°$ C to be 0.003265 times its value at one atmosphere pressure at the same temperature.

(i) Calculate the pressure exerted by one mole of ethylene when occupying a volume of 0.1000 litre at $24.95°$ C according to the ideal gas law.

(ii) Assuming that ethylene obeys the van der Waals equation, calculate from the critical data above, the critical volume of ethylene and the value of its a and b coefficients in the van der Waals equation.

(iii) From the results of (ii) calculate the pressure exerted by one mole of ethylene when occupying a volume of 0.1000 litre at $24.95°$ C according to the van der Waals equation.

(iv) Compare the result of (iii) with the experimental observation of Masson and Dolley.

(v) In order to visualize the average distance apart of

molecules under pressure, calculate the percentage of the total volume of 0·100 litre occupied by the molecules contained in one mole of ethylene if these can be assumed to be spheres with a diameter of 4·54 Å, as inferred from viscosity measurements.

NOTE: The calculation of the equation of state for a substance from a quantitative understanding of the various types of intermolecular interactions is possible in principle but turns out to be a problem of great complexity. Ch. 2 (by J. A. Beattie and W. H. Stockmayer) of vol. 2 of the third edition of a *Treatise on Physical Chemistry*, edited by H. S. Taylor and S. Glasstone (Van Nostrand, New York, 1951), or ch. 6 of the *Molecular Theory of Gases and Liquids* by J. O. Hirschfelder, C. F. Curtis, and R. B. Bird (Wiley, New York, Chapman & Hall, London, 1954), may be consulted. Sections 9 and 10 of ch. 17 of *Physical Chemistry* by W. J. Moore (Prentice-Hall, Englewood Cliffs, 1962) give a good general picture.

143 VIRIAL COEFFICIENT OF A GAS

J. D. Lambert and V. J. Wilkinson (unpublished work) have measured P and V for ethyl chloride vapour at various temperatures.

The values of P and V at 78·2° C are given in the table opposite.

(i) Plot PV against P and find the value of B in the equation

$$PV = n(RT + BP)$$

The ratio of the density of mercury at 78·2° C to that at 0° C is 0·98605. Express B in cm³/mole.

(ii) Evaluate the critical constants in terms of the Berthelot equation

$$\left(P + \frac{a}{TV^2}\right)(V - b) = RT$$

and rewrite the Berthelot equation in terms of $P_c V_c$ and T_c instead of a and b.

Hence express the second virial coefficient, B, in terms of the critical constants.

(iii) The critical constants of ethyl chloride are (Landolt-Börnstein Tabellen, 5, Auflage 1936) $T_c = 182 \cdot 9°$ C; $P_c = 54$ atm.

Compare the calculated value of B from these data, with that found from the PV measurements of Lambert and Wilkinson.

Berthelot found that the equation expressed in terms of the critical constants gave better agreement with experiments at low pressures when the numerical constants were modified to give

$$\left(P + \frac{16 P_c V_c^2 T_c}{3 T V^2}\right)\left(V - \frac{V_c}{4}\right) = RT.$$

(iv) Find B, using this modified equation.

NOTE: It is found experimentally that the relation
$$P_c V_c = 9RT/32$$
holds fairly closely for many gases.

P.V data for ethyl chloride

P in cm Hg at 78·2° C	V cm³	P.V
25·305	41·413	1048·0
32·227	32·454	1046·0
35·717	29·247	1044·6
41·153	25·362	1043·7
46·403	22·467	1042·5
51·491	20·218	1041·0
56·800	18·312	1040·1
60·591	17·141	1038·6
118·425	8·657	1025·3
106·432	9·665	1028·7
93·159	11·065	1030·8
63·038	16·475	1038·6
70·285	14·752	1036·9
77·349	13·389	1035·6
82·085	12·600	1034·3

144 SURFACE FILMS ON WATER[1]

For each substance calculate the area per molecule and the surface pressure (in dynes cm^{-1}) and plot surface pressure against area. Interpret the curves obtained.

(a) HEXADECYL ALCOHOL

N. K. Adam, *Proc. Roy. Soc.* A, **101**, 452, 1922.

0·210 cm^3 of a solution, containing 6·186 mg of *n*-hexadecyl alcohol in 25 cm^3 of benzene, was placed on a trough 14·0 cm wide. The floating barrier at one end was 13·8 cm long and the gaps past the ends were blocked by jets of air directed along the surface of the water. The force observed on the float at different lengths of the film was as follows:

Length of film (cm)	Force on float (dynes)
20·9	4·14
20·3	8·56
20·1	26·2
19·6	69·0
19·1	108
18·6	234
18·3	323
18·1	394
17·8	531

(b) MYRISTIC ACID ON WATER AT LARGE AREAS PER MOLECULE

N. K. Adam and G. Jessop, *Proc. Roy. Soc.* A, **110**, 423, 1926; N. K. Adam and J. B. Harding, ibid., **138**, 411, 1932.

Three solutions of myristic acid ($C_{13}H_{27}COOH$) in petroleum ether were prepared with the following compositions:

A: 0·0329 g in 30·78 g of solvent
B: 0·0330 g in 27·93 g of solvent
C: one-fifth the concentration of B.

[1] Professor Adam kindly selected the detailed experimental data of this problem from his laboratory note-books.

N drops of solution, each weighing 1·82 mg, were placed on a trough 14·0 cm wide fitted with a float of effective length 12·33 cm. Below is tabulated the force on the float with various values of N and various lengths of film.

The surface potential (that is, the amount by which the contact potential between the air and water was changed by the presence of the film) of these films was also measured. It was found that, when the amount of myristic acid corresponded to the figures marked with an asterisk, the surface potential fluctuated violently as the surface of the film was explored in various places. At surface concentrations higher and lower than those asterisked, this phenomenon was not observed.

Solution	Drops of solution (N)	Length of film (cm)	Force on float (dynes)
A	1	35	2·00
	2 *	,,	2·49
	5 *	,,	2·52
B	1	35	2·26, 2·53
	2 *	,,	2·39
	10 *	,,	2·46
	15	,,	2·49
	,,	28	3·52
	,,	27·5	5·06
C	1	35	0·80
	2	,,	1·45
	3	,,	2·04
	4	,,	2·20

NOTE: It is particularly desirable in plotting surface film data to choose a scale which permits of the inclusion of all the experimental points even where it involves an inconvenient compression of part of the graph.

Problem (a). This is a typical example of a condensed film; the cross-sectional area of the molecule may be derived from the graph.

Problem (b). This illustrates the behaviour of a film over a very wide range of values of the area per molecule; duplicate measurement of the film with one drop of solution B are given to illustrate the possibilities of experimental error in these delicate measurements.

Appendix

Some short exercises from Oxford Examinations

(**1**) P^{32} is an artificially produced β-emitter. A preparation of 8.8×10^{-15} g of Na_2HPO_4 (containing 100 per cent P^{32}) emits a total of 1250 β-particles per minute. Calculate the disintegration constant and half-life of P^{32}.

$$(\lambda = 3.372 \times 10^{-5} \text{ min}^{-1}$$
$$t_{\frac{1}{2}} = 14.27 \text{ days})$$

(**2**) The following table gives bimolecular reaction velocity constants (in moles per litre per second) for two different reactions in benzene solution over a range of temperature. Draw as many conclusions as you can from these data.

Reaction between benzoyl chloride and aniline—

Temperature (° C)	.	.	.	5	25	40	70
$k \times 10^2$	.	.	.	.	3.08	7.55	12.2	41.7

Reaction between benzoyl chloride and p-nitraniline—

Temperature (° C)	.	.	25	40	70	100
$k \times 10^2$	.	.	.	0.00421	0.0110	0.062	0.253

$$(E_I = 7.92 \text{ kcal mole}^{-1}$$
$$E_{II} \quad 12.16 \text{ kcal mole}^{-1}$$
$$\frac{P_I}{P_{II}} = 1.23 \text{ assuming } Z_1 = Z_2$$

(**3**) The equilibrium mixture of NO_2 and N_2O_4 has a density relative to air of 1.778 at 49.7° C and 93.8 mm pressure. Under the same conditions the density of pure N_2O_4 would be 3.181. The heat of dissociation of N_2O_4 is sensibly constant over the range 0–100° C, and when 100 g of N_2O_4 dissociate at constant pressure, 14782 calories are absorbed. Calculate the degree of dissociation of N_2O_4 at 75° C and 760 mm pressure.

$$(\alpha = 0.772)$$

(**4**) The following data were obtained for the solubility of oxygen in molten silver just above the melting point:

Oxygen pressure (mm)	440	760	1000	1200
Dissolved oxygen (g/100 g Ag)	0·232	0·305	0·350	0·383

What conclusions can you draw about the state of the dissolved oxygen?

The melting-point of silver *in vacuo* is 962° C. Given that the latent heat of fusion of silver is 25·0 cal/g, estimate the change of melting-point caused by the presence of oxygen at a pressure of one atmosphere. (Oxygen is monatomic in molten silver

$$\Delta T = 23\cdot1° C)$$

(**5**) Comment upon the possibility of drying chlorine by subliming it, given that the latent heat of vaporization of chlorine at its boiling-point ($-34\cdot6°$ C) is 5·3 kcal per g mol, and its melting-point is $-103\cdot5°$ C; the vapour pressure of ice at 0° C is 4·58 mm of mercury and its latent heat of sublimation is 12·1 kcal per g mol.

(vapour pressure of ice at $-103\cdot5°$ C $= 5\cdot6 \times 10^{-6}$ mm)

(**6**) Gaseous azomethane decomposes photochemically according to the equation:

$$CH_3N_2CH_3 \rightarrow C_2H_6 + N_2.$$

In an experiment at 293° K azomethane vapour was exposed to ultra-violet radiation of wavelength 3130 Å for 120 min. The radiation absorbed amounted to $2\cdot45 \times 10^2$ ergs/sec. The total volume of nitrogen produced was 0·02 cm³ at n.t.p. Calculate the quantum yield, and comment on your result. (1·93)

(**7**) The viscosity of nitrogen at 0° C is

$$1665 \times 10^{-7} \text{ cm}^{-1} \text{ g sec}^{-1}.$$

Calculate,

(i) the mean free path at 0° C and pressure 1 atm;
(ii) the collision diameter of nitrogen.

($l = 8\cdot803 \times 10^{-6}$ cm; $\sigma = 3\cdot08$ Å)

(8) The following lines, given in units of ν/R, are adjacent members of a Rydberg series:

$$0\cdot28517, \quad 0\cdot33385, \quad 0\cdot35638, \quad 0\cdot36862 \ (\nu/R).$$

Calculate a value for the ionization limit of this series in cm^{-1}, assuming that 1 Rydberg unit is equivalent to 109700 cm^{-1}.

$$(43472 \ cm^{-1})$$

(9) Sulphuryl chloride dissociates according to the equation

$$SO_2Cl_2 \rightleftharpoons SO_2 + Cl_2.$$

The vapour density of sulphuryl chloride was found to be $50\cdot08$ at $50°$ C and 450 mm Hg, and $36\cdot6$ at $102°$ C and 700 mm Hg. Calculate the heat-content change for this reaction. Outline briefly how you would calculate the standard Gibbs free energy change and the standard entropy change.

$$(\Delta H = 16\cdot025 \ \text{kcal mole}^{-1}$$
$$\Delta G° = -616\cdot2 \ \text{cal mole}^{-1}$$
$$\Delta S = 44\cdot37 \ \text{e.u.})$$

(10) In a solution containing a very small concentration of an alcohol and a much larger concentration of ether, an equilibrium is set up

$$ROH + R_2'O \rightleftharpoons ROH \cdots OR_2'.$$

The concentration of non-hydrogen-bonded alcohol was measured from the intensity of the infra-red absorption at 3620 cm^{-1}. A_0 is the value of this intensity if no hydrogen bonds occur, and A is the intensity observed. Find the heat of formation of the hydrogen bond, assuming that the concentration of the ether is so large as to remain constant.

$T \ (°C)$	A_0	A
25	4620	2450
34	4560	2690
84	4240	3090
94	4180	3200

$$(\text{approx.} \ -3\cdot1 \ \text{kcal mol}^{-1})$$

(11) Find the e.m.f. of the cell with transference at $25°$ C

$$Ag \mid 0\cdot1 \ M \ AgNO_3aq. \mid 0\cdot01 \ M \ AgNO_3aq. \mid Ag$$

given the following data for $f_\pm$, the mean activity coefficient, and n_+, the cationic transport number.

$$0\cdot1 \text{ M AgNO}_3 \quad f_\pm = 0\cdot733 \quad n_+ = 0\cdot468$$
$$0\cdot01 \text{ M AgNO}_3 \quad f_\pm = 0\cdot892 \quad n_+ = 0\cdot466$$
$$(57\cdot7 \text{ mV})$$

(**12**) Calculate the heat of forming the dative link in the compound $(CH_3)_3N \rightarrow BF_2CH_3$ from the following data: $0\cdot540$ millimoles, in a bulb of volume 171 cm^3, give the following pressures: at $140°$ C, $105\cdot25$ mm; at $150°$ C, $115\cdot0$ mm; at $160°$ C, $125\cdot6$ mm. $(\Delta H = -23 \text{ kcal mole}^{-1})$

(**13**) Water vapour is partially associated to $(H_2O)_2$. The percentage association at various temperatures, when the vapour is at a pressure of 1 atm, is given below:

Temperature (°C)	40	70	100	150
Percentage association . . .	4·32	2·06	1·03	0·35

Calculate the heat of formation of the dimer, the standard free energy of association at $100°$ C, and the standard entropy of association. Comment briefly on your results.

$$(\Delta H = -5\cdot90 \text{ kcal mole}^{-1}$$
$$\Delta G° = 3\cdot89 \text{ kcal mole}^{-1}$$
$$\Delta S° = -26\cdot3 \text{ e.u.})$$

(**14**) The following pressure–time relations were observed in the decomposition of an organic compound in the gas phase at $160°$ C:

Pressure (mm Hg) 50	78·6	94·3	107·9	121·5	132·3	139·2	147·1
Time (min) . . 0	10	20	30	45	60	80	∞

At $130°$ C and the same initial pressure the time of half change was 636 min. What can you deduce about the stoicheiometry, order, and activation energy of the reaction?
$$\text{(first order}; E = 37\cdot7 \text{ kcal mole}^{-1})$$

(**15**) A sample of a metallic oxide absorbs the following quantities of argon:

Pressure of argon (mm) .	100	200	300	400	500	600
Argon absorbed (ml at n.t.p.)	26·7	40·0	48·0	53·3	57·1	60·0

Assuming that an argon atom occupies 1×10^{-15} cm^2 on the surface, and that the system obeys Langmuir's adsorption isotherm, calculate the accessible surface area of the sample.

$$(2 \cdot 17 \times 10^6 \text{ cm}^2)$$

Answers

The student must not expect that a correct solution of a problem will invariably lead to a result identical to the last significant figure with the value quoted below. Especially where graphs are concerned an arbitrary factor enters into the calculation which may lead to small numerical differences between individual solutions. Somewhat larger differences will sometimes be found between the answers below and the results contained in the original paper since the latter are usually based on a much wider selection of experimental data. For some of the longer problems numerical values obtained at intermediate stages of the calculation are quoted (in square brackets) as well as the final answers.

1 $7\cdot4 \times 10^{23}$, $6\cdot8 \times 10^{23}$.

2 $6\cdot6$, $6\cdot9$, $6\cdot4$, $6\cdot1 \times 10^{23}$; mean $= 6\cdot5 \times 10^{23}$.

3

$$\sqrt{\left(\frac{9\eta}{2g}\right)} = 9\cdot145 \times 10^{-4}$$

$$\frac{4\pi}{3}\left(\frac{9\eta}{2}\right)^{\frac{3}{2}}\frac{300}{g^{\frac{1}{2}}} \times 1\cdot49174 = 1\cdot405 \times 10^{-3}$$

Drop	v_G (mean) (cm/sec)	$v_G + v_F$ (mean) (cm/sec)
5	0·02554	0·01024
12	0·03497	0·00927
14	0·02146	0·01226

(i)	*Drop*	*Apparent radius*	*Apparent value of electronic charge*
	5	0·0001525	$5·15 \times 10^{-11}$ e.s.u.
	12	0·0001784	5·45 ,,
	14	0·0001397	5·66 ,,

(ii) True value of electronic charge $= 4·8_5 \times 10^{-10}$ e.s.u. (extrapolated from the three selected drops).

4 (i) Stopping voltages: $-2·04_7$, $-0·91_7$, $-0·30_0$ volts.
(ii) Planck's constant $= 6·6_8 \times 10^{-27}$ erg.sec.

5 (i) 138·92   (ii) 138·91.

6 (i) Both elements are probably simple unless by a rare coincidence both elements have isotopes in just the right proportion to make the 'chemical' mass ratio equal to the 'physical' mass ratio.
(ii) Hydrogen must have one or more heavy isotopes; if there is one isotope, whose mass is twice that of ordinary hydrogen, then it must be present in a proportion of about one in four thousand.
(iii) A comparison of Aston's *revised* 'physical' mass of hydrogen with the chemical atomic weight indicates that hydrogen contains *no* isotope. The anomaly is explained by the fact that the purification of hydrogen for atomic-weight purposes automatically eliminates nearly all the heavy isotope.

7 $_6C^{13} = 13·007463$ on the 'physical' ($_8O^{16}$) scale.

8 (i) Extrapolated pressure ratios are 1·14222 and 1·74623. At. wts. are 14·0078 and 12·0112.
(ii) Compressibility of $N_2 = 0·00025$ atm^{-1}.

9 (i) 1·059473.
(ii) $C^{12}/C^{13} = 0·922802$ assuming $S^{32}/C^{12} = 31·98/12·00$
$\qquad\qquad = 0·922815 \qquad\qquad\qquad = 32·00/12·00$
$\qquad\qquad = 0·922848 \qquad\qquad\qquad = 32·05/12·00$.

10 [35100, 33900.] Mean $= 34500$.

11 (i) The plot for the cyclohexane solutions shows upward concavity to an extent that makes extrapolation to zero concentration somewhat arbitrary. In benzene solution the plot shows a much smaller variation of the osmotic pressure/concentration ratio with concentration. On the basis of both plots the limiting value of the ratio must lie between 0·30 and 0·40 corresponding to number-average molecular weights of 840000 and 630000 respectively. The limits of uncertainty with macromolecules of lower molecular weight would be narrower. In choosing the appropriate value of R to use in the molecular weight calculation it is well to note the units in which the osmotic pressure and concentration have been expressed.

(ii) and (iii).

Sample	$\dfrac{\ln \eta_r}{c}$	Number-average molecular weight
1	0·494	80300
2	0·370	51300
3	0·304	39700
4	0·137	11000

(iv) The log–log plot shows a good straight line; it does *not*, however, have the slope of unity that Staudinger's equation would predict.

12 [Degree of dissociation = 0·064, 0·201, 0·415.]
(i) K_p = 9·19, 126, 848 (mm of mercury).
(ii) K_c = 1·37, 15·9, 92·3 × 10^{-4} (moles/litre).
(iii) ΔE = 33100 cal.

13 (i)
$$\frac{dm_2}{dt} \Big/ \frac{dm_1}{dt} = \frac{P_2 a_2}{P_1 a_1} \sqrt{\left(\frac{T_1}{T_2}\right)} \frac{\{1 + (\sqrt{2}-1)\alpha\}}{(1+\alpha)}$$

(ii)
$$\alpha = \frac{1 - \left(\dfrac{a_1}{\sqrt{T_1}} d\ln P_2 \Big/ \dfrac{a_2}{\sqrt{T_2}} d\ln P_1\right)}{\left(\dfrac{a_1}{\sqrt{T_1}} d\ln P_2 \Big/ \dfrac{a_2}{\sqrt{T_2}} d\ln P_1\right) - \{\sqrt{2}-1\}}$$

	572° K	658° K
(iii) Degree of dissociation (α)	0·034	0·247
$K_p = P_F^2/P_{F_2}$ (atm)	3·37 × 10^{-9}	2·03 × 10^{-7}

(iv) 37·2 kcal mole^{-1}.

14 K = 1·836 at 698·6° K and 1·672 at 666·8° K. When corrected for the diffusion error the values are 1·812 and 1·644 respectively.
(ii) 1·41$_5$ kcal for *one* mole of hydrogen iodide.

	698·6° K	666·8° K
(iii) Rate constant (cm³ mole^{-1} sec^{-1})	1·26	0·253

(iv) 46 kcal (46·7 kcal before correction).
(v) 5·5 × 10^{-8} cm. The close approach of this value to typical molecular dimensions played an important role in the early development of the picture; such a close approximation is by no means universal.

15 (i)

$$\begin{array}{ccc}
T\ °K & x & K_p\ (atmosphere^{-\frac{1}{4}}) \\
625 & 0\cdot8696 & 4\cdot15 \\
625 & 0\cdot8082 & 3\cdot95 \\
659 & 0\cdot8447 & 2\cdot93 \\
659 & 0\cdot8038 & 3\cdot01 \\
\end{array}$$

The mean values of K_p are $4\cdot05$ at $625°$ K and $2\cdot97$ at $659°$ K. $\Delta H = -7\cdot47$ kcal per mole of HCl reacted.
(ii) $\Delta H = -6\cdot9$ kcal from thermochemical data.
(iii) $\Delta G = -27\cdot85$ kcal.
(iv) $K_p = 10^{-19\cdot4}$ (atmosphere$^{\frac{1}{4}}$).
(v) $1\cdot20_8$ volt.

All the above results ignore the temperature-dependence of the enthalpy changes.

16 (i) $K_p = \dfrac{p_{CO}^2}{p_{CO_2}} = 5\cdot3$ at $1073°$ K, $28\cdot7$ at $1173°$ K, 222 at $1323°$ K (atmospheres).

(ii) $\Delta H_{1173} = 42\cdot16$ kcal (from equilibrium data).
$\Delta H_{298} = 41\cdot23$ kcal (from thermochemical data).

(iii) $K_{p_{1400°}} = 530$ (atmospheres).

(iv) $K_p = \dfrac{p_{CO}^2 p_{O_2}}{p_{CO_2}^2} = 1\cdot37,\ 7\cdot81,$ and $52\cdot2 \times 10^{-12}$ atmospheres respectively.

(v) $\Delta H_{1\,443} = 146\cdot8$ kcal (from equilibrium data).
$\Delta H_{298} = 135\cdot3$ kcal (from thermochemical data).

(vi) $K_{p_{1400°}} = 1\cdot5_9 \times 10^{-12}$ atmospheres.

(vii) e.m.f.$_{1400°} = 1\cdot01$ volt.

(viii) $\left[\begin{array}{l}\text{In the expansion for } 2\cdot303 \log_{10} K_p,\ \Delta H_0 = -93937 \text{ cal and } I, \\ \text{the integration constant} = 1\cdot54; \text{ this leads to} \\ \qquad\qquad \log_{10} K_{p_{1400°}} = 69\cdot4.\end{array}\right]$

e.m.f.$_{298°} = 1\cdot03$ volt.

(ix) $\left[\begin{array}{l}\dfrac{p_{H_2}^2 p_{O_2}}{p_{H_2O}^2} = 1\cdot49 \times 10^{-12} \text{ at } 1457°\text{ K} \\[4pt] \qquad\qquad 9\cdot84 \times 10^{-12} \text{ at } 1537°\text{ K} \\[4pt] \qquad\qquad 3\cdot41 \times 10^{-13} \text{ at } 1400°\text{ K}\end{array}\right]$ $K_{p_{1400°}} = \dfrac{p_{CO}\,p_{H_2O}}{p_{CO_2}\,p_{H_2}} = 2\cdot1_6.$

17 $\left[\begin{array}{l}\text{For iodine atoms the contribution of the }^2P_{\frac{1}{2}} \text{ state to } Z_{\text{int.}} \text{ is} \\ \text{negligible at each temperature.} \quad \therefore\ Z_{\text{int.}} = 4\cdot00. \\ \text{For iodine molecules } Z_{\text{rot.}} = 9\cdot3077T.\end{array}\right]$

$T\ °K$	298·1	1073·1	1473·1
$\dfrac{G° - E_0°}{T}$ cal deg^{-1} g atom^{-1} for I atoms	$-38\cdot200$	$-44\cdot561$	$-46\cdot134$

$\dfrac{G° - E°_\circ}{T}$ cal deg^{-1} g mole^{-1} for I$_2$	$-54{\cdot}137$	$-64{\cdot}927$	$-67{\cdot}686$
K_p (calculated)	$\sim 10^{-21}$	$0{\cdot}0112$	$1{\cdot}25$
K_p (Prob. 12)		$0{\cdot}012$	$1{\cdot}12$

18 (i) The phase-rule diagram will be found on p. 153 of the original paper.

(ii) A compound AuSb$_2$ is formed.

(iii) The diagram may be divided into the following areas: (1) homogeneous liquid, (2) liquid+solid Au, (3) liquid+solid AuSb$_2$, (4) liquid+solid Sb, (5) solid Au+solid eutectic, (6) solid AuSb$_2$+solid eutectic, (7) solid Sb+solid AuSb$_2$. (5 and 6 may be regarded as a single area.)

19 A diagram will be found on p. 1469 of the original paper. A double salt, K$_2$SO$_4$,BeSO$_4$,2H$_2$O, is in equilibrium with solutions containing between 37·2 and 84·8 per cent of BeSO$_4$ in the anhydrous solute. The solid in equilibrium with solutions containing a smaller percentage of beryllium sulphate is K$_2$SO$_4$; with a greater percentage of beryllium sulphate it is BeSO$_4$,4H$_2$O.

20 A diagram will be found on p. 149 of the original paper.

(i) The double salt is obtained when solutions are evaporated for which the molar ratio FeCl$_3$/NH$_4$Cl lies between c. 7·3 and 0·9: an equimolecular solution would obviously be a convenient source of the double salt.

(ii) The solid which would separate out is respectively (a) FeCl$_3$,6H$_2$O, (b) (NH$_4$Cl)$_2$,FeCl$_3$,H$_2$O, (c) mixed crystals containing about 1·5 per cent FeCl$_3$.

21 (i) A diagram will be found on p. 78 of the original paper. The four solid phases are:

	Approximate composition (per cent)	
Formula	Li$_2$O	CrO$_3$
LiOH,H$_2$O	35·6	0
Li$_2$CrO$_4$,2H$_2$O	18·0	60·2
Li$_2$Cr$_2$O$_7$,2H$_2$O	11·2	75·2
CrO$_3$	0	100

(ii) The solubility of the normal hydrated chromate, calculated as Li$_2$CrO$_4$, is 49 per cent.

The solubility of the hydrated dichromate, calculated as Li$_2$Cr$_2$O$_7$, is 56 per cent.

22 (i)

Temperature (°K)	Pressure (atmospheres) $\times 10^6$
2282	10·76
2175	2·50
2089	0·768
2046	0·360

(ii) $\log_{10} p = 7 \cdot 696 - \dfrac{2 \cdot 89 \times 10^4}{T}$.

(The original paper uses a good many more experimental points, leading to somewhat different values.)

(iii) and (iv)

(a) If the T^{-2} term in the heat capacity of the solid is taken into account:

$$\Delta H_T = 149030 - 7 \cdot 8T - \frac{4 \times 10^5}{T} \text{ cal.}$$

(b) If the T^{-2} term is ignored:

$$\Delta H_T = 148850 - 7 \cdot 8T \text{ cal.}$$

(The equation arrived at in the original paper from a much larger number of measurements is somewhat different: the contrast is instructive.)

23 (i)

	1002° C	1105° C
Rate of input of carbon monoxide (millimoles/min) . . .	3·887	3·768
Rate of formation of zinc (mg-atoms/min)	0·253	0·730
Rate of output of carbon monoxide (millimoles/min) . . .	3·634	3·038
Molar percentage of carbon monoxide in effluent gas =	43·04	34·26
$K_p = \dfrac{p_{Zn} \times p_{CO_2}}{p_{CO}}$ (atmospheres) =	0·0364	0·1293

(ii) $\Delta H = 42 \cdot 9_8$ kcal.

(iii) $\Delta H = 47557 - 2/69T + 4 \cdot 5 \times 10^{-5}T^2 + \dfrac{1 \cdot 31 \times 10^{-6}}{T}$ cal.

(iv) $\Delta G° = 47557 + 6 \cdot 194T \log T - 4 \cdot 5 \times 10^{-5}T^2 + \dfrac{6 \cdot 55 \times 10^3}{T} - 49 \cdot 83T$ cal.

24 (i)

Temperature (°C)	Pressure (mm)
1100	10·0
1150	18·6
1190	30·1

230

(ii) $A = 10641$, $B = 8.751$. (From a more extensive set of data Pidgeon and King arrive at values of 10875 and 8.916 respectively.)

(iii) $\Delta G = 122400 + 11.74T \log T - 100.38T$.

(iv)

Temperature (°C)	log p	p (mm)
1100	0.08	1.2
1190	0.65	4.5

The discrepancy between the results of (i) and (iv) is presumably due to the intervention of other reactions besides the one cited in the first paragraph of the problem.

25 (ii) (a) The reduction is clearly impossible; from the graph ΔG for the reduction of two-thirds of a mole of alumina is in the neighbourhood of *plus* 92 kcal.

(b) The reduction process is clearly feasible with carbon; ΔG is approximately *minus* 42 kcal for the reduction of two-thirds of a mole of chromic oxide. Carbon monoxide is not a plausible reducing agent as ΔG is about plus 43 kcal for the same amount of chromic oxide.

(iii) 10^{-19} atmosphere.

(iv) $p_{CO_2}/p_{CO} = 58$.

26

	636° K,	732° K.
p_{TiCl_3} (mm)	1.58×10^{-4}	1.59×10^{-2}.
p_{TiCl_4} (mm)	4.69×10^{-3}	2.66×10^{-1}.

(ii) $\Delta G = 15.1_6$ kcal at 636° K, 11.5_7 at 732° K.

$\Delta H = 38.9$ kcal.

(iii) $\Delta H = 44.7$ kcal per mole.

The last two quantities are higher than those quoted in the paper, which are based on a wider selection of experimental data.

27 (i)

Pressure, mm .	0.001	0.002	0.004	0.006	0.008	0.010
Volume adsorbed at 90° K (cm³ corrected to n.t.p.)	0.130	0.147	0.160	0.169	0.177	0.182
Volume adsorbed at 193° K . ..		0.002	0.004	0.0063	0.00825	0.01028

(ii) The results fit a Langmuir equation such as the following:

$$x = \frac{400p}{1 + 2180p} \quad \text{or} \quad \frac{505p}{1 + 2870p}.$$

(iii) Percentage of surface covered at saturation is about 97 per cent.

28 [Mass of gas adsorbed *uncorrected* for buoyancy: 0.01552, 0.01889, 0.01895, 0.01830, 0.01475 grammes.]

(i) 0.0156, 0.0194, 0.0202, 0.0211, and 0.0213 grammes respectively.

(ii) The results do not conform to the Freundlich isotherm, but are moderately well represented by the Langmuir form of equation with coefficients such as the following:

$$x = \frac{0 \cdot 11p}{1 + 5 \cdot 34p}.$$

29 1 'cm³-mm' is equivalent to $1 \cdot 205 \times 10^{-3}$ cm³ measured at s.t.p. For the meaning of the symbols used in this table of intermediate results, see the latter part of the answer.

p	$\dfrac{p}{v(p_0 - p)}$	$\log p/p_0$	$\dfrac{1}{1000v'^2}$
22·30	0·2958	$\bar{1}$·8267	6·44
12·70	0·0904	$\bar{1}$·6180	11·18
7·30	0·0488	$\bar{1}$·3784	16·71
4·48	0·03109	$\bar{1}$·1656	22·60
2·74	0·01973	$\bar{2}$·9553	27·77
1·85	0·01399	$\bar{2}$·7818	32·55
1·32	0·01041	$\bar{2}$·6345	36·73

(i) The data are not compatible with the Langmuir isotherm because there is no levelling-off of the amount of adsorption at higher pressures. A plot of (equilibrium pressure/amount adsorbed) against the equilibrium pressure is concave to the axis of the latter; a plot of amount adsorbed against the equilibrium pressure gives an S-shaped curve.

(ii) A plot of $p/v(p_0 - p)$ against p/p_0, where 'v' is the amount adsorbed (in the units of the table) at equilibrium pressure 'p' and where 'p_0' is the vapour pressure of ethylene at the temperature of the experiment, gives a good straight line. The intercept when p/p_0 is zero is 0·0016 and the slope is 0·208. From the intercept and slope it can be calculated that for this particular 17·6 mg sample the amount of gas corresponding to a monomolecular layer is 4·8 cm³-mm. The gas laws show that 1 cm³-mm at 25° C contains $5 \cdot 38 \times 10^{-8}$ mole of an ideal gas. The cross-section of the ethylene molecule can be used to calculate the area of a monomolecular layer of one mole of ethylene and it is then easy to show that the area of the sample is 273 cm².

(iii) If $\log p/p_0$ against $1/v'^2$, where 'v'' is the volume adsorbed measured in cm³ at s.t.p., a good straight line is obtained except at the highest pressures. The slope 'A' is $3 \cdot 77 \times 10^{-5}$. The area of the sample in square metres is then given by $5 \cdot 16A^{\frac{1}{2}}$ or 317 cm² in fair agreement with the value arrived at using the B.E.T. equation.

30 (i) Surface excess in 10^{-8} g/cm² = 7·3, 7·9 (mean 7·6) ($c = 3 \cdot 987$)
= 4·9, 5·8 (mean $5 \cdot 3_5$) ($c = 1 \cdot 498$).

(ii) Unimolecular layer = $10 \cdot 3 \times 10^{-8}$ g/cm².

(iii)

	Concentration	Slope of plot	Gibbs adsorption
	3·987	−2·8	$6·9 \times 10^{-8}$ g/cm²
	1·498	−5·2	4·8 ,, ,,

31

I	$-\log \gamma$	[indicator in basic form] / [indicator in acid form]	pK_A for hydroxylammonium ion
0·0857	0·0961	$2·80_2$	$5·96_6$
0·0794	0·0940	$1·25_7$	$5·97_7$

32   (i) $S_0 = 6·16$ mg/100 ml.
(ii) $pK_a' = 6·47$, $pK_b' = 11·94$.

33   (i) $E_0 = -0·0205$
(ii) $[E_0' = -0·0030$ at $\sqrt{c} = 0·1]\, f_{0·01} = 0·717$.
(iii) ⎡The e.m.f. of the corresponding concentration cell *without* liquid⎤
⎣junction is 0·1153 volt. ⎦
$n_{H^+} = 0·732$.

34   (i)

c (moles/litre) . .	3·021	4·570	5·559	7·546	8·256
p (mm) . . .	0·0078	0·0558	0·1727	1·820	4·117

(ii) [The vapour pressure of the 5N solution is by interpolation 0·0883 mm]

c . .	3·021	8·256
$a_{\pm}$ . .	3·73	85·7

35   (i) ⎡The successive values of the function are 0·22505, 0·22511,⎤
⎣0·22485, 0·22441 and 0·22372 volt respectively. ⎦
$E_0 = 0·2254 \pm 0·0002$ volt.
(ii) ⎡At $m = 0·01$ the function = 0·2246 volt and the e.m.f. of the⎤
⎣cell at this concentration will be 0·4631 volt. ⎦
$\gamma_{0·01} = 0·90_5$.
(iii) [Slope of graph = 0·081.] $b = 0·69_6$.
(iv) Successive values of the activity coefficient are 0·793, 0·760, 0·848, 1·128, 1·324, 1·854 respectively.

36   (i) $[p_{4·484m} = 0·030$ mm$]p_{0·01m} = 2·9 \times 10^{-8}$ mm.
(ii) [HCl] $= 5 \times 10^{-10}$ m.
(iii) [HCl] $= 10^{-11}$ m.

37   (i)

	√Ionic strength	Activity coefficient
1–1 salt . .	0·0183	0·980
	0·0366	0·961
	0·0731	0·920
	0·1018	0·895
	0·0484	0·948
	0·0660	0·924
	0·1018	0·891

	√Ionic strength	Activity coefficient
3–1 salt . .	0·0174	0·941
	0·0364	0·881
	0·0483	0·838
	0·0427	0·865

(ii) For the 1–1 salt a line is obtained with a slope between 0·45 and 0·50 (Debye–Hückel: 0·50).

For the 3–1 salt a line is obtained with a slope between 1·50 and 1·55 (Debye–Hückel: 1·50).

38 (i)

m .	0·004134	0·019330	0·02420	0·03982	0·05206	0·08067	0·09746
j .	0·00157	0·00911	0·00986	0·01335	0·01734	0·02067	0·02385

	m .	.	0·01	0·03	0·05	0·10
(ii) j/m .		.	$0·4_2$	$0·36_5$	$0·32_0$	$0·23_7$
(iii) γ .		.	0·992	$0·977_2$	$0·965_6$	$0·945_0$

Alternative values for (ii) and (iii) will be found in the original paper; the slight differences between the two sets of figures are due partly to the limited selection of data embodied in the problem and partly to the latitude with which the (j/m)–m graph may be drawn.

39 (i)

C_2 .	0·004984	0·006978	0·019934	0·03985	0·05976
$\Delta\log_{10}f$	−0·0758	−0·0705	−0·0489	−0·0300	−0·0176

(ii) Conformity with an equation of the type suggested is shown by the linear graph obtained when $\Delta \log f - \alpha \sqrt{C}$ is plotted against $(-0·11 - \Delta \log f)\sqrt{C}$. A second approximation establishes the value of A ($= \log_{10}f$ when $C = 0·09953$) as $-0·1081$ and β as 1·46.

(iii) Since $\beta = 1·46$, the distance of closest approach is $4·4_6$ Å.

(iv) For $C = 0·004984$ $f = 0·928$.

$C = 0·09953$ $f = 0·779$.

40 (i) $K = 1·417 \times 10^{-3}$ (A) and $1·396 \times 10^{-3}$ (B) at 25° C $0·719 \times 10^{-3}$ (C) at 0° C.

(ii) $\Delta H = -4·36$ kcal.

(iii) $E = 0·6848$ volt at 25° C and 0·6796 volt at 0° C.

(iv) $\Delta G = -15·79$ kcal at 25° C and $-15·67$ kcal at 0° C.

(v) $\Delta S = 4·8$ e.u.

(vi) $\Delta H = 14·36$ kcal.

(vii) 0·0216 volt.

41 (i) c .

c .	.	.	0·003	0·005	0·010	0·015	0·100	0·300
$K_c(\times 10^3)$	.		1·53	1·55	1·58	1·59	1·64	1·69

(ii) $\log K_c = \bar{3}·1505 + \sqrt{\mu} - 3·12\mu$

$K_a = 1·41_4 \times 10^{-3}$.

42 (i) With the limited selection of data supplied in the problem the extrapolation to the limiting value of the quotient at infinite dilution is somewhat arbitrary but it clearly lies between 0·218 and 0·219. A value of 0·2184 is used in part (ii).

(ii)

$[OH^-]$	$[CaOH^-]$	K_c
0·01346	0·00096	0·0876
0·02000	0·00162	0·1135
0·02603	0·00279	0·1084
0·03173	0·00396	0·1113

(The values of K_c in Table II of the original paper are lower than those quoted above owing to some minor arithmetical error in the former; the values of K'_d in the same table are correct.)

(iii)

μ	K_a
0·0197	0·050
0·0292	0·058
0·0376	0·051
0·0456	0·050

43 At 20° C $\frac{RT}{F}\ln 10 = 0{\cdot}058165$ volt.

The values of the function, whose limiting value at zero ionic strength is $-\frac{RT}{F}\ln K_a$, are at successively higher concentrations 0·27670, 0·27696, and 0·27685.

With such a limited selection of experimental data as are provided in the problem the extrapolation is somewhat arbitrary; a plausible value would be $0{\cdot}2768_4$ leading to a value of $1{\cdot}740\times 10^{-5}$ for the dissociation constant.

44 (i) Values of the function for cell A:

m_{KCl}	Function 15° C	Function 25° C
0·02	0·82020	0·82802
0·05	0·82032	0·82818
0·10	0·82047	0·82837

Limiting values of function: 0·82012 at 15° C.
0·82789 at 25° C.

(ii) $K = 0{\cdot}4524\times 10^{-14}$ at 15° C.
$= 1{\cdot}0012$,, ,, 25° C.
$\Delta H = 13{\cdot}75$ kcal.

45 (i) Mean value of $[OH^-]/[Br^-] = 0.202$.
(ii) $K_w = 1.018 \times 10^{-14}$.

46 If 'p' is the absorbance of each solution for 1 cm optical path and 'y' is the quotient $[I_2]_0/p$, we find:

$[I_2]_0 \times 10^5$	p	$y \times 10^5$
3.26	0.317	10.29
10.42	0.829	12.59
17.4	0.700	24.9
43.5	0.853	51.0

When y is plotted against $1/A$ (the reciprocal of the mole fraction of benzene in the solution), a straight line is obtained as would be expected from the formation of a 1–1 complex between benzene and iodine. The value of y when $1/A$ is zero is approximately 6.4×10^{-5}, leading to a molar extinction coefficient of about 15600λ for the complex. The latter quantity can be used to find the concentration of complex and of un-complexed iodine in each solution and thence to calculate for each solution the value of the equilibrium constant defined as the molarity of the complex divided by the product of the molarity of the uncomplexed iodine and the mole fraction of benzene in the solution. The values obtained are 1.65, 1.67, 1.63, and 1.67 respectively.

47

pH	$[I_2]$ $\times 10^3$	$[I_3^-]$ $\times 10^6$	$\dfrac{[I_3^-]^2 f_\pm^2}{[I_2]^2 K_2}\left(1 + \dfrac{1}{K_2[I_2]}\right)$ $\times 10^8$
4.54	1.233	3.55	1.81
4.89	1.213	4.98	3.71
5.32	1.221	8.20	9.90
5.67	0.865	8.00	22.75

The plot of the expression in the fourth column against the reciprocal of the hydrogen-ion concentration gives a straight line, whose slope leads to a value of 4.8×10^{-13} for K_1.

48 (i) $[I_3^-] = 224.5 \times 10^{-5}$ mole litre^{-1}
$[I_2] = 21.5$,, ,,
$[I^-] = 1465.5$,, ,,
(ii) $[I^-]^2/[I_2] = 2.291 \times 10^3$ in the right half-cell.
(iii) $[I^-] = 1940 \times 10^{-5}$, $[I_2] = 1.64 \times 10^{-7}$, $[RH] = 2170 \times 10^{-5}$,
$[RI] = 248 \times 10^{-5}$, $[H^+] = 3.02 \times 10^{-5}$.
(All these concentrations are expressed as molarities.)
$K_a = 0.26_1$ mole litre^{-1}.

49 (iii) [Equivalent point $= 8.50$ cm^3]
$K = 6.6 \times 10^{-5}$.
(iv) [Equivalent point $= 8.09$ cm^3]
$K_1 = 9.1_8 \times 10^{-4}$; $K_2 = 7.2_7 \times 10^{-5}$.

50

(i) $\lim_{m_2=0} (\pi_2 + \pi_3)$

$m_1 = 0.05$	0.10	0.20
0.7383	0.7310	0.7221 volt.

(ii) $\pi_0 = 0.7470$ volt (extrapolation rather elastic).

(iii) $K_a = 0.1295$.

(iv) ⎡ The ionic strengths and equilibrium constants (in gramme-⎤
ion/litre units) are as follows:

0.01167	8.93×10^{-3}
0.00675	9.93×10^{-3}

$K_a = 0.01884$ and 0.01751 respectively. Mean $= 0.0182$.

(v) $\pi_0 = 0.7471$ volt.

51 (i) Experiment 8a.

⎡ From the first column of figures:
c.p.m./gramme of original tagged $Na^{24}Cl$ solution
$= 1.562 \times 10^6$.

From the second column of figures:
c.p.m. added to system as $Na^{24}Cl$ $= 1.545 \times 10^6$
c.p.m. in total solution at equilibrium $= 0.754 \times 10^6$
c.p.m. in resin at equilibrium $= 0.781 \times 10^6$.
(c.p.m./gramme of resin)/(c.p.m./gramme of solution $= 1470$. ⎦

$K_a = 1.79_1$.

(ii) ⎡ The difference between weight of solution and weight of solvent ⎤
cannot be neglected with the relatively concentrated hydrochloric acid involved in Experiment 12.
At equilibrium in Experiment 12:
(c.p.m./gramme of resin)/(c.p.m./gramme of solution) $= 8.44$. ⎦

If $\gamma_{HCl} = 0.789$, $\gamma_{NaCl} = 0.768$.

52 KCl, 27.9, 20.9, and 26.9 millimoles/litre^{-1}.

53 The average number of chloride ions bound to each albumin molecule are respectively 0.91, 5.7, and 8.5.

(These figures have not been corrected for the influence of impurities
present in protein and conductivity water; their contribution to the
conductivity leads to an overestimate of the concentration of sodium
chloride outside the sac and therefore to an underestimate of the amount
of chloride ion bound to each protein molecule.)

54

	kcal mole^{-1}				
Fluorides (Mean 81.7)	81.8	82.0	79.3	83.1	82.5
Chlorides (Mean 87.3)	88.2	87.1	84.5	86.7	90.2
Bromides (Mean 81.8)	83.6	81.7	79.0	81.4	83.2
Iodides (Mean 74.3) .	77.2	74.3	71.4	73.5	75.3

55 $\Delta H_{1873} = 59{\cdot}09$ kcal mole^{-1}.

56 (i)

$$\begin{bmatrix} & S \\ \textit{Temperature range} & \textit{(entropy units/mole)} \\ 0\text{--}157{\cdot}4° \text{ K} & 14{\cdot}88 \\ 157{\cdot}4\text{--}175{\cdot}2° \text{ K} & 1{\cdot}28 \\ 175{\cdot}2\text{--}298° \text{ K} & 9{\cdot}63 \end{bmatrix}$$

$S_{298}° = 31{\cdot}1$ entropy units/mole.

(ii) $\Delta H_{298}° = -57{\cdot}3$ kcal/mole.

(iii) $\Delta G_{298}° = -40{\cdot}3$,, ,,

57 $\Delta G_{298} = -6{\cdot}94$ kcal mole^{-1}.
$K_{p_{298}} = 1{\cdot}22 \times 10^5$.

58 (a) $\dfrac{p_{C_2H_4O}^2}{P_{C_2H_4}^2 \cdot p_{O_2}} = 9{\cdot}08 \times 10^{27}$ atm^{-1}.

(b) $2{\cdot}74 \times 10^{-6}$ atm or $2{\cdot}08 \times 10^{-3}$ mm.

(c) $1{\cdot}62 \times 10^{-4}$ atm.

(d) $a_{Fe}^{++}/a_{Fe}^{+++} = 1{\cdot}07 \times 10^{13}$.

(e) $1{\cdot}77 \times 10^{-10}$.

(f) $m = 1{\cdot}324 \times 10^{-3}$. (The free energy data used here are from W. M. Latimer, *Oxidation Potentials* (Prentice-Hall, Englewood Cliffs, 1952), and not from the NBS circular.)

(g) $0{\cdot}0573$ atm.

(h) $p_{CO}/p_{CO_2} = 3{\cdot}18 \times 10^{-11}$.

(i) $0{\cdot}0045$ atm.

(j) $0{\cdot}2224$ volt.

59

Concentration (per cent)	Specific heat
3	0·9627
12	0·8741

60 $S_{298}° = 6{\cdot}9_3$ cal/° K per mole

The graphical integration introduces an uncertainty of up to $0{\cdot}2$ cal/° K. Landolt-Börnstein gives a rather higher value.

61 (i) $39{\cdot}57$ e.u., $63{\cdot}94$ e.u.
(ii) (a) $-21{\cdot}66$ e.u., (b) $-23{\cdot}18$ e.u.
(iii) (a) $-21{\cdot}72$ e.u., (b) $-23{\cdot}19$ e.u.

62

	C_v(joules)	C_v(cal)	Temperature (°K)
(i)	10·90	2·605	20
	19·35	4·625	40
	22·10	5·282	60
	23·25	5·557	80
	23·88	5·707	100
	24·45	5·844	150
	24·77	5·920	200
	24·99	5·973	250
	25·19	6·020	298·15

(ii)

T (°K) .	.	13·4	22·3	33·5	67	134	268	402
C_v(calc.)	.	1·017	2·955	4·314	5·485	5·835	5·930	5·941

(iii)

T	.	. $n =$	0	1	2	5
67	.	.	0·632	0·233	0·0855	0·00426
335	.	.	0·181	0·148	0·121	0·0667
536	.	.	0·117	0·104	0·091	0·083

63

(i) The method of least squares leads to the equation

$$\log_{10} p = 7\cdot840 - \frac{9878}{T}.$$

(ii) 45200 cal per gramme-atom from the least squares equation.

(iii) 199_2° K from the least squares equation.

(If visual inspection is used to determine the 'best' straight line, results differing by several per cent from those above might be obtained. The measurements were difficult and the observations are compatible with a range of numerical values for the coefficients in the equation.)

64

(i) Entropy of liquid at 695° K $= 17\cdot99$ e.u.

Entropy of vapour at 695° K $= 59\cdot38$ e.u.

$\Delta H = 28\cdot77$ kcal mole^{-1}.

(ii) ΔH_{298} sublimation $= 31\cdot16$ kcal mole^{-1}.

(iii) ΔH_0 sublimation $= 31\cdot39$ kcal mole^{-1}.

ΔH_{298} sublimation $= 31\cdot17$ kcal mole^{-1}.

65

(i) $\Delta H = -14940$ cal (from KI)

$= -15020$ cal (from NaI). Mean $= 14980$

(ii) $S_{298} = 14\cdot0$ cal/°K.

66

(i)

T (°K) .	.	79·8	94·8	197·2	248·4	273·0	288·1
$C_p - C_v$(obs.)	.	0·84	0·77	0·52	0·49	0·49	0·49
$C_p - C_v$(calc.)	.	0·836	0·772	0·525	0·494	0·490	0·490

(ii) $\Delta G_T = 332\cdot8 + 1\cdot368T - 4\cdot39 \times 10^{-3}T^2 + 9\cdot73 \times 10^{-6}T^3 - $
$$- 8\cdot1 \times 10^{-9}T^4.$$

(iii) $\Delta F_T = 332\cdot8 - 3\cdot150\,T \log_{10} T + 5\cdot69T + 4\cdot39 \times 10^{-3}T^2 - $
$$- 4\cdot86 \times 10^{-6}T^3 + 2\cdot7 \times 10^{-9}T^4.$$

(iv) A graph will be found on p. 487 of the original paper.

67 $\Delta H = 15\cdot1$ kcal mole^{-1}.

68 (i) $A = 2\cdot088$, $B = 893$ (typical values from visual inspection).
(ii) $A = 2\cdot156$, $B = 915$.
(iii) $\Delta H = 4\cdot19$ kcal in the neighbourhood of 65° C.
(iv) $\Delta H_{298} = 4\cdot16$ kcal.
    $\Delta S_{298} = 9\cdot8$ entropy units.

69

$$\begin{bmatrix} g/1000\ g\ water & moles/litre\ (c) & c\ d\Delta/dc \\ 499\cdot7 & 1\cdot508 & 0\cdot2774 \\ 472\cdot2 & 1\cdot437 & 0\cdot2701 \\ 428\cdot9 & 1\cdot322 & 0\cdot2551 \\ 395\cdot0 & 1\cdot231 & 0\cdot2381 \\ 313\cdot9 & 1\cdot001 & 0\cdot1972 \end{bmatrix}$$

Osmotic pressures (atmospheres): 132·2, 113·3, 87·0, 71·2, 41·7.

70 (i)

T (°K)	$C_{\text{vibrational}}$ (cal/mole)
270	0·981
452	1·528

(ii) If to the above values are added $\frac{3}{2}R$ calories for translational heat capacity, R calories for rotational heat capacity (assumed classical about two axes of rotation) and R calories for external work $(C_p - C_v)$ we get 7·936 for C_p at 270° K and 8·483 for C_p at 452° K. The concordance supports the validity of the Einstein equation for the vibrational energy of the chlorine molecule and also the assumption that the rotational energy may be treated as classical ($\equiv$ high quantum numbers of rotation) as these temperatures.
(iii) At 298° K 93·5 per cent of molecules have no vibrational quanta and 6·1 per cent have one vibrational quantum; at 813° K 63·2 per cent of molecules have no vibrational quanta and 23·2 per cent have one vibrational quantum.

71 $\Lambda_0 = 30\cdot6$. $K = 3\cdot5 \times 10^{-5}$.

72 (i) $\Lambda_0 = 126\cdot42$; observed slope $= 83$.
(ii) $\Lambda_0 = 126\cdot41_5$.
(iii) Slope from Onsager equation $= 88\cdot5$.

73 $K = 9 \times 10^{-15}$ mole^2 litre^{-2}.

74 (i) $1\cdot840 \times 10^{-6}$ ohm^{-1} cm^{-1}.
(ii) Solubility, making no allowance for interionic attraction, $1\cdot331 \times 10^{-5}$ mole litre^{-1}. After correcting for interionic attraction, the value of $1\cdot334 \times 10^{-5}$ mole litre^{-1} is obtained.

(iii) $\left[\left(\dfrac{1{\cdot}334\times 10^{-5}\times 0{\cdot}9958}{0{\cdot}9970}\right)^2=\right]$ $1{\cdot}775\times 10^{-10}$.

75 (i) Lithium bromide in acetophenone:
A fair straight line is obtained when $1/\Lambda$ is plotted against Λ/v, leading to the values $\Lambda_0 = 34{\cdot}5$, $K = 1{\cdot}4\times 10^{-4}$.
(ii) Tetraethylammonium picrate in chloroform:
$\Lambda_0 = 104{\cdot}65$ leading to the following values of the dissociation constant:

$v =$	5852	24140	49620	95520
$K\times 10_9 =$	2·8	3·3	4·9	4·8

The graph of $1/\Lambda$ against Λ/v is very irregular.

76 (i) $\Lambda_0 = 52{\cdot}3\pm 0{\cdot}4$; the slope $d\Lambda/d\sqrt{c}$ is about 1000, the Onsager slope being 138.
(ii) At $v = 11680$ the 'true' degree of dissociation is $0{\cdot}83_8$, whereas the conductivity ratio is $0{\cdot}82_0$.

77

Approximate concentration		0·02	3·0
Change in amount of KCl (in grammes) due to electrolysis			
	anolyte	$-0{\cdot}05428$	$-0{\cdot}933$
	catholyte	$+0{\cdot}05409$	$+0{\cdot}931$
Transport number of K			
	from anolyte	0·490	0·486
	from catholyte	0·488	0·485

78

	Anolyte	*Catholyte*
Composition of solution *after* electrolysis (in grammes)		
Raffinose	5·018	3·763
Lithium chloride	4·636	4·534
Water	94·746	73·173
Weight of LiCl in same solution *before* electrolysis (in grammes)		
(a) assuming water and raffinose stationary	5·1835	3·997
(b) assuming raffinose only stationary	5·240	3·929

(i) Apparent n_{Li^+} 0·278   0·273
(ii) 'True' n_{Li^+} 0·307   0·307
(iii) Water transfer (moles/Faraday)   1·30   1·57
(iv) N_w^{Li} $(4{\cdot}7+2{\cdot}2x)$

79 $n_{Na^+} = 0{\cdot}389_5$.

80 (i) $\begin{bmatrix}\text{Values of the function at successively higher concentrations:}\\ 91\cdot01_2,\ 91\cdot07_7,\ 91\cdot09_4,\ 91\cdot21_6,\ 91\cdot35_3.\end{bmatrix}$

$\Lambda_0 = 90\cdot99$.

Shedlovsky equation: $\Lambda_{\text{NaAc}} = 90\cdot99 - 80\cdot48\sqrt{c} + 86c(1 - 0\cdot2274\sqrt{c})$.

(ii) $\Lambda_{\epsilon\text{HAc}} = 390\cdot61 - 148\cdot62\sqrt{c_i} + 162\cdot0c_i(1 - 0\cdot2274\sqrt{c_i})$.

c_i	Λ_ϵ
0·000036	389·82
0·0001	389·14
0·0002	388·54
0·0006	387·07
0·0010	385·40

(iii), (iv), and (v)

$c \times 10^3$	(iii) $K_{\text{Ostwald}} \times 10^5$	(iv) 'true α'	(v) $K' \times 10^5$
0·02801	1·759	0·5392	1·766
0·15321	1·767	0·2875	1·777
1·02831	1·777	0·1238	1·794
9·8421	1·804	$0\cdot0422_2$	1·831
52·303	1·809	$0\cdot0186_5$	1·851

(vi) and (vii) The graph of $\log K'$ against $\sqrt{c_i}$ leads to a limiting value at infinite dilution of $\bar{5}\cdot2434$; the thermodynamic dissociation constant is therefore $1\cdot752 \times 10^{-5}$. The limiting slope is $0\cdot96 \pm 0\cdot03$, the theoretical value being $1\cdot01$.

81 (i) *Assuming* linearity of Λ_c with $\sqrt{c}$ below $c = 10\cdot79 \times 10^{-5}$ Λ_0' is $82\cdot6 \pm 0\cdot5$.

(ii) The Onsager slope based on Λ_0' is about 471; the observed slope is about 2190. Dissociation must be incomplete and the true curve of Λ_c against $\sqrt{c}$ must become concave to the $\sqrt{c}$ axis at very high dilutions and Λ_0' must be somewhat larger than the true value of Λ_0.

(iii)

Molarity $\times 10^5$	$\dfrac{1}{\Lambda S} \times 10^2$	$c\Lambda Sf^2 \times 10^3$
10·79	1·588	4·764
6·564	1·486	3·316
3·328	1·385	1·946

The above figures were obtained by taking a provisional value of 83 for Λ_0 and approximating S to $(1+Z)$; calculations based on $S = 1 + Z + \dfrac{Z^2}{2}$ (i.e. including one further term in the expansion) give results that are not significantly different.

$\Lambda_0 = 80\cdot2$; $K = 2\cdot1_7$ mole litre^{-1}.

82 (i) $-143\cdot1$ kcal mole^{-1}.
(ii) -201 kcal mole^{-1}.

83 (i) $\pi_0 = 0\cdot7646$ volt.
(ii) $L = 8\cdot63 \times 10^{-14}$ (in activity units based on molalities).
(iii) $\pi_0 = 1\cdot1280$ volt.

84 (i) $\left[\dfrac{N\varepsilon^2 z^2}{JD} \sqrt{\left(\dfrac{8\pi\varepsilon^2 z^2 N}{1000\,DkT}\right)} = 1279z^3.\right]$

	dD/dT	A
	$-0\cdot349$	-322 (a)
	$-0\cdot365$	-486 (b)

(ii) and (iii) $\qquad\qquad V_{c_1 c_2}$ $(cal/mole)$

Observed	Calculated	
	(a)	(b)
$-13\cdot7$	$-11\cdot9$	$-18\cdot1$
$-18\cdot3$	$-17\cdot1$	$-25\cdot9$
$-30\cdot9$	$-30\cdot9$	$-46\cdot7$
$-38\cdot3$	$-53\cdot3$	$-80\cdot6$

85 The equation $\dfrac{d\log I}{dV} = \dfrac{K}{T}$ seems to express the variation of current density with overvoltage for both discharge processes, with K the same in both cases within the (not inconsiderable) experimental error:

	Temperature $(^\circ K)$	$d\log I/dV$	$Td\log I/dV$
Hydrogen at mercury	273	$9\cdot14$	$2\cdot5 \times 10^3$
,, ,, ,,	345	$7\cdot00$	$2\cdot4$,,
Oxygen at platinum	273	$10\cdot3$	$2\cdot8$,,
,, ,, ,,	254	$6\cdot65$	$2\cdot3$,,

where I is the current density in amps$\times 10^{-6}$/cm^2 and V is the overvoltage in volts.

If the equation is written in the form $\dfrac{d\log I}{dV} = \dfrac{\alpha}{2\cdot303RT}$ and R is expressed in volt-faradays/$^\circ$ C, α has the value $0\cdot5 \pm 0\cdot05$.

86

	$D/(D+H)$
Original water . . .	$0\cdot01062$
Original solution . . .	$0\cdot01057$
Final water . . .	$0\cdot03374$

$\alpha = 7\cdot7.$

87 ⎡During each stage of electrolysis the deuterium content of the electrolyte is changed so that for each stage $D_{final}/D_{initial} = 0.9647$. Assuming that the D/H ratio in the original water was 0.00025, the D/H ratio in the cathode gas from the first three stages would be 3.53×10^{-5}, 4.98×10^{-6}, and 7.02×10^{-7} respectively.⎤

(i) 7×10^{-7}.

(ii) 0.07 parts per million.

(iii) The specific gravity of deuterium-free water must be 0.999981 relative to ordinary water; the D/H ratio in ordinary water must therefore be about $1/5700$.

(iv) $\alpha = 1.008_8$.

(v) About 10^{34} cm^3.

88 The ratio must lie between 1.6 and 2.3.

89 (i)

Current (amp)	Rate constant (litre mole^{-1} min^{-1})	
0·100	3.64×10^2	
0·200	3·74 ,,	
0·055	3·56 ,,	(pH 8·55)
0·055	3·33 ,,	(pH 8·58)

(ii) When corrected for cumulative nitroethane depletion the rate constant calculated from the equilibrium pH of 8·58 at 0·055 amp becomes 339 instead of 333; an error of 0·05 unit in the pH value changes the rate constant by 37 and is clearly a more significant source of uncertainty.

(iii) 0.056 min or 3.3_6 sec. It is important here (a) to keep track of powers of ten in converting pH units to hydroxide ion concentrations, (b) to distinguish between the amount of hydroxide ion generated in the 250 ml sample solution and the amount generated per litre.

90 (i) $e^{-36.9}$ ($\simeq 10^{-16}$).
(ii) $e^{-36.9}$ ($\simeq 10^{-16}$).

(iii) $\left(\dfrac{E}{RT} + 1\right) 10^{-16} \simeq 4 \times 10^{-15}$.

(iv)

Number of quadratic terms	Proportion of collisions
6	7×10^{-14}
12	6×10^{-11}
18	8×10^{-9}
24	4×10^{-7}

244

91 (i) Second order.

(ii) 3·70, 0·84, and 0·135 respectively.

(iii) 58 kcal.

(iv) ⎡Root-mean-square velocity $= 7·64 \times 10^4$ cm/sec. At a concentration of one mole per litre the number of molecules reacting per cm^3 per sec is $5·09 \times 10^{20}$; the number of molecules colliding per cm^3 per sec is $1·38 \times 10^{32}$.⎤

To account for the observed reaction rate at 1030° K, an activation energy of 53·9 kcal is necessary.

92 The reaction is homogeneous and first order; the rate constant may be expressed by an equation such as:

$$k = 3·5 \times 10^{10} e^{-41600/RT}.$$

The slight uncertainty in the gradient of the $\log k \Big/ \dfrac{1}{T}$ graph naturally affects both the exponential term and (more conspicuously) the non-exponential portion of the expression; a value of as high as 42400 for the heat of activation is not inconsistent with the data selected for the problem and such a value would lead to a corresponding increase in the coefficient by which the exponential term is multiplied.

93 (i) First order.

(ii) 29·5 kcal.

94 On *tungsten* the reaction is of zero order with respect to ammonia and is uninfluenced by the pressure of hydrogen present; this points to the tungsten surface being almost completely covered by ammonia.

On *platinum* the rate is roughly proportional to the ammonia pressure and almost inversely proportional to the hydrogen pressure; this suggests that the catalyst is nearly covered with hydrogen which must be much more strongly adsorbed than ammonia.

95 (i) The order is about 2·8; the reaction is therefore predominantly third order.

(ii) Reaction velocity $\propto p_{NO}^2 p_{H_2}$.

(iii) 1·48, 1·27, 1·29, and $1·64 \times 10^{-7}$ respectively.

(iv) 1·28 and $1·19 \times 10^{-7}$.

(v) The anomalies originally attributed to the heterogeneous reaction are now interpreted otherwise; the references quoted in the note should be consulted.

(vi) $39·5 \pm 1$ kcal.

96 (i) The order of reaction is $\frac{3}{2}$; this suggests the mechanism mentioned in (ii).

(ii) 6·5 kcal; 5·5 kcal if the temperature dependence of collision rate is allowed for.

97
$$\begin{bmatrix} \text{Time spent by gases in reaction bulb} = 0\cdot0164 \text{ sec.} \\ \text{Partial pressures in bulb (mm): } H_2 = 0\cdot1306,\ Cl_2 = 0\cdot1679, \\ Cl = 0\cdot0415 \end{bmatrix}$$

(i) $1\cdot0$ (ii) $2\cdot9 \times 10^4$.   (iii) $1\cdot7 \times 10^{-5}$.

98 (i) $k_1 = \dfrac{2\cdot303K}{2t[\text{HCl}]\sqrt{(Ka+\frac{1}{4}K^2)}} \times$
$$\times \left[\log_{10}\frac{\sqrt{(Ka+\frac{1}{4}K^2)}+(x+\frac{1}{2}K)}{\sqrt{(Ka+\frac{1}{4}K^2)}-(x+\frac{1}{2}K)} - \log_{10}\frac{\sqrt{(Ka+\frac{1}{4}K^2)}+\frac{1}{2}K}{\sqrt{(Ka+\frac{1}{2}K^2)}-\frac{1}{2}K} \right].$$

(ii) $[K = 0\cdot405.]$

t (sec)	k_1 (mole/litre/sec)
1350	$3\cdot53 \times 10^{-3}$
2070	$3\cdot54$
3060	$3\cdot75$
5340	$3\cdot49$
7740	$3\cdot71$

99 (i) $E = 5500$, 6800, and 12100 cal respectively.
(ii) [Calculated velocity constants: $7\cdot4 \times 10^7$, $4\cdot2 \times 10^6$, and $7\cdot4 \times 10^2$.] $P = 1\cdot2 \times 10^{-8}$, $2\cdot9 \times 10^{-7}$, and $1\cdot5 \times 10^{-7}$ respectively.
(iii) In these experiments E plotted against $\log_{10} kM^{\frac{1}{2}}$ lies on a line of gradient close to $2\cdot303RT$, therefore P varies comparatively little and the differences in reaction velocity are primarily due to differences in the energy of activation.

100 (i)

Flask	Velocity constant (equiv/litre/min)
1	$0\cdot296_0$
2	$0\cdot299_6$
3	$0\cdot308_3$

(ii) $\begin{bmatrix} \text{The ionic strength of the reaction mixture is four times the} \\ \text{normality of the reactants in it.} \end{bmatrix}$

$\dfrac{d\log_{10}K}{d\sqrt{\mu}}$ for the experimental values is distinctly less than the theoretical value of $+2\cdot0$ if the correct ionic strengths are used.

101 $1\cdot42_3$ min^{-1}.

102 (i) $K_0 = 5\cdot30 \times 10^{-3}$.
(ii) $k_{H_2O} = 0\cdot146$.
(iii) $k_{M^-} = 0\cdot011_5$.
$k_{Py} = 0\cdot079$.
$k_{HM} = 0\cdot006_5$.
$k_{PyH^+} = 0$. $k_{H_2O} = 9\cdot5 \times 10^{-5}$.
(iv) The graph will be found on p. 2583 of the original paper.

103 (i) 1.81_3 micro-moles of ferrous iron.

(ii)

Wave-length (Å) . .	4360	4050	3660
Rate of absorption of radiation by *solution* corrected for area of cell face, transmission by cell face and solution (microwatts)	206	68·6	150
Ergs absorbed during irradiation . .	3.71×10^6	1.85×10^6	1.80×10^6
Einsteins absorbed during irradiation .	1.35×10^{-6}	6.27×10^{-7}	5.51×10^{-7}
Quantum efficiency (moles of ferrous iron produced per Einstein absorbed) . .	1·14	1·16	1·27

104 $\begin{bmatrix} \text{Quanta absorbed in first experiment} = 1.13 \times 10^{19} \\ \quad,, \qquad ,, \quad ,, \text{ second } \quad ,, \quad = 4.12 \times 10^{19}. \end{bmatrix}$

0·51 and 0·56 molecules/quantum respectively.

105 See pp. 145 and 146 of the original paper.

106 (i) Rate $\propto [C_2H_4I_2]$ and independent of $[I_2]$.
(ii) Rate $= k\sqrt{I_0}\,[C_2H_4I_2]$.
(iii) Quantum efficiency $= 26.4$ and 23.5 respectively.
(iv) See the original paper.

107

Wave-length (Å)	Quanta/sec per cm deflexion of photo. cell	x (mm)	Number of molecules of NO_2 decomposed per second in cell	Number of quanta absorbed per second
4360	6.44×10^{13}	0	0	..
4050	3.45×10^{13}	1·22	2.9×10^{14}	4.0×10^{14}
3650	1.44×10^{13}	1·68	7.5×10^{14}	3.6×10^{14}

Wave-length (Å)	Quantum efficiency
4360	0
4050	0·72
3650	2·07

108

		Methyl acetate	*Ethyl acetate*	
(i)	E	12·0	11·6	kcal/mole
(ii)	$\Delta H^{\ddagger}$	11·4	11·0	,, ,,
(iii)	$\Delta S^{\ddagger}$	$-24·1$	$-26·2$	cal deg^{-1} mole^{-1}
(iv)	$\Delta S^{\ddagger}$	$-10·4$	$-12·5$	,, ,, ,,

The change of concentration units multiplies the rate constants by 10^3 and raises their logarithms by 3; the effect of this is to increase the entropy of activation algebraically by $3 \ln R$ or 13·7 cal deg^{-1} mole^{-1}. The dependence of the entropy of activation on the concentration units is not surprising since the entropy of activation is a *standard* entropy change and is equal to the entropy increase when the appropriate number of moles of each reactant, initially at unit concentration (e.g. 1 mole/litre or 1 mole/cm^3), are transformed into one mole of activated complex also at unit concentration. For all but first-order reactions the entropy of activation will depend on the concentration unit selected. The textbook reference in the note may be consulted for amplification.

109

If k_0 is the rate constant under atmospheric pressure and k is the rate constant at higher pressures, the values of $\log k/k_0$ for the five pressures tabulated are 0, 0·0781, 0·1473, 0·2156, and 0·2853 respectively. The plot of $\log k/k_0$ against p has a slope of $1·80 \times 10^{-5}$ in^2 lb^{-1}.

$\Delta V^{\ddagger} = -14·9$ cm^3/mole.

110

(i) $(R_{\text{methane}}/R^{\frac{1}{2}}_{\text{ethane}}) \times [\text{acetone}] = k_3/k_2^{\frac{1}{2}}$.

(ii)

Run	R_{methane}	R_{ethane}	$[acetone]$
	(*molecules*/*cm*^{3}/*sec* $\times 10^{-12}$)		(*molecules*/*cm*^{3} $\times 10^{-18}$)
26	9·21	1·03	0·816
27	6·33	14·3	2·14
29	14·4	8·10	1·98
30	25·4	1·89	1·72
158	1·61	0·738	2·20
160	0·69	0·175	2·20

(iii) $F \times 10^{13} = 112, 7·82, 25·5, 107·6, 8·52$, and 7·50 respectively.

(iv) (Quanta/second) $\times 10^{-14} = 38·6, 3·8$, and 1·2 respectively. F does not vary significantly with light intensity.

(v) F is essentially the same at both pressures.

(vi) It follows from (i) that the slope of the plot is $(E_3 - \frac{1}{2}E_2)/2·303R$; if E_2 is zero, $E_3 = 9·9$ kcal.

(vii) From the condition that the concentration of excited ethane molecules does not change with time it can be shown that:

$$[C_2H_6^*] = \frac{k_2[CH_3]^2}{k_6 + k_7[A]}.$$

248

When this is substituted in the expression for F we get:

$$F = \frac{k_3}{k_2^{\frac{1}{2}}} \times \left[\frac{k_6}{k_7} \cdot \frac{1}{[A]} + 1 \right]^{\frac{1}{2}} \text{ and, since } G = F \times [A]^{\frac{1}{2}},$$

$$G = \frac{k_3}{k_2^{\frac{1}{2}}} \times \left[\frac{k_6}{k_7} + [A] \right]^{\frac{1}{2}}.$$

(viii)

Run	101B	97B	100B	104B	103B
$F \times 10^{13}$	264	138	110	88·1	86·1
$G \times 10^4$	18·8	17·7	25·9	39·9	52·3

(ix) The fall of F to a limiting value as the acetone pressure *increases* and the fall of G to a limiting value as the acetone pressure *falls* are both to be anticipated from the answers to (vii). The operation of a third body restriction in the low-pressure region is clearly confirmed.

111

(i) There is a close approximation to direct proportionality between the rate of nitrogen production and the intensity of absorbed light.

(ii) Quantum yield of nitrogen (molecules of nitrogen produced per quantum of light absorbed): 0·93, 0·93, 0·88, and 0·94.

(iii) (Rate of formation of methane)/(rate of formation of ethane)$^{\frac{1}{2}}$ is fairly closely proportional to the initial pressure of the azomethane.

(iv) The observations recorded in (i), (ii), and (iii) fit in well with the reaction scheme proposed. The reason for the constancy of $(R_{CH_4})/(R_{C_2H_4})^{\frac{1}{2}} \times$ [azomethane] will be seen if rate equations for steps (2) and (3) of the reaction scheme are combined so as to eliminate the concentration of the methyl radical.

(v) 7·3 kcal. Use is made here of the fact that $d \ln (k_2/k_3^{\frac{1}{2}})/d(1/T)$ is very simply connected with the activation energy of step (2) diminished by half that of step (3), together with the assumption that the activation energy for the recombination of methyl radicals is zero.

112

(i) The experimental data are well represented by the equation if $a = 1$, $b = \frac{1}{2}$, and $c = -\frac{1}{2}$. With these exponents k' has the successive values of 7·2, 7·2, and 7·3 × 10^{-4} respectively.

(ii) $k' = 2·84$, 0·818, and 0·185 × 10^{-4} respectively. The energy of activation is $18·4_6$ kcal, uncorrected for the variation of collision number with temperature, or 18·0 kcal after correction.

(iii) The reaction rate is very nearly proportional to the square root of the light intensity since $(1-0·555)^{\frac{1}{2}} = 0·667$.

(iv) $k_4/k_3 = 0·212$.

(v) The rate laws obeyed without and with the addition of hydrogen bromide beforehand can be derived by writing down the equations for steady state concentrations of bromine atoms and of methyl radicals. The rate of reaction measured is determined by the third step in the postulated mechanism. It should be remembered that in any given set of observations the incident light intensity was constant and the experimental conditions were such that the rate of absorption of light by molecular bromine was proportional to its partial pressure.

113 (i) For methyl methacrylate the number of initiator fragments per polymer molecule is 1·15; for styrene the corresponding quantity is 2·03.

(ii) In the polymerization of methyl methacrylate under these conditions chain termination by disproportionation is more frequent than that by combination. In the polymerization of styrene chain ending by combination is predominant.

114 (i) If the proportion of carboxyl groups esterified, 'p', is defined as the quotient of the number of ester groups divided by the sum of the number of ester groups and of unesterified carboxyl groups, its value at successive stages is 0·7899, 0·8674, 0·8975, 0·9221, and 0·9304.

(ii) $1/(1-p)^2$ = 22·65, 56·81, 95·24, 164·7, and 206·2. This quantity increases linearly with time during the period of reaction covered by the data; the latter are accordingly compatible with the hypothesis cited in the statement of the problem.

115 (i) [Intercept on $(\varepsilon-1)vT$ axis at $T = 0$ is 0·87.]
$\mu = 1·02 \times 10^{-18}$ e.s.u. = 1·02 Debyes.

(ii) (electronic charge) $\times$ (internuclear distance) = 6·2 Debyes.

116

$k \times 10^{-5}$ dynes cm^{-1}	F_2	Cl_2	Br_2	I_2	
	4·45	3·29	2·46	1·72	
	HF	HCl	HBr	HI	H_2
	6·72	5·16	4·12	3·14	5·76

117 (i) $1·65 \times 10^6$ dynes/cm.
(ii) 1·36 ,, ,,
(iii) (Stokes line at 170 cm^{-1} Anti-Stokes at 168 cm^{-1}.)
$k = 1·69 \times 10^5$ dyne cm^{-1}.

118 $I = 2·68 \times 10^{-40}$ g cm^2. Internuclear distance = 1·28 Å.

119 $B = \dfrac{5·0536 \times 10^{-5}}{\mu r^2}$ μ in at. wt. units, r in cm.

	CsCl^{35}	CsCl^{37}
B_e =	$2·161 \times 10^9$ c/s	$2·069 \times 10^9$ c/s
r_e =	2·899 Å	2·899 Å
r_0 =	2·909	
r_4 =	2·937	
r_8 =	2·966	

120

	HCl^{35}		DCl^{35}	
	Accurate	*Approximate*	*Accurate*	*Approximate*
ν_0	2886·01 cm^{-1}	2885·70 cm^{-1}	2091·04 cm^{-1}	2090·9 cm^{-1}
$x_e\omega_e$		51·7		27·6
ω_e		2989·2		2146·1
k_e		5·156 × 10^5 dynes cm^{-1}		5·165 × 10^5 dynes cm^{-1}
B_0	10·427 cm^{-1}	10·436 cm^{-1}	5·392 cm^{-1}	5·393 cm^{-1}
B_1	10·123	10·138	5·280	5·280
B_e	10·579	10·589	5·448	5·450
α	0·3035	0·306	0·1123	0·114
r_0	1·284$_5$ Å	1·284 Å	1·281 Å	1·280 Å
r_e	1·274$_4$ Å	1·275 Å	1·2746 Å	1·275 Å

121

(i) Gaps occur at about 11370 cm^{-1} and 14830 cm^{-1}.
The difference is 3460 cm^{-1} and $11370/3 = 3790$ and $14830/4 = 3710$. We therefore have the 3,0 and 4,0 bands.

(ii) $R(J-1)-P(J+1)$ for 3,0 band; for 4,0 band

$J = 1$	123·21	123·20
2	205·25	205·24
3	286·95	286·96
4	368·33	368·32
	&c.	

(iii) $\Delta_2 F(J) \approx 4B(J+\frac{1}{2})+8D(J+\frac{1}{2})^3$.
The slopes of the plots of $\Delta_2 F(J)/(J+\frac{1}{2})$ against $(J+\frac{1}{2})^2$ vary, but there is not much error in B.
$B_0 = 20·546$. $B_3 = 18·299$. $B_4 = 17·561$.
$D \approx -1·9 \times 10^{-3}$.

(iv) $R(J+1)+P(J) = 2\nu_0+2J^2(B'-B'')+2J^2(J^2+1)(D'-D'')$.
ν_0 for 3,0 band $= 11372·84$ cm^{-1}
4,0 band $= 14831·69$ cm^{-1}.
$\omega_e = 4123·0_4$ cm^{-1}. $x_e\omega_e = 83·02$ cm^{-1}.

(v) $B_0 = 20·546$. $I_0 = 1·3621 \times 10^{-40}$ gm cm^2.
$r_0 = 0·9258$ Å. $k_e = 9·584 \times 10^5$ dynes cm^{-1}.

(vi) $D_0 \approx 49150$ cm^{-1} $= 6·0$ eV $= 140·_4$ kcal mole^{-1}.

122

(i) 2·46 eV. (ii) 56·9 kcal.

123

17·5 kcal (= 0·76 cV).

124

263 kcal (≡ 11·41 eV).

125

(i) $\Sigma\Delta G_v = 7773$ cm^{-1} $= D_0$.
$D_e = 8119$ cm^{-1}.

(ii) Dissociation products are $^3P + {}^1D$.

(iii) D_0 for $^3\Sigma_g^-$ state $= 41259$ cm^{-1} per molecule $= 117·96$ kcal mole^{-1}.

126 CO_2 Linear symmetrical.

N₂O N_2O Not symmetrical. The rotational fine structure of the vibrational spectrum show NNO to be linear.

$\left.\begin{array}{l} ZnCl_2 \\ ZnBr_2 \\ ZnI_2 \end{array}\right\}$ Linear. In strong aqueous solutions, additional lines occur in the Raman spectrum due to ions of the kind $ZnCl_{2+n}^{n-}$.

SCl_2 Non-linear.
NO_2^- Non-linear.
NO_3^- Planar symmetrical.
NF_3 Pyramidal.

127 (i) $4 \times 58 \cdot 45$.   (ii) $5 \cdot 65$ Å.   (iii) $0 \cdot 589$ Å.

128

$\dfrac{\sin \theta}{\gamma}$		0·1	0·2	0·3	0·4	0·5	0·6	0·7	0·8	0·9	1·0
NaCl $\begin{cases} f_{Na} \\ f_{Cl} \end{cases}$	(9·5)	7·9	5·5	3·9	2·6	1·7	1·1	0·8	0·5	0·4	
	(15·7)	11·4	8·05	6·1	4·9	3·8	3·0	2·2	1·6	1·15	
NaF $\begin{cases} f_{Na} \\ f_F \end{cases}$	(9·7)	8·1	6·2	4·5	3·25	2·3	1·6	1·15	..	..	
	(8·9)	7·2	4·85	3·1	1·9	1·3	0·9	0·65	..	..	

129 (i) $F_{hkl} = 2 \cos 2\pi(hx + ky + lz)$.

(ii) $F_{hkl} = \sqrt{(A^2 + B^2)}$,

where $A = \cos 2\pi(hx + ky + lz) + \cos 2\pi\{-hx + k(y + \tfrac{1}{2}) - lz\}$
$B = \sin 2\pi(hx + ky + lz) + \sin 2\pi\{-hx + k(y + \tfrac{1}{2}) - lz\}$.

(iii) $F_{hkl} = \sqrt{(A^2 + B^2)}$,

where $A = \cos 2\pi(hx + ky + lz) + \cos 2\pi\{h(x + \tfrac{1}{2}) - ky + lz\}$
$B = \sin 2\pi(hx + ky + lz) + \sin 2\pi\{h(x + \tfrac{1}{2}) - ky + lz\}$.

(iv) In the case of (i) all reflections appear for 0k0 (k odd) and h0l (h odd).

In the case of (ii), 0k0 reflections are absent when k is odd.

In the case of (iii), k0l reflections are absent when h is odd.

(v) If the screw axis is placed at the origin, the centres of symmetry are at $\tfrac{1}{4}\,\tfrac{1}{4}\,0$, $\tfrac{3}{4}\,\tfrac{1}{4}\,0$, $\tfrac{1}{4}\,\tfrac{3}{4}\,0$, and $\tfrac{3}{4}\,\tfrac{3}{4}\,0$.

(vi) 1172; two nickel atoms in cell.

(vii) Maximum m.w. (from crystallographic data) = 586.
Minimum m.w. (from analytical data) = 559.

(viii) The molecule must have a centre of symmetry and the nickel atoms be placed at the crystallographic centres of symmetry.

130 Electrons per Å:

$2\pi x/d$		0	10	20	30	40	50	60	70	80	90
86° K	.	32·6	27·3	16·1	8·5	6·3	5·7	4·5	3·3	2·9	2·5
290° K	.	27·1	24·0	17·4	11·0	7·2	5·6	4·6	3·7	3·1	2·8
900° K	.	18·0	17·4	15·6	13·2	10·5	8·2	6·3	4·9	4·1	3·7

$2\pi x/d$.	100	110	120	130	140	150	160	170	180	..
86° K .	2·4	2·4	3·1	4·3	5·4	7·2	11·2	16·6	19·2	..
290° K .	2·8	2·8	3·4	4·4	5·4	8·3	11·6	14·7	16·0	..
900° K .	3·7	4·1	4·8	6·0	7·3	8·9	10·3	11·3	11·7	..

131 (i) $F = f_{Fe}\{\cos \pi h + \cos \pi k + \cos \pi l + \cos \pi(h+k+l)\{+$
$\qquad + 2f_s[\cos 2\pi u(h+k+l) + \cos 2\pi\{u(h-k-l) + \tfrac{1}{2}(h+k\} +$
$\qquad + \cos 2\pi\{u(h+k+l) + \tfrac{1}{2}(k+l)\} +$
$\qquad + \cos 2\pi\{u(k+l-h) + \tfrac{1}{2}(h+l)\}\}].$

For $h00$ (h even) this becomes $4[f_{Fe} + 2f_s \cos 2\pi hu]$.

(ii) To save space, values of $F/4$ are given below for the 200 plane only:

$2\pi x/d$.	0°	40°	60°	80°	90°	120°	180°
u . .	0	0·0555	0·0833	0·111	0·125	0·167	0·250
$F/4$.	40·1	36·0	30·2	23·1	8·8	−1·9	19·5

$u = 0.114$. (The data of the problem do not permit of any certainty as to the third significant figure; the value given here is that obtained by Fourier analysis.)

(iii) With $u = 0.114$, the calculated F values are:

200	400	600	800	1000
23·45	−1·20	5·80	17·02	11·84

and $R = 8.6$ per cent.

(A small improvement in R could be effected by modifying $F_{calc.}$ by a term $e^{-B\frac{\sin^2 \theta}{\lambda^2}}$ to allow for the thermal movement of the atoms.)

(iv)

$2\pi x/d$	0	10	20	30	40	50	60	70	80	90
ρ_x	120·2	79·2	29·6	46·9	74·7	51·2	17·2	11·2	13·0	9·2

(v)

$2\pi x/d$	0	10	20	30	40	50	60	70	80	90
P_x	880	519	53	122	326	55	$\overline{390}$	$\overline{522}$	$\overline{429}$	$\overline{374}$

These figures have been calculated from the Fs of (ii), i.e. on the $\tfrac{1}{4}$ scale.

Fe–Fe, $x = 0$ and $x = \tfrac{1}{2}$.
Fe–S, $x = u$, $\tfrac{1}{2} - u$.
S–S, $\tfrac{1}{2} - 2u$, $2u$.

and positions related by the centre of symmetry at $x = 0$.

(vi) S–S $= 2.14$
Fe–S $= 2.26$ (based on $u = 0.114$).

132 (i) Three types of arrangement consistent with tetragonal symmetry are shown diagrammatically overleaf; of these (1) is centrosymmetric and excluded by the space group data; (3) may be centrosymmetric with suitable choice of z parameters; it is very unlikely from the cell dimensions.

For (1) and (2) there are two possible projections, b_1 and b_2, parallel with mirror planes in (a) at 45° to one another.

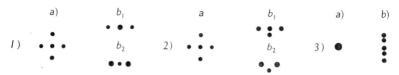

(ii) The diagrams below correspond with the structure types in (i), the points being weighted according to the number of vectors involved.

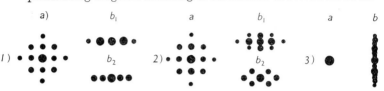

(iii) The boron atoms have parameters:
B1, $00z$, B2, $x0z$, $\bar{x}0z$, $0xz$, $0\bar{x}z$.

The values given by Lipscomb and Dulmage for these parameters from three dimensional calculations are:

	x	y	z
B1	$0\cdot000$	$0\cdot000$	$0\cdot202 \pm 0\cdot004$
B2	$0\cdot175 \pm 0\cdot002$	$0\cdot000$	$0\cdot000$

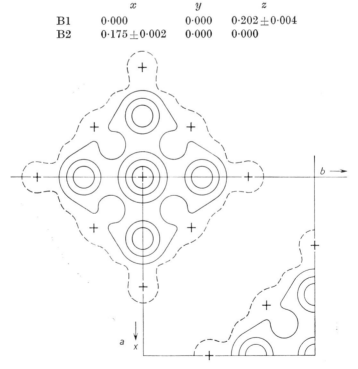

Slightly different values are given by the two dimensional maps.

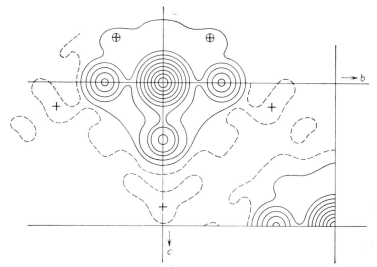

(iv) The drawings illustrate maps drawn from the figure fields of the electron density projections (3) and (4). The hydrogen atom positions are marked with a cross. The molecule, B_5H_9, has considerable thermal motion in the crystals. The maps given have been calculated from the measured Fs multiplied by $e^5 \frac{\sin^2\theta}{\lambda^2}$ partly to counteract the effects of this motion and make the peaks better defined.

The interatomic distances calculated from the parameters of Lipscomb and Dulmage are:

B2–B2, 1.77 ± 0.02; B1–B2, 1.66 ± 0.02; B1–H1, 1.21 ± 0.05; B2–H2, 1.20 ± 0.07; B2–B3, 1.35 ± 0.04.

133 1.98 Å; the binding must be homopolar.

134 (ii) From the decay curve $\left(\text{plotting} \quad \log \dfrac{a}{a-x} \text{ against} \quad t\right)$,
$t_{\frac{1}{2}} = 4.0$ days and $K = 0.17_4$ day^{-1}.

From the regeneration curve (applying the Guggenheim method to the results of days 2 to 10), $K = 0.16_3$ day^{-1}; if the results for the latter period of regeneration are used, lower values of K are obtained.

(iii) The shape of the earliest portion of both curves is due to the decay and regeneration respectively of the short-lived products from thorium-X.

135 (i) $3.1_4 \times 10^{10}$ (ii) 1.18×10^{-11} sec^{-1} (iii) 1860 years.

136 [Decay constant of radon $= 0.1812$ day^{-1}.]
(i) 0.02085 mm^3.   (ii) 158.6 mm^3.   (iii) 6.06×10^{23}.

137 (i) 0·003454 (0·00236 g of Pb on surface of 1 g of $PbSO_4$).
(ii) 12740 cm^2/g.

138 (i) Calculated energy per α-particle $= 7\cdot2\ (\pm1\cdot4)$ million volts.
(ii) Calculated energy per α-particle (based on second set of nuclear masses) $= 8\cdot6$ million volts.

139 (i) 24320 counts/min/mg.
(ii) N-ethylpiperidine salt   2464 counts/min/mg.
    Potassium salt   2961 counts/min/mg.
(iii) 1·44 mg of potassium salt per ml.
(iv) 2300 international units/ml.

140 (i) 8·4. (The values of α quoted in Table II of the original paper relate to the individual stages of the enrichment process and not to the over-all enrichment.)
(ii) 2130.
(iii) $9\cdot5\times10^6$.
(iv) $4\cdot3\times10^{-14}$.
(v) $2\cdot0\times10^{-17}$. Kaufman and Libby showed a rather wide range of abundances in the samples they measured.

141 (i) The activity of the hydrazone corresponds to 96·8 per cent of what would have been expected if the carbon atom in the methyl group of the ethanol had been derived exclusively from the aldehyde carbon of the original glucose.
(ii) The barium carbonate made from the carbon dioxide produced by fermentation shows only 1·8 per cent of the activity that would have been expected if the carbon dioxide had been derived exclusively from the aldehyde carbon of the original glucose.

142 (i) 244·6 atm.
(ii) $V_c = 0\cdot1717$ litre mole^{-1}, $a = 4\cdot48$ litre^2 atm mole^{-2}, $b = 0\cdot572$ litre mole^{-1}.
(iii) 124·1 atm.
(iv) The experimental results of Masson and Dolley indicate that one mole of ethylene occupies a volume of about 0·08 litre at 125 atm and 24·95° C; the observed pressure–volume product in this region is therefore nearly 20 per cent lower than the value expected from the van der Waals equation.
(v) The volume occupied by one mole of spherical molecules of diameter 4·54 Å would be 29·5 ml (or 29·5 per cent of a total volume of 0·100 litre).

143 (i) $B = -504$ cm^3/mole at 78·2° C.
(ii) $\left(P+\dfrac{3P_cV_c^2T_c}{TV^2}\right)\left(V-\dfrac{V_c}{3}\right) = RT.$

(iii) $B = \dfrac{3RT_c}{32P_c}\left(1 - \dfrac{81T_c^2}{32T^2}\right) = -212$ cm^3/mole.

Using modified equation, $B = -443.3$ cm^3/mole.

The higher value of B obtained experimentally than the calculated value has been interpreted in terms of association of the ethyl chloride vapour.

144 (a) To save space the results for a few selected points only are given below:

Length of film (cm)	Area/molecule (Å^2)	Surface pressure (dynes cm^{-1})
20·9	22·47	0·30
20·1	21·61	1·90
19·1	20·53	7·82

The cross-sectional area of the molecule = 22Å^2.

(b) To save space the results for a few selected points only (at film-length = 35 cm) are given below:

Solution	Drops	Area/molecule (Å^2)	Surface pressure (dynes cm^{-1})
A	1	947	0·162
B	10	85·7	0·199
C	1	4284	0·065

Between about 50 and 850 Å^2/molecule the surface pressure is practically constant; it falls off more or less according to the two-dimensional gas law at higher areas and increases very sharply at lower areas, being here a liquid film under compression. The fluctuating surface potential is observed in the region where the film consists of floating islands of coherent film in equilibrium with saturated two-dimensional vapour film. Above 850 Å^2/molecule only vapour film is present.

Useful Quantities and†
their Logarithms

Principal physical constants			Logarithm
Avogadro's number	N	$6{\cdot}0238 \times 10^{23}$	$23{\cdot}7799$
Electronic charge	e (e.s.u.)	$4{\cdot}8022 \times 10^{-10}$	$\bar{1}0{\cdot}6814$
	(coulomb)	$1{\cdot}6019 \times 10^{-19}$	$\bar{1}9{\cdot}2046$
Faraday constant	F (coulomb)	96493	$4{\cdot}9845$
Planck constant			
(ergsec/molecule)	h	$6{\cdot}6238 \times 10^{-27}$	$\bar{2}7{\cdot}8211$
Gramme-molecular volume	G.M.V.	$22{\cdot}414$	$1{\cdot}3505$
Velocity of light (cm/sec)	c	$2{\cdot}9979 \times 10^{10}$	$10{\cdot}4768$
Boltzmann constant			
(erg/degree-molecule)	k	$1{\cdot}3803 \times 10^{-16}$	$\bar{1}6{\cdot}1400$
Ice-point (degrees Kelvin)		$273{\cdot}16$	$2{\cdot}4364$
Gas constant (cal/degree-mole)	R	$1{\cdot}9872$	$0{\cdot}2982$
(litre-atm/degree-mole)		$0{\cdot}082054$	$2{\cdot}9141$
(ergs/degree-mole)		$8{\cdot}3144 \times 10^{7}$	$7{\cdot}9198$

Factors related to the gas constant		
$R \times \ln 10$ (cal/degree-mole)	$4{\cdot}5757$	$0{\cdot}6605$
RT at 25° C (cal/mole)	$592{\cdot}50$	$2{\cdot}7727$
$RT \times \ln 10$ at 25° C (cal/mole)	$1364{\cdot}3$	$3{\cdot}1349$
$\dfrac{RT}{F} \times \ln 10$ at 25° C (volt)	$0{\cdot}059157$	$\bar{2}{\cdot}7720$

Energy conversion factors			
1 calorie (by definition)	$=$	$4{\cdot}184$ joule	$0{\cdot}6216$
	$=$	$0{\cdot}041292$ litre-atm	$\bar{2}{\cdot}6159$
1 reciprocal cm/molecule	$=$	$2{\cdot}8589$ cal/mole	$0{\cdot}4562$
	$=$	$1{\cdot}9857 \times 10^{-16}$ ergs/molecule	$\bar{1}6{\cdot}2979$
1 eV/molecule	$=$	23064 cal/mole	$4{\cdot}3629$
	$\approx$	$8067{\cdot}1$ reciprocal cm	$3{\cdot}9067$

Miscellaneous		
π	$3{\cdot}1416$	$0{\cdot}4971$
$\ln 10$	$2{\cdot}3026$	$0{\cdot}3622$
$\log e$	$0{\cdot}4343$	$\bar{1}{\cdot}6378$

† See note 1, page xv.